C000132217

BIOLOGY
for AQA

Ann Fullick

Heinemann

Heinemann Educational Publishers
Halley Court, Jordan Hill, Oxford OX2 8EJ
a division of Reed Educational & Professional Publishing Ltd
Heinemann is a registered trademark of Reed Educational
& Professional Publishing Ltd

OXFORD MELBOURNE AUCKLAND
JOHANNESBURG BLANTYRE GABORONE
IBADAN PORTSMOUTH NH (USA) CHICAGO

© Ann Fullick, 2001

First published 2001

ISBN 0 435 58355 7

05 04 03 02 01
10 9 8 7 6 5 4 3 2 1

Edited by Liz Jones

Designed and typeset by Gecko Ltd

Original illustrations © Heinemann Educational
Publishers 2001

Illustrated by Harvey Collins, Stephen Crumly,
Neil Falconer, Alan Johnson, Joe Little, Richard Morris
and Tony Wilkins.

Printed and bound in Italy by Printer Trento S.r.l.

Tel: 01865 888058 www.heinemann.co.uk

Acknowledgements
The authors and publishers would like to thank the
following for permission to use photographs:

Cover photos: SPL/T J O'Donnell; inset: Stone

p3: SPL; p4: Bruce Coleman; p5: SPL; p6: Corbis UK Ltd;
p8: SPL; p9: OSF; p10,16,24,25,27,28,29,30: SPL; p31:
Bruce Coleman; p34,35,38,40,42,44: SPL; p45: Hulton
Getty; p46: Topham Picturepoint; p47R: Hutchison
Library; p47L: Corbis UK Ltd; p52T: OSF; p52B,53: SPL;
p54: Mary Evans Picture Library; p55L: SPL; p56T: SPL;
p56M: Robert Harding Picture Library; p56B: Hutchison
Library; p58: NHS Health Promotion, England; p60T:
Robert Harding Picture Library; p60B,62: Topham Picture
Point; p63L: OSF; p63R: SPL; p64: Hulton Getty; p68T:
OSF; p68B: Peter Gould; p70: Heather Angel; p71,72T:
SPL; p73,74,75: SPL; p76: OSF; p77: Heather Angel; p78:
SPL; p82: OSF; p83: Corbis/Bettman; p84T: Corbis UK
Ltd; p84B: SPL; p86L: Kobal Collection; p86R: SPL; p88:
Cystic Fibrosis Trust; p90T: Corbis UK Ltd; p90B: Heather
Angel; p91: P. Adams; p92T: Kobal Collection; p92B:
Advertising Archives; p93: Bruce Coleman; p94: SPL;
p98: Corbis UK Ltd; p100: SPL; p101: Ardea;
p102T,102R: Corbis UK Ltd; p102L: OSF/Tony Martin;
p104: Corbis UK Ltd; p105T: SPL; p105M: FLPA; p105B:
Kew Gardens Press Office, Royal Botanic Gardens; p106:
Heather Angel; p107: Ardea; p108: SPL; p109: Bruce
Coleman; p112T: FLPA; p112BL: Ecoscene; p112BR:
Corbis UK Ltd; p113,114T: SPL; p114B,115,116,117:
Corbis UK Ltd; p118: SPL; p119: Corbis UK Ltd; p120:
SPL; p121: Corbis UK Ltd; p122T: SPL; p112B: Ecoscene;
p123L: SPL; p123R: Corbis UK Ltd; p126: OSF; p129:
SPL; p130T,130M: Corbis UK Ltd; p130B: Bruce
Coleman; p131: FLPA; p132T: SPL; p132M: Bruce
Coleman; p132B: SPL; p134: Ardea; p138: SPL; p139T:
OSF; p139M: Corbis UK Ltd; p139B: Photographers
Library; p140,143: SPL; p144: OSF; p145: Corbis UK Ltd;
p146,147: SPL; p148L: OSF; p148R: FLPA; p149: Ardea;
p152R,152L: Bruce Coleman; p153,154T,154TR: SPL;
p154MR: Corbis; p154BR: Oxford Scientific Films; p155:
SPL; p156T: Peter Gould; p156B,157,158,160T: SPL;
p160B: Ardea; p162T: Bruce Coleman; p162B: SPL; p163:
Oxford Scientific Films; p166T: SPL; p166M: Oxford
Scientific Films; p167: SPL; p168T: Bruce Coleman;
p168B: Oxford Scientific Films; p170: SPL; p171T: Bruce
Coleman; p172T,172B: SPL; p173T: Ardea; p173M:
Oxford Scientific films; p176T: SPL; p176B: The Wellcome
Trust Medical Photo Library; p178: SPL; p179: Hulton
Getty; p180T,180B: The Wellcome Trust Medical Photo
Library; p182T: Hulton Getty; p182B: Department of
Health, Heath Education Authority; p184T: SPL; p184BL,
184BR: The Wellcome Trust Medical Photo Library;
p185,186,188: SPL; p189: The Wellcome Trust Medical
Photo Library; p192: SPL; p193: Corbis; p194T: Ancient
Art and Architecture; p194BL,194BR: SPL; p195,196:
Corbis; p197: Oxford Scientific Films; p198T,198B,200,
202T,202M: SPL; p202TBR,202BR: Mary Evans Picture
Library; p303: SPL; p204: Panos Pictures; p206T: SPL;
p206B: Corbis.

Picture research by Sally Smith

The publishers have made every effort to trace the
copyright holders, but if they have inadvertently
overlooked any, they will be pleased to make the
necessary arrangements at the first opportunity.

AQA examination questions are reproduced by
permission of the Assessment and Qualifications Alliance.

Introduction

Biology – the science which looks at the world around us and at all living things. Biology is exciting, fascinating and helps us understand how the most interesting organism in the world works – ourselves! In this book you will find the secrets of the living cell, the mystery of plants and the complex interactions of all the living organisms in an environment.

This book has been written to support you as you study the AQA Separate Science GCSE. As well as lots of facts and clear explanations with diagrams and photos to illustrate the science, there are some other features which will add interest and depth to your learning.

⊙ **Science people** introduces you to some of the scientists who have worked out the science we now take for granted.
⊙ **Ideas and evidence** looks at the way ideas about biology have developed and grown over the years.

At the end of each double page spread there are questions to help you check that you have understood the material you have just read, and at the end of each chapter there are GCSE style questions which will allow you to test your knowledge for the exams ahead.

Studying biology will give you an increased understanding of environmental issues, of health and disease and of the human condition. I hope this book will help you in your studies, and help you enjoy biology throughout your course.

Contents

The Earth is covered with a teeming variety of life, but one thing all living organisms have in common is that they are made up of cells.

Basic cell structure – animal cells

All cells have some features in common and we can see them clearly in animal cells (Figure 1).

- The **nucleus** controls all the activities of the cell. It also contains the instructions for making new cells or new organisms.
- The **cytoplasm** is a liquid gel in which most of the chemical reactions needed for life take place. One of the most important of these is respiration, where oxygen and sugar react to release the energy the cell needs.
- The **cell membrane** controls the passage of substances such as carbon dioxide, oxygen and water in and out of the cell.

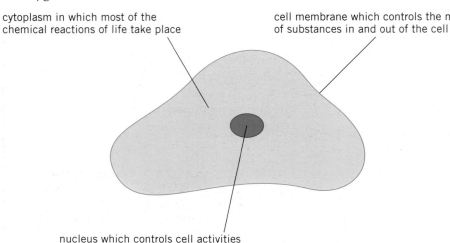

cytoplasm in which most of the chemical reactions of life take place

cell membrane which controls the movement of substances in and out of the cell

← **Figure 1:** A simple animal cell like this shows the features which are common to all living cells.

nucleus which controls cell activities

Basic cell structure – plant cells

Plants are very different from animals – they do not move their whole bodies about and they make their own food by photosynthesis. So while plant cells have all the features of a typical animal cell, they also have structures which are needed for their very different way of life (Figure 2).

- The **cell wall** is made of cellulose which strengthens the cell and gives it support.

Many (but not all) plant cells also have these other features.

- **Chloroplasts** are found in all of the green parts of the plant. They are green, which gives the plant its colour, and they absorb energy from light to make food by photosynthesis.
- A **permanent vacuole** (a space in the cytoplasm filled with cell sap) is found in many cells. It is important for maintaining rigid cells to support the plant.

↓ **Figure 2:** A plant cell has many features in common with an animal cell, but others which are unique to plants.

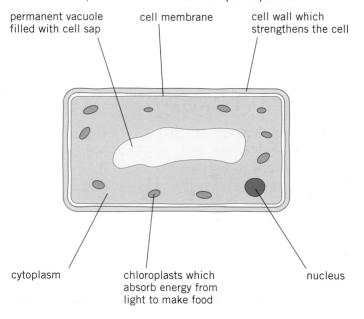

permanent vacuole filled with cell sap

cell membrane

cell wall which strengthens the cell

cytoplasm

chloroplasts which absorb energy from light to make food

nucleus

Chemical control in cells

Imagine 100 mixed reactions going on in a laboratory test-tube – chemical chaos and probably a few explosions would be the result! But this is the level of chemical activity going on in a cell at any one time. Cell chemistry works because each reaction is controlled by an **enzyme**, a protein designed to control the rate of a very specific reaction and ensure that it takes place without becoming mixed up with any other reaction. Enzymes are found throughout the structure of a cell, but particularly in the mitochondria. The mitochondria are structures in the cytoplasm and are very important in releasing energy from food by respiration (see page 30).

Ideas and Evidence

Over the past three centuries our ideas about cells have developed as our ability to see them has developed. In 1665 the English scientist Robert Hooke designed the first working microscope and saw cells in cork. At around the same time a Dutchman, Anton van Leeuwenhoek (1632–1723), produced a microscope which enabled him to see bacteria, microscopic animals and blood cells for the first time ever (Figure 3).

← **Figure 3:** The work of the early pioneers of the microscope led the way in revealing the structure of living cells.

Almost two centuries later, by the 1840s, scientists had accepted that cells are the basic units of all living things. From then on, as light microscopes improved, more details of the secret life inside a cell were revealed as cells were magnified up to 1000 times (Figure 4).

With the invention of the **electron microscope** in the 1930s it became possible to magnify things much more – now we can look at cells magnified up 500 000 times!

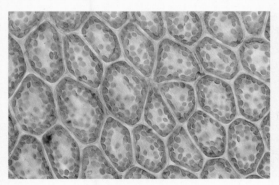

Plant cell ×250

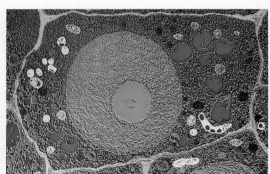

Plant cell ×2825

← **Figure 4:** The ability to see cells and the secret worlds inside them has developed in an amazing way since the days of the early microscopes.

Questions

1 Make a table to show the similarities and differences in structure between animal and plant cells.

2 Root cells in a plant do not have chloroplasts. Why not?

3 What happens in the cytoplasm of a cell?

4 Which two features of a plant cell help the plant to stay firm and upright? Explain how they do this.

5 Explain what enzymes do in the cell.

Key Ideas

⊙ Cells are the basic units of life.

⊙ All cells contain a nucleus, cell membrane and cytoplasm.

⊙ Plants cells may also have a cell wall, a permanent vacuole and chloroplasts.

The very smallest living organisms are single cells which carry out all of the functions of life – feeding, respiration, the excretion of waste, growth, movement and reproduction. As organisms get bigger and are made up of many cells, some of these cells become **specialised** to carry out particular jobs. Muscle cells have a different structure to blood and nerve cells in animals. In plants the cells where photosynthesis happens are very different to root hair cells.

Seeing colours

An interesting example of specialised cells is those involved in colour vision in the human eye (Figure 1).

These cells, known as **cone cells**, are found in the retina of the eye (see page 36). They have an outer segment which is filled with a special chemical known as a visual pigment, which changes when coloured light hits it. When this happens it sends a signal along the optic nerve to the brain. The pigment then has to be changed back to its original form, ready to register more coloured light. This needs energy, and the middle of the cell is stuffed with structures called mitochondria which provide the energy.

Minute predators

Hydra are tiny multicellular animals, but in spite of their small size they are carnivores (Figure 2). They capture prey using their tentacles and then push it into their body cavity to be digested. *Hydra* have specialised nerve cells which allow them to be co-ordinated enough to hunt, and specialised sting cells in their tentacles which shoot out poisoned barbs and sticky threads to paralyse and help trap the prey – often water fleas.

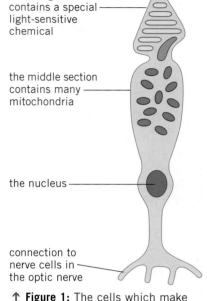

outer segment contains a special light-sensitive chemical

the middle section contains many mitochondria

the nucleus

connection to nerve cells in the optic nerve

↑ **Figure 1:** The cells which make it possible for us to see in colour are an excellent example of the way the basic animal cell structure can be adapted to carry out a particular function.

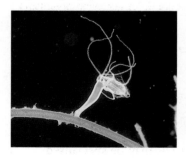

before release the 'sting' is coiled up inside the cell

lid

when the cell is triggered by the nervous system the sting shoots out, releasing poison into the prey or tangling it in a sticky thread

← **Figure 2:** Without these specially adapted stinging cells Hydra would not survive as a predator.

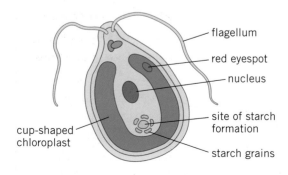

flagellum

red eyespot

nucleus

site of starch formation

cup-shaped chloroplast

starch grains

Chlamydomonas is a single-celled organism which lives under water. It can move itself to the light to photosynthesise, and stores excess food as starch

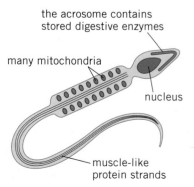

the acrosome contains stored digestive enzymes

many mitochondria

nucleus

muscle-like protein strands

sperm are usually released a relatively long way from the egg they must fertilise

← **Figure 3:** Throughout the living world cells are adapted to carry out very specific functions, sometimes becoming so different from the so-called 'typical' cell that it is hard to recognise them as the same thing!

Organised cells

Specialised cells are often grouped together to form a **tissue** – in animals, connective tissue joins bits of the body together, while nervous tissue carries information around the body and muscles move the body about. Similarly in plants, photosynthetic tissues make food by photosynthesis, whilst storage tissues store any extra food made to help with survival in adverse conditions.

Tissues make up an **organ** and there is usually more than one type of tissue in an organ. For example, the pancreas is an organ in our bodies which has two important functions: to make hormones to control our sugar levels and to make some of the enzymes which digest our food. Figure 4 shows these two different tissues in the pancreas.

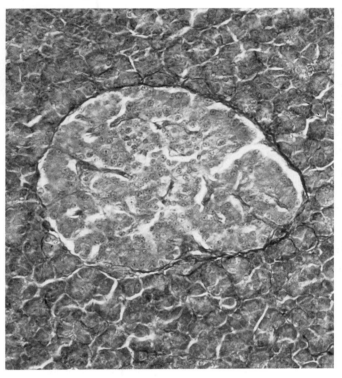

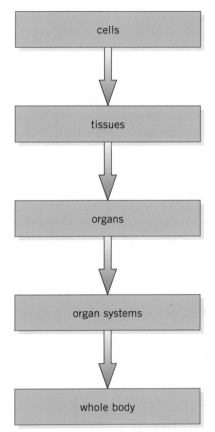

← **Figure 4:** Within an organ like the pancreas at least two very different tissues can be seen. The cells in each type of tissue are specialised to make a very different chemical product, and so they take up stains differently which allows them to be seen.

a) The cells which are stained blue make hormones which help to control the sugar levels in the blood

b) The cells which are stained red make enzymes needed to digest the food in the gut

↑ **Figure 5:** Larger living organisms have many levels of organisation which means that each part of the body is perfectly adapted to carry out the jobs it has to do.

In turn, different organs are combined in **organ systems** to carry out major functions in the body such as transporting the blood or reproduction (Figure 5).

? Questions

1 Describe how the sperm cell is adapted for its long journey to the egg.

2 Describe the special features of a cone cell in the eye which enable it to do its job.

3 What is the name of:

  a the tissue of which the cone cell is part

  b the organ of which it is part?

4 *Chlamydomonas* is a single-celled organism.

  a What features does it have in common with other cells in plants and animals?

  b What features are different to other cells and how do they help it to survive?

Key Ideas

⊙ Cells may be specialised to carry out particular functions in an organism.

⊙ Specialised cells are adapted to carry out their functions.

⊙ Specialised cells are often organised into groups known as tissues.

⊙ Organs are groups of different tissues which work together to perform particular functions.

Substances which cells need for chemical reactions, such as oxygen and glucose, must move into the cell across the membrane. Waste products, or chemicals which the cell has made to be used elsewhere in the body must leave the cell. The movement of water and many other substances in and out of cells depends largely on two physical processes – diffusion and osmosis.

Diffusion

Sharks can smell their prey from a long way away – the smell reaches them by **diffusion** (Figure 1). Diffusion happens when particles of a gas, or a solid in a solution, spread out. Particles move from an area where they are at a high concentration to an area where they are at a lower concentration until they are evenly distributed throughout both areas.

Diffusion is possible because of the random movements of the particles of a gas or of a substance in solution. All the particles, of the air and water as well as the substance, are moving and bumping into each other and this moves them all around.

Imagine a room containing a group of boys and a group of girls. If everyone closes their eyes and moves around briskly but randomly, people will bump into each other and scatter until the room contains a mixture of boys and girls. This gives us a good working model of diffusion (Figure 2).

↑ **Figure 1:** Everyone knows that bleeding in the sea when there are sharks around is a bad idea, because sharks are sensitive to just a few molecules of blood in the water and blood from an injury spreads quickly through the water by diffusion.

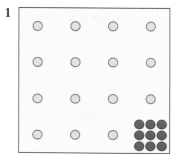 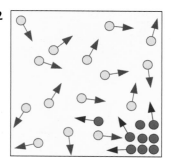 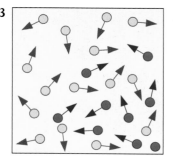 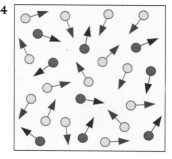

1 At the moment of adding the blue particles to the yellow mixture they are not mixed at all.

2 As the particles move randomly the blue ones begin to mix with the yellow ones.

3 As the particles move and spread they bump into each other and keep spreading as a result of all the random movement.

4 Eventually the particles are completely mixed and diffusion is complete.

↖ **Figure 2:** The random movement of particles results in substances spreading out or diffusing from an area of higher concentration to an area of lower concentration.

If there is a big difference in concentration between two areas, diffusion will take place quickly. For example, in our room with the two groups of girls and boys, the girls will very quickly get mixed in among the boys because almost as soon as anyone moves they are likely to meet the 'opposite particle'! There is a large concentration gradient between the all-girls group and the all boys group.

However, when a substance is moving from a higher concentration to one which is just a bit lower, the movement toward the less concentrated area will be appear to be quite small. This is because although some particles move into the area of lower concentration by random movement, at the same time other identical particles are leaving that area by random movement. So:

overall or **net** movement = particles moving in − particles moving out

In general, the bigger the difference in concentration, the faster the rate of diffusion. This difference between two areas of concentration is called the **concentration gradient** – the bigger the difference, the steeper the gradient (Figure 3).

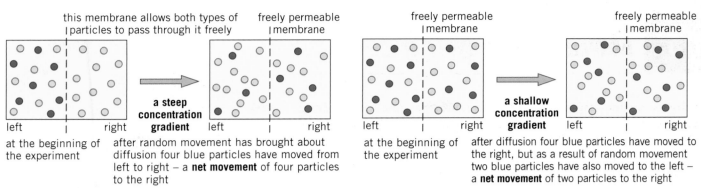

this membrane allows both types of particles to pass through it freely | freely permeable membrane

a steep concentration gradient

left | right

at the beginning of the experiment

after random movement has brought about diffusion four blue particles have moved from left to right – a **net movement** of four particles to the right

freely permeable membrane

a shallow concentration gradient

left | right

at the beginning of the experiment

after diffusion four blue particles have moved to the right, but as a result of random movement two blue particles have also moved to the left – a **net movement** of two particles to the right

↑ **Figure 3:** This diagram shows us how the overall movement of particles in a particular direction is more effective if there is a big difference (a steep concentration gradient) between the two areas. This is why so many body systems are adapted to maintain steep concentration gradients.

Osmosis

Diffusion takes place where particles can spread freely from one place to another. However, in cells the solutions inside are separated from those outside by the cell membrane which does not let all types of particles through. Because it only lets some types of particles through it is known as **partially permeable**.

Cell membranes will allow water to move across them. The water particles move from a dilute solution (containing lots of water particles and very few solute particles) to a more concentrated solution (with fewer water molecules and more solute particles). This special case, where only water particles move across a partially permeable membrane, is known as **osmosis**. Figure 4 shows some model cells and what happens if the concentrations of the solutions inside or outside of the cell change.

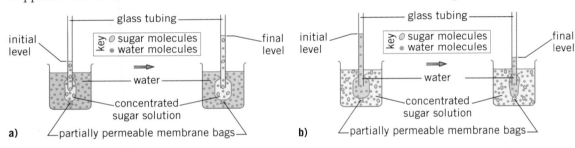

← **Figure 4:** Using bags of partially permeable membrane we can clearly see the effect of osmosis as water moves across the membrane from a dilute to a concentrated solution.

? Questions

1 Explain the following in terms of diffusion and the movement of particles:

   a A cake baking in the oven can be smelt all over the house.

   b When trying on new perfumes or aftershaves, you are advised to try no more than two at a time.

   c A cut in water looks much worse than a cut on land.

2 Explain clearly with the help of diagrams the difference between diffusion and osmosis.

3 Describe what is happening in terms of osmosis to each of the model cells shown in Figure 4.

4 **a** Someone suggests that diffusion and osmosis will both take place faster as the temperature increases. Do you think that temperature would have any effect? Explain your answer carefully.

   b Suggest an investigation you could do to show whether temperature has any effect on the speed of osmosis or diffusion.

🔑 Key Ideas

⊙ Diffusion is the net movement of particles from an area of high concentration to an area of lower concentration.

⊙ The steeper the concentration gradient, the more rapid the rate of diffusion.

⊙ Osmosis is the movement of water from an area of high concentration to an area of lower concentration through a partially permeable membrane.

Diffusion in living cells

Diffusion is very important to living organisms in a number of different ways. Within the bodies of many living things and in many individual cells we can see special adaptations which have evolved to make diffusion more efficient.

Diffusion in living organisms

Many important substances can move across the cell membrane by diffusion. Water is one. Simple sugars like glucose and amino acids (from the breakdown of proteins in food) can also pass through the membrane by diffusion.

Another important group of substances which can move through membranes by simple diffusion is mineral ions such as iron, nitrates and sodium. Minerals are only needed in minute amounts, but they are vital for the healthy functioning of plant and animal cells, so it is important that they are easily transported into the cells by diffusion.

Individual cells may be adapted to make diffusion easier and more rapid. As movement of substances into and out of cells takes place across the cell membrane, the most common adaptation is to increase the **surface area** of the cell membrane over which diffusion occurs (Figure 1).

How does increasing the surface area increase diffusion?

Only so many particles of a substance such as oxygen can diffuse over a given surface area, so increasing the surface area means there is more room for diffusion to take place. By folding up the membrane of a cell, or the tissue lining an organ, the area over which diffusion can take place is greatly increased and so the amount of substance moved by diffusion is also greatly increased (Figure 2).

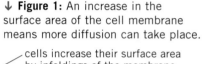
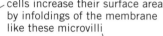
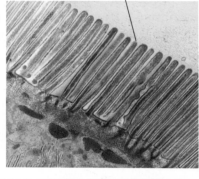

↓ **Figure 1:** An increase in the surface area of the cell membrane means more diffusion can take place.

cells increase their surface area by infoldings of the membrane like these microvilli

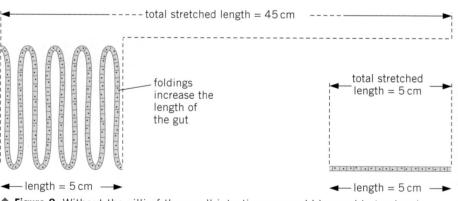

- - - - - total stretched length = 45 cm - - - - -

foldings increase the length of the gut

total stretched length = 5 cm

◄—— length = 5 cm ——►

◄—— length = 5 cm ——►

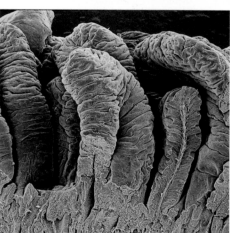

↑ **Figure 2:** Without the villi of the small intestine we would be unable to absorb enough digested food to survive. They increase the surface area available for diffusion many times.

Adaptations of organs for diffusion

The lungs of human beings and many other animals are specially adapted to make the movement of oxygen into the body and the removal of waste carbon dioxide more efficient. The tissue is arranged into clusters of **alveoli**, tiny air sacs which give ideal conditions for rapid gas exchange by diffusion (see page 23). Together they have a surface area about the size of a tennis court! This makes it possible for enough diffusion to take place to supply us with the oxygen we need and get rid of carbon dioxide.

Both the lungs (Figure 3) and gut also have an excellent **blood supply** which carries away the oxygen or glucose as soon as it has diffused from one side to the other. This maintains a steep concentration gradient all the time, which ensures diffusion is as rapid and efficient as possible.

↘ **Figure 3:** The multitude of tiny air sacs in the lungs gives them a much larger surface area than if they were single balloon-like sacs, making lots of rapid diffusion possible.

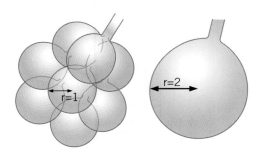
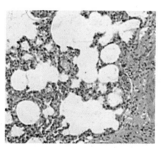

The volume of this one large sphere is the same as the volume of the eight smaller spheres.

But the smaller spheres have twice the surface area of the larger one.

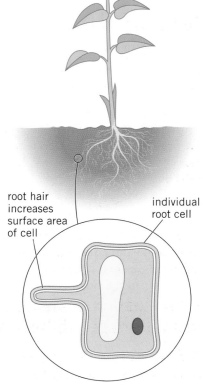

root hair increases surface area of cell

individual root cell

↑ **Figure 5:** Many small roots and the presence of microscopic root hairs on the individual root cells all increase diffusion of substances from the soil into the plant.

Plants also rely heavily on diffusion to obtain the carbon dioxide they need for photosynthesis and to obtain minerals from the soil. The flattened shape of the leaves increases the surface area for diffusion, and the many air spaces inside the leaf allow carbon dioxide to come into contact with lots of cells to aid diffusion (Figure 4). Plant roots also have adaptations to help in the uptake of water and minerals. The roots and the individual root cells have adaptations to increase the surface area for the uptake of substances from the soil (Figure 5).

↓ **Figure 4:** The wide, flat shape of most leaves increases the surface area for collecting light and exchanging gases.

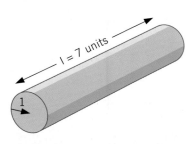
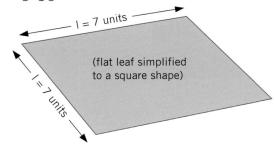

(flat leaf simplified to a square shape)

surface area = 22 units^2

surface area = 98 units^2

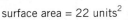

? Questions

1 Give three examples of substances which are transported by diffusion in animals or plants.

2 Explain why a folded gut wall can absorb more nutrients than a flat one.

3 a What substances diffuse through the cell walls of our lungs?

  b How does the structure of lungs make this as effective as possible?

4 Describe **two** ways in which a leaf is adapted to take in as much carbon dioxide as possible.

0—ⅲ Key Ideas

- ⊙ Cells and organs of living organisms are often adapted to make diffusion more efficient. The most common adaptations are:
  - increasing the surface area of a membrane or part of an organ so more diffusion can take place
  - maintaining a steep concentration gradient to encourage rapid diffusion.

A cell is basically some chemicals in solution in water inside a partially permeable bag. This internal concentration needs to stay the same all the time for the reactions of life to take place. Outside the cell are more solutions of chemicals, sometimes at different concentrations to the inside of the cell (Figure 1). This can make water move into or out of the cells by the process known as osmosis (see page 7).

Osmosis is an important way of moving water in and out of the cell when needed. If a cell uses up water in its chemical reactions, the cytoplasm becomes more concentrated and more water will immediately move in by osmosis. Similarly, if the cytoplasm becomes too dilute because water is produced during chemical reactions, water will leave the cell by osmosis, restoring the balance.

However, osmosis can also cause some problems:

⊙ If the solution outside the cell is more dilute than the cell contents, then water will move into the cell by osmosis, diluting the cytoplasm and causing swelling.

⊙ If the solution outside the cell is more concentrated than the cell contents, then water will move out of the cell by osmosis, the cytoplasm will become too concentrated and the cell will shrivel up (Figure 2).

Both plants and animals have sophisticated mechanisms to ensure that they have the right concentration of the solutions around their cells. We will see some of these later in the book (see Chapter 3.7 on homeostasis).

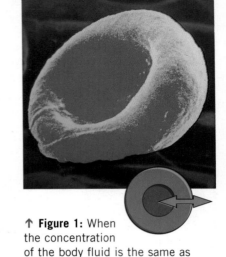

↑ **Figure 1:** When the concentration of the body fluid is the same as the red blood cell contents, equal amounts of water enter and leave the cell by random movement.

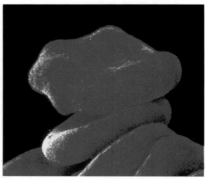

← **Figure 2:** If the concentration of the solution around the red blood cells is higher than the concentration of substances inside the cell, water will leave the cell by osmosis, making it shrivel and shrink so it can no longer carry oxygen around the body.

Plants rely on well-regulated osmosis to support their stems and leaves. Water moves into plant cells by osmosis, making the cytoplasm swell and press against the cell walls. The pressure builds up until no more water can physically enter the cell, which is hard and rigid. This swollen state (known as **turgor**) keeps the leaves and stems of the plant rigid and firm. So for plants it is important that the fluid surrounding the cells always has a higher concentration of water (it is a more dilute solution of chemicals) than the cytoplasm of the cells, to keep osmosis working in the right direction (Figure 3).

concentration the same inside and outside the plant cell

water moves in and out equally

the concentration of the solution outside the plant cell is stronger than inside

the concentration of the solution outside the plant cell is weaker than inside

water moves out by osmosis

water moves in by osmosis

The vacuole and cytoplasm shrink away from the cell wall.

The vacuole is full, and the cytoplasm pushes against the cell wall. The cell is rigid – this is how plant cells need to be.

↑ **Figure 3:** Osmosis plays an important role in maintaining the rigid structure of plants.

Active transport

Diffusion and osmosis both depend on the presence of a concentration gradient to enable them to work. However, sometimes substances needed by the body have to be moved against a concentration gradient. The only way this can be done is to use energy produced by respiration. The process is known as **active transport**.

For example, the mineral ions in the soil are usually in very dilute solutions, more dilute than within the plant cells themselves. By using active transport plants can absorb these mineral ions needed for making proteins and other important chemicals from the soil, even though it is against a concentration gradient (Figure 4).

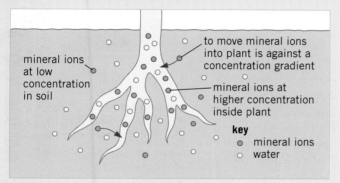

↑ **Figure 4:** It takes the use of energy in active transport to move mineral ions against a concentration gradient like this.

In animals, between meals, sugar may be found in very low concentrations in both the gut and the kidney tubules but in a high concentration in the blood where it is travelling to the other body cells. There is a danger

that it will diffuse into the gut and kidney tubules and then be passed out of the body in faeces from the gut or urine from the kidney. This would be a waste of precious food. Active transport systems in the lining of the small intestine and in the kidney tubules use energy to transport the sugar from the gut and the kidney back into the blood (Figure 5).

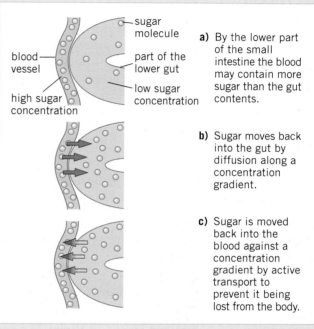

a) By the lower part of the small intestine the blood may contain more sugar than the gut contents.

b) Sugar moves back into the gut by diffusion along a concentration gradient.

c) Sugar is moved back into the blood against a concentration gradient by active transport to prevent it being lost from the body.

↑ **Figure 5:** Sometimes it is worth using up energy when a resource is particularly valuable and its transport really important.

Questions

1 Animals which live in fresh water have a constant problem with their water balance. Explain what you think will be the difficulties for:

  a a single-celled organism such as *Amoeba*

  b a freshwater fish.

2 Plants do not have skeletons in the way that animals do. Instead, osmosis is a very important part of the plant support system. Explain how osmosis is involved in keeping the plant cells rigid.

3 When a plant is short of water it wilts. Explain why this happens in terms of osmosis and what happens to the cells. Draw a diagram to help your explanation.

4 **a** Give some examples of when a substance cannot be moved into a cell by osmosis or diffusion.

  b The processes of diffusion and osmosis do not need energy to take place. Why does the organism have to provide energy for active transport?

  c Where does the energy for active transport come from?

Key Ideas

⊙ Differences in the concentrations of the solutions inside and outside a cell cause water to move into or out of the cell by osmosis.

⊙ In animal cells, water moving in or out by osmosis can cause problems.

⊙ In plant cells water needs to move into the cells by osmosis; if it moves out there are problems.

New cells are needed for an organism, or part of an organism, to grow. They are also needed to replace cells which become worn out or damaged, so it is very important for cells to reproduce.

Chromosomes and genes

Each cell has a nucleus containing the instructions for making a whole new cell and even an entire new organism. The instructions are carried in the form of **genes**. A gene is a small packet of information which controls a characteristic, or part of a characteristic, of the body. The genes are grouped together on **chromosomes**. A chromosome may carry several hundred or even thousands of genes (Figure 1).

Matching pairs

The number of chromosomes found in the nucleus of a cell depends on the species of the organism. Each species has its own number of chromosomes – each normal human cell has 46 chromosomes, whilst those of turkeys have 82! The chromosomes are usually found in pairs, one inherited from the female parent and one from the male. So human chromosomes are grouped in 23 pairs.

Genes and alleles

Many of the genes we carry on our chromosomes have different forms, and these different forms of the genes are known as **alleles**. The gene for eye colour may be the allele for blue eyes or the allele for brown eyes; the gene for tongue rolling may have the rolling or the non-rolling allele in place. There can be a number of possible alleles for a particular feature.

Making new cells

Body cells divide to make new cells. Before they divide they produce new copies of the chromosomes in the nucleus, so that when division takes place two genetically identical **daughter cells** are formed (Figure 2). In some areas of the body of an animal or plant, cell division like this carries on rapidly all of the time. The human skin is a good example – cells are constantly being lost from the surface and new cells are constantly being formed by cell division to replace them.

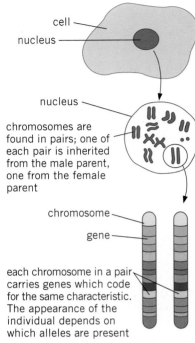

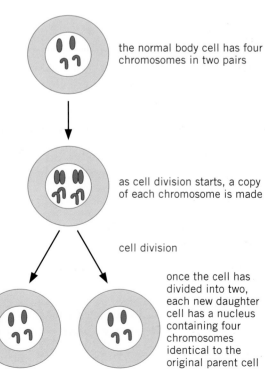

the normal body cell has four chromosomes in two pairs

as cell division starts, a copy of each chromosome is made

cell division

once the cell has divided into two, each new daughter cell has a nucleus containing four chromosomes identical to the original parent cell

↑ **Figure 1:** The nucleus of the cell contains the chromosomes which carry the genes which control the characteristics of the whole body.

cell
nucleus

nucleus

chromosomes are found in pairs; one of each pair is inherited from the male parent, one from the female parent

chromosome
gene

each chromosome in a pair carries genes which code for the same characteristic. The appearance of the individual depends on which alleles are present

← **Figure 2:** The formation of identical daughter cells by simple division means there are always plenty of new cells available when they are needed in the body for growth, replacement or repair. For simplicity, the cell is shown with only two pairs of chromosomes.

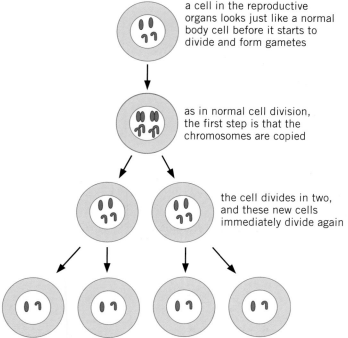

a cell in the reproductive organs looks just like a normal body cell before it starts to divide and form gametes

as in normal cell division, the first step is that the chromosomes are copied

the cell divides in two, and these new cells immediately divide again

this gives four sex cells each with a single set of chromosomes-in this case two instead of the original four

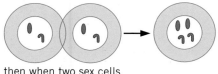

then when two sex cells combine at fertilisation…

…the new cell formed has a full set of chromosomes, like any other body cell. It will grow and reproduce to form a new individual

↑ **Figure 3:** The formation of sex cells involves a special kind of cell division to halve the chromosome number. For simplicity, the cell is shown with only two pairs of chromosomes.

The cell division which takes place in the normal body cells and produces identical daughter cells is known as **mitosis**. As a result of mitosis, every body cell has the same genetic information.

However, there is another type of cell division which takes place only in the reproductive organs (the ovaries and testes in human beings). Special cells divide to make the sex cells or **gametes** (in humans, the eggs and sperm). These sex cells contain only one member of each pair of chromosomes, which is exactly *half* of the full chromosome number, so that when the sex cells join during fertilisation the new cell formed has a full set of chromosomes. In humans, the egg cell has 23 chromosomes and so does the sperm. When they join together they produce a new normal cell with the full human complement of 46 chromosomes (23 pairs).

When a cell divides to form gametes, the first stage is very similar to normal body cell division. The chromosomes are copied so there are four sets of chromosomes. The cell then divides twice in quick succession to form four gametes, each with a single set of chromosomes. This type of cell division where the chromosome number is reduced to form sex cells is known as **meiosis** (Figure 3).

1 Give a definition for each of the following terms:

   a nucleus **b** chromosome **c** gene **d** allele **e** chromosome number.

2 **a** How many *pairs* of chromosomes are there in a normal turkey body cell?

   b How many chromosomes are there in a turkey egg cell?

   c How many chromosomes are there in a fertilised turkey egg?

3 **a** Division of the body cells is taking place all the time in living organisms. Why is it so important?

   b Explain why the chromosome number must stay the same when cells divide to make other normal body cells.

H 4 **a** What is mitosis?

   b What is meiosis and where does it take place?

   c Why is meiosis important?

Key Ideas

⊙ The instructions for making a new cell or a new organism are carried in the genes which are carried on long strands called chromosomes.

⊙ Different forms of the same gene are known as alleles.

⊙ Division to make identical daughter cells with the same number of chromosomes as the parent is known as mitosis.

H ⊙ Division to make sex cells with half the chromosome number of the parent is known as meiosis.

1 The diagram shows a cell from a blade of grass.

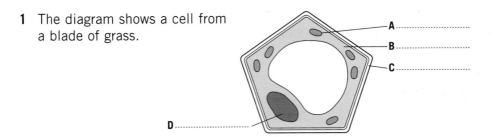

   a Use words from the list below to name the parts labelled A–E   (5 marks)

     cell membrane   cell wall   chloroplast   cytoplasm   nucleus   vacuole

   b Name **two** parts of the grass cell which are not found in any of the cells in an animal.   (2 marks)

                                                          (Total 7 marks)

                                                 AQA specimen question

H 2 **a** The diagram shows four ways in which molecules may move into and out of a cell. The dots show the concentration of molecules.

      The cell is respiring aerobically.
      Which arrow, **A**, **B**, **C** or **D** represents
      i the movement of oxygen molecules?
      ii the movement of carbon dioxide molecules?   (2 marks)

   b Name the process by which these gases move into and out of the cell.   (1 mark)

   c Which arrow, **A**, **B**, **C** or **D**, represents the active uptake of sugar molecules by the cell? Explain the reason for your answer.   (2 marks)

                                                      (Total 5 marks)

                                                 AQA specimen question

3 The diagram shows three cells labelled **A**, **B** and **C** which are specialised for very different functions. One is a fat storage cell, one is a light-sensitive cell from the eye which gives us vision in dim light and one is a sperm cell.

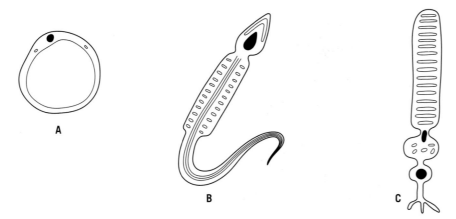

   a Identify which cell is which.   (2 marks)

   b Explain how each type of cell is specialised and adapted to carry out its particular function.   (6 marks)

                                                      (Total 8 marks)

4 a Why is diffusion important in the gut? (1 mark)

  b The gut cell in the diagram has microvilli.
How do they increase the uptake of
digested food? (2 marks)

  c How else is the lining of the gut adapted to increase absorption
of the digested food? (1 mark)

  d Give **two** examples of other cells, tissues or organs which are
adapted to allow as much diffusion as possible to take place. (2 marks)

                                                   (Total 6 marks)

5 The movement of water into and out of cells is very important in
maintaining them in their correct shape and functioning properly.

The diagram shows three
red blood cells which have
been exposed to solutions
of different concentration:

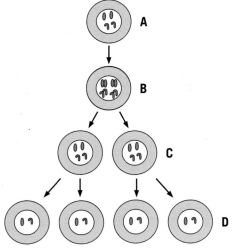

The normal red blood cell has been kept in a solution which is the same
concentration as blood. Explain carefully, in good English and with the aid
of diagrams if you wish, what has happened to the other two cells and why. (Total 6 marks)

6 a How many chromosomes would you expect to find in
a normal human body cell? (1 mark)

  b A cotton plant has 52 chromosomes in the normal body cells.
How many chromosomes would you expect there to be in
   i a cotton pollen grain
   ii a cotton seed? (2 marks)

                                                   (Total 3 marks)

(H) 7 a What is mitosis? (2 marks)

  b Why is a different type of cell division needed for the
formation of gametes? (2 marks)

  c The diagram shows the
main stages of meiosis.

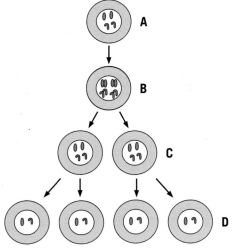

Explain clearly in your own words what is happening at
the stages labelled **A**, **B**, **C** and **D**. (4 marks)

                                                   (Total 8 marks)

2.1 Food for life

People, like all living organisms, need a source of energy to survive (Figure 1). It doesn't matter what the food is as long as it contains the right balance of chemicals – carbohydrates, fats, proteins, as well as minerals and vitamins.

However, in the form that they are usually eaten neither carbohydrates, proteins nor fats are useful to the body. These large, insoluble food molecules need to be broken down or digested to form smaller, soluble molecules which can be absorbed by the body and used by the cells. Carbohydrates must be broken down into simple sugars, proteins into amino acids, and fats to fatty acids and glycerol.

↑ **Figure 1:** The link between the food that comes in and what the body needs is the **digestive system**.

How digestion works

The working of the digestive system is based on two things: muscle action and enzyme action.

The gut is a muscular tube and its squeezing action is very important for several reasons. It helps to break up the food into very small pieces with a large surface area for enzyme action to take place. It also helps the chemical breakdown of the food, mixing it with various digestive juices which chemically break down its molecules. The muscles also move the food along the gut from one area of chemical digestion to another.

Enzyme action

Enzymes are chemicals which speed up (catalyse) other reactions. They do not actually take part in the reaction or change it in any way except to make it happen faster. Each type of enzyme acts on a specific type of food:

⊙ Amylase breaks down complicated carbohydrates such as starch into simple sugars such as glucose which the body can use.

⊙ Protease enzymes break down the proteins in food into amino acids.

⊙ Lipase breaks down fats and oils (lipids) into fatty acids and glycerol.

The effects of temperature and pH

Enzymes work best under very specific conditions of temperature and pH. Like most other chemical reactions, the rate of enzyme-controlled reactions increases with an increase in temperature. However, this is only true up to temperatures of about 40 °C. Higher than this the structure of the enzyme is affected by the temperature so that it no longer acts as a catalyst. We say the enzyme has been **denatured**. The rate of the reaction drops dramatically (Figure 2).

← **Figure 2:** Once the temperature gets too high the enzyme stops working and the rate of the reaction falls rapidly.

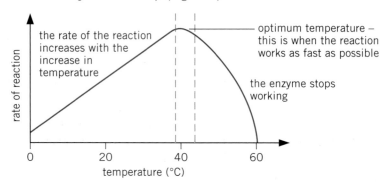

the rate of the reaction increases with the increase in temperature

optimum temperature – this is when the reaction works as fast as possible

the enzyme stops working

rate of reaction

temperature (°C)

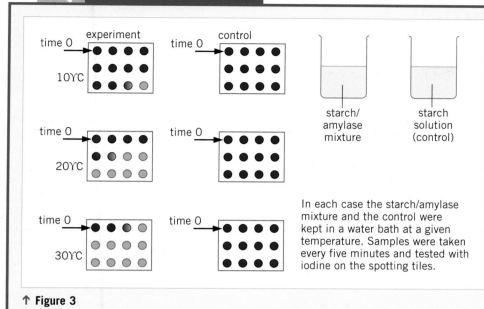

↑ Figure 3

In the experiment in Figure 3, samples of starch solution and the enzyme amylase (which breaks starch down into simple sugars) are mixed together and kept at different temperatures. Samples from each experiment are tested with iodine at regular intervals. In the presence of starch iodine turns blue-black, but when there is no starch present the iodine stays yellowy-brown. When the iodine no longer changes colour we know all the starch has been broken down. It is evidence such as this which demonstrates the effect of temperature on the rate of enzyme-controlled reactions.

In each case the starch/amylase mixture and the control were kept in a water bath at a given temperature. Samples were taken every five minutes and tested with iodine on the spotting tiles.

The pH also affects the way an enzyme works. Different enzymes have different pH levels at which they work their best — and a change in the pH can stop them working completely (Figure 4).

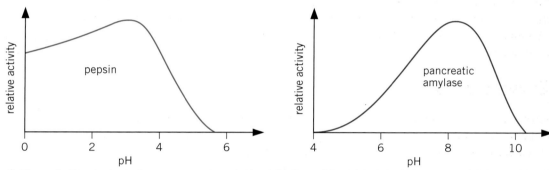

↑ Figure 4: Pepsin (a protease enzyme) works best in the acid environment of the stomach, but in the alkaline conditions which suit the amylase made in the pancreas, pepsin does work well at all.

Questions

1 a Why does food need to be digested?

   b What role do

   i muscles

   ii enzymes play in the work of the digestive system?

2 a How do temperature and pH affect the rate of an enzyme-controlled reaction?

   b Using the graphs in Figure 4, at which pH do

   i pepsin

   ii pancreatic amylase work best?

3 a Use the information in Figure 3 to draw a graph of the effect of temperature on the rate of the reaction of amylase on starch.

   b Draw on the graph what you would expect to happen if two more samples were set up, one at 40 °C and one at 50 °C. Explain what you have drawn.

Key Ideas

⊙ Carbohydrates, proteins and fats are large insoluble molecules which need to be broken down into small soluble molecules before they can be used by the body.

⊙ The breakdown of large molecules into smaller molecules is speeded up (catalysed) by enzymes.

⊙ Enzymes are proteins and their activity is affected by temperature and pH.

The digestive system is a hollow tube running from the mouth to the anus (Figure 1).

Following a cheese sandwich on its journey through the gut can help us understand how the digestive system works. In your **mouth**, the sandwich is coated with saliva which contains amylase. Your **teeth** chop the sandwich into smaller pieces which gives amylase a greater surface area to work on, so that it works faster (Figure 2).

The sandwich then travels down the **gullet** to the stomach, squeezed along by muscular contractions known as **peristalsis**.

↓ **Figure 1:** The human digestive system.

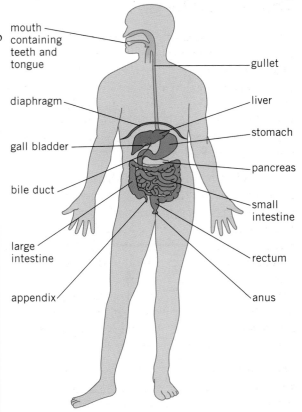

↓ **Figure 2:** The idea of increasing the surface area available for enzymes to work on is an important one – the more food the enzymes come into contact with, the faster the food molecules will be broken down and made ready for the body to use.

the volume of this cube of bread is $3 \times 3 \times 3 = 27\,cm^3$

the surface area of this cube is $(3 \times 3) \times 6$ (the number of faces of the cube) $= 9 \times 6 = 54\,cm^2$

If the same volume of bread is broken into cubes with sides of 1 cm, there will be 27 small cubes.

$1 \times 1 \times 1 = 1\,cm^3$

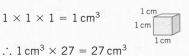

the surface area of 27 of these small cubes of bread is $(1 \times 1) \times 6$ (the number of faces) $= 6\,cm^2$

$\therefore 1\,cm^3 \times 27 = 27\,cm^3$

the total surface area of all 27 cubes $= 6\,cm^2 \times 27 = 162\,cm^2$

So the surface area of the smaller cubes is 3 times that of the single large cube.

Stomach churning activity

The **stomach** produces protease enzymes to digest protein. It also produces a concentrated solution of hydrochloric acid. The acid kills most of the bacteria which are taken in with our food. It also makes the protease enzymes more effective because they need a low pH to work as fast as possible.

After about 4 hours a thick paste of partly digested sandwich is squeezed out of the stomach into the **small intestine**. As soon as it arrives it is mixed with two more liquids from the liver and pancreas.

The liver . . .

The liver carries out lots of important jobs in the body. One of them is producing bile, a greenish yellow alkaline liquid stored in the gall bladder until needed. As food comes into the small intestine bile is squirted onto it. The bile does two important jobs:

- ⊙ It **neutralises** the acid from the stomach and then makes the semi-digested food alkaline. This is ideal for the enzymes in the small intestine, which work most effectively in an alkaline environment.

- ⊙ It **emulsifies** the fats in the food, that is, it breaks down large drops of fat into smaller droplets. This provides a much bigger surface area for the lipase enzymes to work on to break down the fats completely into fatty acids and glycerol.

... and the pancreas

The enzymes in the first part of the small intestine are supplied by the pancreas. It makes amylase, protease and lipase enzymes. As food enters the small intestine these enzymes are released and mixed with the food paste.

The rest of the gut

The rest of the small intestine is a long (about 5 m) coiled tube which produces amylase, protease and lipase enzymes of its own. Once the food molecules have been completely digested into soluble glucose, amino acids, fatty acids and glycerol, they leave the small intestine by diffusion and move into the blood supply to be carried around the body to the cells which need them.

This is why it is so important that the food molecules are broken down into a soluble form. Only when the molecules are dissolved in water can diffusion take place. The digested food molecules are small enough to pass freely through the walls of the small intestine into the blood vessels. They move in this direction because there is a very high concentration of food molecules in the gut and a much lower concentration in the blood. In other words they move into the blood along a steep concentration gradient (see page 7).

The lining of the small intestine has a large surface area for diffusion (see page 8) and a rich blood supply which carries away the digested food molecules (Figure 3).

The end of the story

After the digested food molecules have been absorbed into the blood, a watery mixture of enzymes and undigested food moves into the **large intestine**. In this wide, thin-walled tube water is absorbed back into bloodstream by diffusion. By the end of the large intestine a thick paste called **faeces** remains which leaves the body through the anus.

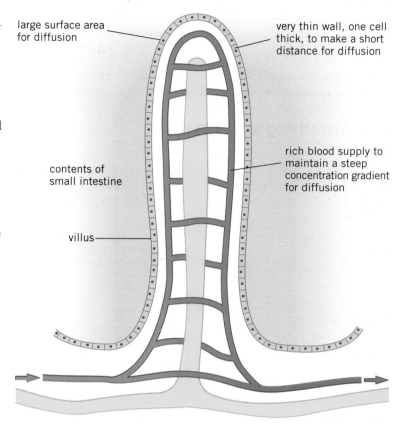

↑ **Figure 3:** Thousands of finger-like projections in the small intestine wall – called villi – provide a large surface area for soluble molecules to diffuse into the blood.

Labels on figure:
- large surface area for diffusion
- very thin wall, one cell thick, to make a short distance for diffusion
- contents of small intestine
- rich blood supply to maintain a steep concentration gradient for diffusion
- villus

? Questions

1 What is the starch in the bread of the sandwich broken down into?

2 Which bits of the sandwich start being digested in the stomach?

3 Stomach acid has two functions – what are they?

4 Draw a diagram to show how the bile produces a greater surface area for lipase to work on.

5 Make a table showing where all the three main food groups in the sandwich are digested in the body, the types of enzyme which do this and the conditions they need to work in.

Key Ideas

⊙ As food is moved along the gut, large insoluble molecules are broken down into smaller soluble molecules.

⊙ Different parts of the gut use different enzymes to break down the food.

⊙ The small soluble molecules leave the small intestine and move into the blood by diffusion along a concentration gradient.

The first breath a baby takes when it is born signals the start of a new independent life. Why is breathing so important, and how does it work? During **cellular respiration**, oxygen is used to release energy from our digested food molecules. Carbon dioxide, a poisonous waste, is produced and must be constantly removed.

Breathing is the answer to both of these problems – it brings oxygen into the body and removes the waste carbon dioxide produced by the cells as they work.

The breathing system

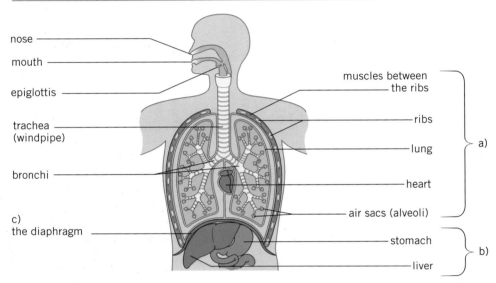

← Figure 1: The breathing system supplies the body with vital oxygen and removes poisonous carbon dioxide.

a) The lungs are in the upper part of the body – the **thorax**.

b) The **abdomen** contains the digestive system and many other body organs.

c) The **diaphragm** is a sheet of muscle separating the thorax and the abdomen, keeping the contents of each part of the body quite separate.

How is air brought into the lungs?

The job of the breathing system is to continually move air into the lungs and then move it out again. This is brought about by movements of the ribcage which we can see and feel, and by movements of the diaphragm which we can't.

When we breathe in our ribs move up and out, and the muscles of the diaphragm contract so it flattens from it's normal domed shape. This pulls air into the lungs. When we breathe out the ribs move down and in and the diaphragm returns to its domed shape, forcing air out of the lungs again. This movement of air in and out of the body is known as **ventilation** of the lungs (Figure 2).

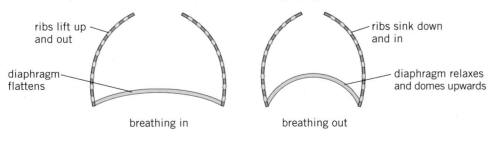

← Figure 2: The movements of the diaphragm are hidden but the movements of the ribs can be seen and felt experimentally.

More about ventilation

The breathing movements are brought about by two different sets of muscles which change the pressure in the chest cavity. The intercostal muscles between the ribs contract, pulling them upwards and outwards at the same time as the diaphragm muscles contract to flatten the diaphragm. These two movements increase the volume of the thorax. Because the same amount of gas is now inside a much bigger space, the pressure inside the chest drops. This in turn means the pressure inside the chest is lower than the pressure of the air outside. As a result air moves into the lungs.

Then when the intercostal and diaphragm muscles relax, the ribs drop and the diaphragm domes up. The volume of the thorax is decreased, so the pressure inside the chest increases as the air is squeezed and forced out of the lungs.

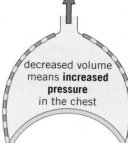

atmospheric air at higher pressure than chest – air moves into the lungs

pressure in chest higher than outside – air is forced out of the lungs

increased volume means **lower pressure** in the chest

decreased volume means **increased pressure** in the chest

as ribs move up and out and diaphragm flattens the **volume** of the chest **increases**

as ribs fall and diaphragm moves up, the **volume** of the chest **gets smaller**

↑ **Figure 3**

Ideas and Evidence

In the earlier part of the twentieth century many people suffered from polio, a disease which could leave them paralysed and even unable to breathe. The lives of many patients, children and adults alike, were saved by a technological advance known as the 'iron lung'. The whole person was inserted into the lung, with just the head left out and a tight seal around the neck. Air was then moved out of the chamber, lowering the pressure inside. As a result the chest of the patient would move up, increasing the volume and decreasing the pressure so that air moved into the lungs. Air was then forced back into the chamber of the iron lung, increasing the pressure inside it and forcing the patients chest to deflate, lowering the volume, increasing the pressure and forcing air out of the lungs. This was known as external negative pressure ventilation, and in this way the iron lung breathed for the patient – some of whom had to spend years encased in these astonishing machines.

? Questions

1 List the main structures of the human breathing system shown in Figure 1 and explain the function of the ribs, the lungs, the alveoli and the diaphragm.

2 Explain as fully as you can how air is moved into and out of the lungs in the human respiratory system.

3 Summarise the differences between the way an iron lung works and a normally functioning human breathing system.

4 Some people stop breathing in their sleep. A nasal intermittent positive pressure ventilation system forces air into the lungs at regular intervals through a small facial mask. The air is under pressure and is forced into the lungs expanding the chest, then squeezed out again as the chest falls.

a Explain how this differs from normal breathing.

b Explain the advantages of a system like this over an iron lung.

Key Ideas

⊙ The breathing system takes air into and out of the body to supply oxygen and remove carbon dioxide.

⊙ The movement of air is brought about by the ribs and the diaphragm.

⊙ Breathing movements cause changes in the volume and pressure of the chest which bring about ventilation of the lungs.

Breathing in supplies us with the oxygen we need for cellular respiration, while breathing out removes waste carbon dioxide from the body. When the air is breathed into the lungs oxygen passes into the blood by diffusion along a concentration gradient. At the same time carbon dioxide passes out of the blood into the air of the lungs, also by diffusion along a concentration gradient. This exchange of gases takes place in the **alveoli**, the tiny air sacs with a large surface area which make up much of the structure of the lungs (Figure 1).

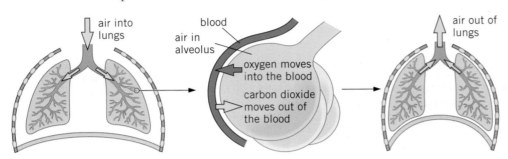

← **Figure 1:** An exchange of gases between the blood and the air takes place in the lungs.

The movement of oxygen into the blood and carbon dioxide out of the blood takes place at exactly the same time – there is a swap or exchange between the two, so this process is known as gaseous exchange.

Ideas and Evidence

It is easy to say that there is an exchange of the gases oxygen and carbon dioxide between the air and the blood, but we need evidence to support that idea. The breathing movements only tell us that air is moved into and out of the lungs – they do not tell us what happens to it there. However an analysis of the gases in inhaled and exhaled air shows clearly the differences in the quantities of some of the main gases (Table 1).

Atmospheric gas	Air breathed in	Air breathed out
nitrogen	about 80%	about 80%
oxygen	20%	16%
carbon dioxide	0.04%	4%

↑ **Table 1:** An analysis of the air taken into and breathed out of the lungs shows how the chemical makeup is changed by the diffusion which takes place in the lungs.

Although a detailed analysis like this is not always possible, a relatively simple experiment can be carried out to demonstrate that the air breathed out is different from the air breathed in. This experiment uses lime-water as an indicator of the presence of carbon dioxide – the clear liquid turns cloudy when carbon dioxide is bubbled through it, and the faster it turns cloudy, the greater the concentration of carbon dioxide present (Figure 2).

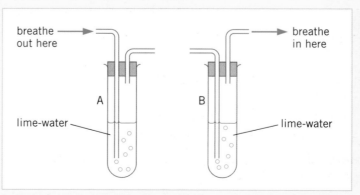

↑ **Figure 2:** Using relatively simple apparatus it is possible to see differences between the air we breathe in and the air we breathe out.

Gas exchange in the alveoli

The air in the lungs ends up in the alveoli. These tiny air sacs provide an ideal site for the most effective possible diffusion (see page 9). They have a very large surface area which is kept moist. This is important for the most effective diffusion of the gases. The alveoli also have a rich blood supply so that a concentration gradient is maintained in both directions – oxygen is constantly removed into the blood and more carbon dioxide is constantly delivered to the lungs. This makes sure that gas exchange can take place along the steep concentration gradients, so that it occurs as rapidly and effectively as possible (Figure 3).

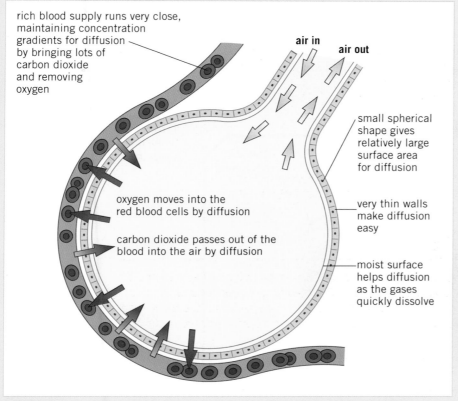

↑ **Figure 3:** The alveoli are the site of very efficient gas exchange in the lungs.

1 What is meant by the term gaseous exchange and why is it so important?

2 How are the lungs adapted to allow gas exchange to take place as effectively as possible?

3 a Draw graphs or bar charts to show the difference in composition between inspired and expired air.

  b On each graph add an extra bar to show what you would expect the moisture content of inspired and expired air to be.

4 a In the experiment shown in Figure 2, what you would expect to happen in tube A and tube B? Explain your answer.

  b What precautions might need to be taken in carrying out this experiment? Suggest a different way of doing the same experiment.

Key Ideas

⊙ In the lungs oxygen from the air diffuses into the bloodstream at the same time as carbon dioxide from the blood diffuses out of the bloodstream into the air. This is known as gas exchange.

⊙ The alveoli provide a very large, moist surface area, richly supplied with blood capillaries to allow the most efficient possible gas exchange.

Human beings are made up of billions of cells, most of them a very long way from a direct source of food or oxygen. A transport system is absolutely vital to supply the needs of the body cells and remove the waste material they produce.

In humans, transport is brought about by the blood circulation system. It has three elements – the pipes (**blood vessels**), the pump (**heart**) and the medium (**blood**).

A double circulation

Actually we have not one transport system but two. We have a **double circulation**, one carrying blood from the heart to the lungs and back again to exchange oxygen and carbon dioxide with the air; the other carrying blood all around the rest of the body and back again (Figure 1).

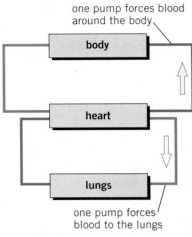

one pump forces blood around the body

body

heart

lungs

one pump forces blood to the lungs

↑ **Figure 1:** The two separate circulation systems supply the lungs and the rest of the body.

 Science people

William Harvey, a 38-year-old doctor, gave lectures correctly explaining the circulation of the blood for the first time in Europe. He is usually given the credit for having worked out the way the blood circulates in the human body, but in fact the Chinese had understood the process well before the birth of Christ. The Arab doctor Ibn An-Nafiis also described the circulation through the lungs in the 13ᵗʰ century AD – long before Harvey worked it out!

← **Figure 2:** William Harvey 1578–1657 – an English doctor who was the first European to understand the circulation of the blood.

The blood vessels

We have three main types of blood vessel which are adapted to carry out particular functions within the body, although they are all carrying the same blood (Figure 3).

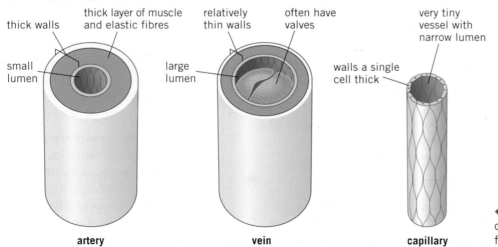

thick walls

thick layer of muscle and elastic fibres

small lumen

artery

relatively thin walls

often have valves

large lumen

vein

very tiny vessel with narrow lumen

walls a single cell thick

capillary

← **Figure 3:** Arteries, veins and capillaries – different blood vessels for different functions in the body.

The **arteries** carry blood *away* from the heart so they have to be able to withstand the pumping of the heart forcing the blood out into the circulation. This is usually oxygenated blood so it is bright red. Arteries have thick walls which contain muscle and elastic fibres, so that they can stretch as the blood is forced through them and go back into shape afterwards.

Arteries have a **pulse** in them which you can feel at certain places in the body (like the wrist) where they run close to the surface. The pulse is the surge of blood from the heart when it beats. Because the blood in the arteries is under pressure, it is very dangerous if an artery is cut because the blood spurts out rapidly every time the heart beats.

The **veins** carry blood *towards* the heart – it is usually low in oxygen and so is a deep purplish-red colour. They have much thinner walls than arteries and the blood in them is under much lower pressure because it is a long way away from the thrust of the heart. They do not have a pulse, but they often have valves to prevent the back-flow of blood as it moves from the various parts of the body back to the heart (Figure 4).

↓ Figure 4: The valves in the veins stop your blood from flowing backwards!

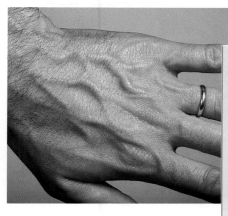

valve open: blood flows towards the heart

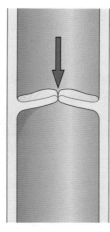

valve closed: blood cannot flow away from the heart

Between the arteries which bring blood from the heart and the veins which collect it up to take back to the heart are very narrow, thin-walled blood vessels called **capillaries**. These take the blood into all the organs and tissues of the body.

The capillaries are narrow with very thin walls so that substances needed by body cells, such as oxygen and glucose, can easily pass out of the blood and into the cells by diffusion. In the same way substances produced by the cells, such as carbon dioxide, pass easily into the blood through the walls of the capillaries.

? **Questions**

1 a Why do we need a circulation system?

 b What are the main parts of the human circulation system?

2 a Draw a diagram which explains the way the arteries, veins and capillaries are linked to each other and to the heart.

 b Label the diagram and explain what is happening in the capillaries.

3 How are the different blood vessels adapted for their function?

4 Blood in the arteries is usually bright red because it is full of oxygen. This is not true of the arteries leaving the heart for the lungs. Why not?

Key Ideas

⊙ The body transport system consists of the blood vessels, the heart and the blood.

⊙ Human beings have a double circulation.

⊙ The three main types of blood vessels are the arteries, veins and capillaries, and they are each adapted for a different function.

The human heart is a bag of reddish-brown muscle which beats from the early days of our development in the uterus until the end of our life, sending blood around the body. The heart is made up of two pumps which beat at the same time so that blood can be delivered to the body about 70 times each minute.

The structure of the heart

The walls of the heart are almost entirely made of muscle tissue. The muscle walls of the left-hand side of the heart are thicker than on the right (see Figure 1). This is because the left-hand side of the heart has to pump blood around the whole body, whilst the right-hand side pumps only to the lungs.

The working of the heart

The two sides of the heart fill and empty at the same time to give a strong, co-ordinated beat, but to understand what happens it is easier to follow a single volume of blood around the heart.

⊙ Deoxygenated blood, which has given up oxygen to the cells of the body and is loaded with carbon dioxide, comes into the right atrium of the heart from the veins of the body.

⊙ The atrium contracts and forces blood into the right ventricle.

⊙ The right ventricle contracts and forces blood out of the heart and into the lungs where it is oxygenated – it picks up oxygen.

⊙ Oxygenated blood returns to the left-hand side of the heart from the lungs and the left atrium fills up.

⊙ The left atrium contracts, forcing blood into the left ventricle.

⊙ The left ventricle contracts, forcing oxygenated blood out of the heart into the aorta and around the body.

Inside the heart there are many different valves. Each time the muscular walls of the heart contract and force blood out some of these valves open to allow the blood to flow in the right direction, and other valves close to make sure that the blood does not flow backwards. The noise of the heart beat we can hear through a stethoscope is actually the sound of these valves working in the surging blood.

↓ **Figure 1:** The structure of the human heart is perfectly adapted to the job it has to do.

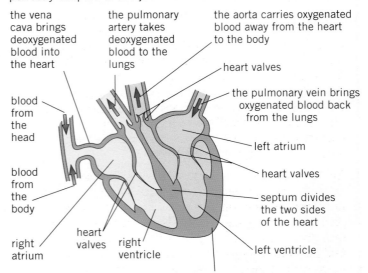

the vena cava brings deoxygenated blood into the heart

the pulmonary artery takes deoxygenated blood to the lungs

the aorta carries oxygenated blood away from the heart to the body

heart valves

blood from the head

the pulmonary vein brings oxygenated blood back from the lungs

left atrium

heart valves

blood from the body

septum divides the two sides of the heart

heart valves

right atrium

right ventricle

left ventricle

muscular heart wall – the muscle is thicker on the left as it has to pump the blood all around the body

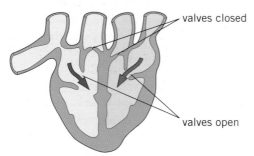

valves closed

valves open

diastole – this is when the heart muscles relax and the chambers fill with blood

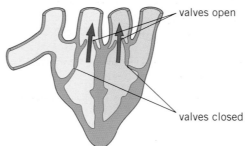

valves open

valves closed

systole – this is when the heart muscles contract and force the blood out of the heart

← **Figure 2:** As the heart fills and empties, the two sides of the heart work in perfect harmony.

Heart disease – the search for an answer

For years many scientists have believed that too much fat in the diet – particularly animal fat – leads to increased heart disease. However, there is growing evidence that the problems of heart disease may be as much to do with vitamin deficiencies in our highly processed diets as with levels of fat.

Thirty years ago a young American researcher at Harvard University, Kilmer McCully, noticed that the arteries of babies who died from a very rare disease looked like the arteries of much older people who died of heart attacks. It seemed as if the build-up of a rogue amino acid caused changes in the blood vessels supplying oxygen to the heart and so caused heart attacks. McCully found that B vitamins, particularly B_6, B_{12} and folic acid, controlled the blood level of the amino acid and prevented it causing any damage. These vitamins are often lacking in modern diets but can easily be taken by changing the diet or taking supplements – a cheap and easy solution to the problem.

But no-one listened to McCully's ideas. People had spent lots of time and money on developing the 'high fat' theory of heart disease and on drugs and low-fat products to help beat the disease. They were not very receptive to a challenging and different approach. McCully was prevented from carrying on his work at Harvard, denied funding, and his career was almost destroyed.

Yet now, 30 years on, in spite of the treatment to counter the effects of fats, deaths from heart disease have not fallen greatly and people are beginning to wonder if there is a different explanation for the problem. McCully's theory is finally being taken seriously, involving major trials of vitamins taking place with heart disease victims around the world. If McCully is proved right, there will be a simple solution to heart disease. If not, then the accuracy of the current model of heart disease will be confirmed.

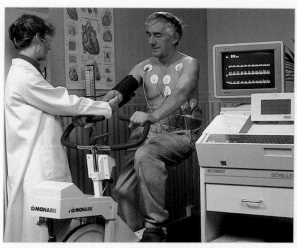

↑ **Figure 3:** There could be far fewer patients with heart disease in the future if Kilmer McCully's ideas turn out to be correct.

1 Draw a diagram of the heart. Then number the areas of the heart to show the route of a single volume of blood returning from the body as it travels around the heart. List the numbers and explain what is happening in the heart at each point you have labelled.

2 ⊙ Deaths from heart disease have been declining since the 1960s in the USA and the late1970s in Britain.

⊙ Cholesterol levels have not changed significantly in that time and neither has the average diet.

⊙ In the 1960s in the USA and in the 1970s in the UK, cereal manufacturers began adding vitamins to breakfast cereals – in particular the B vitamins.

Look at this evidence and explain how it might be used to support Kilmer McCully's theory about the cause of heart disease.

⊙ The heart is mainly made of muscle.

⊙ It pumps blood around the body in response to the needs of the tissues.

⊙ Blood enters the atria of the heart which contract to force blood into the ventricles. When the ventricles contract, blood leaves the heart to go to the lungs (from the right) and around the body (from the left).

2.7 The blood

Our blood is a complex mixture of cells and liquid which carries a huge range of substances around the body.

The structure of the blood

The blood consists of a liquid called plasma which carries red blood cells, white blood cells and platelets.

Plasma

The **plasma** is a yellow liquid which transports all the blood cells but also a number of other things. Carbon dioxide produced in the organs of the body is carried in the plasma back to the lungs. Similarly, urea, a waste product formed in the liver, is carried in the plasma to the kidneys where it is removed from the blood to form urine. All the small, soluble products of digestion pass into the blood from the gut. They are carried in the plasma around the body to the organs and individual cells which need them.

Red blood cells

There are more **red blood cells** than any other type of blood cell. They carry oxygen from the lungs to the cells where it is needed. They can do this because they are full of a special red substance which picks up oxygen (Figure 3).

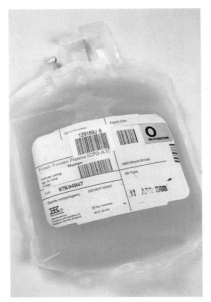

↑ **Figure 1:** In some circumstances – for example when a patient has lost a lot of blood – it is important to restore the blood volume. In cases like this, plasma may be given on its own.

 H **More about red blood cells**

Red blood cells have no nucleus. They are packed with a special pigment called **haemoglobin**, a large protein molecule folded around four iron atoms. In a high concentration of oxygen, such as in the lungs, the haemoglobin reacts with oxygen to form **oxyhaemoglobin**. This is bright scarlet, which is why most arterial blood is bright red.

In areas where the concentration of oxygen is lower, such as the cells and organs of the body, the reaction reverses. The oxyhaemoglobin splits to give purplish-red haemoglobin (the colour of venous blood) and oxygen. The oxygen then passes into the cells where it is needed by diffusion (Figure 2).

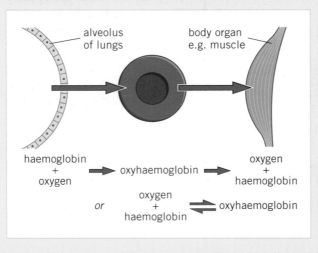

← **Figure 2:** This reversible reaction makes active life as we know it possible by carrying oxygen to all the places where it is really needed.

White blood cells

The **white blood cells** are much bigger than red cells and there are fewer of them. They have a nucleus and form part of the body's defence system against microbes (Figure 3). Some white blood cells form antibodies against microbes whilst others 'eat' invading bacteria.

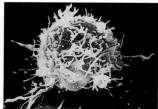
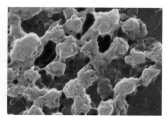

← **Figure 3:** Mixed together with plasma, these different types of cells make up our blood.

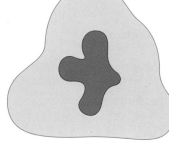

red blood cell

white blood cell

platelets

protein threads

platelets and red blood cells entangled

↑ **Figure 4:** Without platelets, clotting would not occur and we could bleed to death from a simple cut.

Platelets

Platelets are small fragments of cells (Figure 3). They have no nucleus and are very important in helping the blood to clot at the site of a wound. When platelets arrive at a wound site they are involved in the formation of a network of protein threads. Then as more platelets and red blood cells pour out of the wound they become entangled in the mesh of threads forming a jelly-like clot. This soon dries and hardens to form a scab, protecting the body from the entry of bacteria and protecting the new skin as it grows (Figure 4).

Cellular respiration

The digestive system, breathing and circulation systems all exist to provide the cells of the human body with what they need for **respiration**. During this process glucose (a sugar produced as a result of digestion) reacts with oxygen to release energy which can be used by the cell. Carbon dioxide and water are produced as waste products.

The reaction can be summed up as follows:

glucose + oxygen → carbon dioxide + water (**+ energy**)

This is called **aerobic** respiration because it uses oxygen from the air.

H Aerobic respiration takes place in the mitochondria in cells. These are tiny rod-shaped bodies (organelles) which are found in almost all cells. They have a folded inner membrane which provides a large surface area for the enzymes involved in aerobic respiration. Muscle cells contain lots of mitochondria because they use a lot of energy.

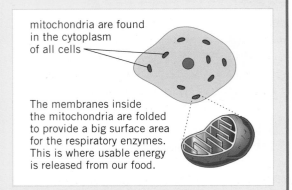

mitochondria are found in the cytoplasm of all cells

The membranes inside the mitochondria are folded to provide a big surface area for the respiratory enzymes. This is where usable energy is released from our food.

↑ **Figure 1:** Mitochondria are the powerhouses which provide energy for all the functions of a cell.

Why is respiration needed?

Respiration releases energy from the food we eat so that the cells of the body can use it. The cells need energy to carry out the basic functions of life. One of their main functions is to build up large molecules from smaller ones to make new cell material. Much of the energy released in respiration is used for these 'building' activities.

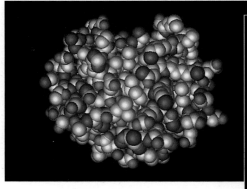
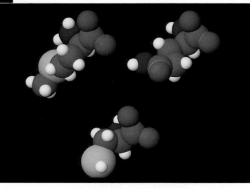

← **Figure 2:** It takes lots of energy to build large molecules like this protein from simpler building blocks like these amino acids.

Another important use of the energy from respiration is in making muscles contract. Muscles are working all the time in our body, even when we are not aware of using them. For example, when we are asleep our heart is beating, our rib muscles and diaphragm contract as we breathe, our gut is churning – and all of these muscular activities use energy.

Finally we are 'warm-blooded'. This means that our bodies are the same temperature inside almost regardless of the temperature around us. On cold days we use energy to keep our body warm (Figure 3), whilst on hot days we use energy to sweat and keep our body cool.

 Aerobic respiration in cells also provides energy for the active transport of some materials across cell boundaries (see 1.5).

Anaerobic respiration

The energy released by aerobic respiration in muscle cells allows them to move. However, during vigorous exercise the muscle cells may become short of oxygen – the blood simply cannot supply it fast enough. When this happens the muscle cells can still obtain energy from the glucose but they have to do it by a type of respiration which does not use oxygen (**anaerobic respiration**).

Anaerobic respiration produces a different waste product called **lactic acid**. The body cannot get rid of lactic acid by breathing it out as it does carbon dioxide, so when the exercise is over lactic acid has to be broken down. This needs oxygen, and the amount of oxygen needed to break down the lactic acid is known as the **oxygen debt**. Even though our leg muscles have stopped working, our heart rate and breathing rate stay high to supply extra oxygen until we have paid off the oxygen debt.

↑ **Figure 3:** Warm-blooded animals like us and this cat use up some of the energy produced by aerobic respiration just keeping a steady body temperature regardless of the weather.

H When muscle cells have been used for vigorous exercise for a very long time they become fatigued, which means they stop contracting efficiently. They often also need to switch to anaerobic respiration. However, anaerobic respiration is not as efficient as aerobic respiration. It does not break down the glucose molecules completely so far less energy is released than during aerobic respiration. After exercise, the lactic acid is oxidised by oxygen to produce carbon dioxide and water.

Anaerobic respiration:
  glucose → lactic acid + energy

Oxygen debt repayment:
  lactic acid + oxygen → carbon dioxide and water

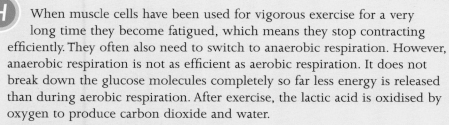

? Questions

1 a What is aerobic respiration?

   b Write a word equation for aerobic respiration.

   c How does aerobic respiration differ from anaerobic respiration?

2 Aerobic respiration provides energy for the cells of the body. Explain why cells need this energy and what they use it for.

3 If you exercise very hard you often puff and pant for some time after you stop. Explain what is happening.

H 4 If you exercise very hard or for a long time your muscles begin to ache and do not work so effectively. Explain why.

0—ᴍ Key Ideas

⊙ Aerobic respiration is the breakdown of glucose with oxygen to provide energy for the cells. Carbon dioxide and water are the waste products.

⊙ Anaerobic respiration is respiration without oxygen. Glucose is broken down to form lactic acid and a small amount of energy.

⊙ After exercise oxygen is still needed to break down the lactic acid which has built up. The amount of oxygen needed is known as an oxygen debt.

1 The diagram shows the human digestive system.

a Which of the parts, labelled **A–I** on the diagram, is where
  i hydrochloric acid is produced
  ii bile is produced
  iii the digestive enzyme amylase is produced?

(3 marks)

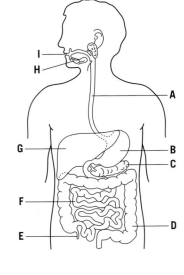

b Describe how starch is digested in the digestive system.

(2 marks)
(Total 5 marks)
AQA specimen question

2 Refer again to the diagram of the human digestive system in question 1. Explain what happens to the food we eat in each of the following areas:
  i I   (2 marks)
  ii B   (3 marks)
  iii F   (4 marks)
  iv D.   (2 marks)
(Total 11 marks)

3 The digestion of our food depends heavily on the action of enzymes.

a What is an enzyme?   (1 mark)

b What are enzymes made of?   (1 mark)

c The graph shows that the rate at which enzyme-controlled reactions take place is affected by temperature.

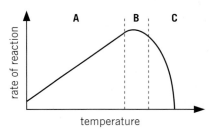

Explain what is happening to the reaction in the areas of the graph labelled **A**, **B** and **C**.

(3 marks)
(Total 5 marks)

4 The table below gives the relative activity of pancreatic amylase under different pH conditions.

pH	Relative activity of the enzyme
4	0
5	1
6	4
7	7
8	10
9	7
10	1

a Plot a graph to show the effect of pH on the activity of the enzyme.   (5 marks)

b Explain why enzymes are so sensitive to pH.   (1 mark)
(Total 6 marks)

5 The bar chart compares the percentages of certain gases in inhaled and exhaled air.

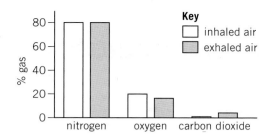

a What are the main differences between inhaled and exhaled air? (2 marks)

b Where in the lungs does gaseous exchange take place? (1 mark)

c Explain in your own words, using good English and diagrams if you wish, how the alveoli are adapted for an efficient exchange of gases in the lungs. (6 marks)

(Total 9 marks)

6 The diagram shows a vertical section through the human heart.

a Which of the parts labelled **A**–**J** on the diagram

   i divides the two sides of the heart

   ii prevents blood flowing in the wrong direction through the heart

   iii brings blood into the heart from the body

   iv carries blood from the heart out around the body? (4 marks)

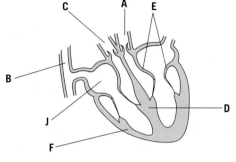

b The blood vessels which carry blood from the heart around the body and then return it to the heart are all well adapted for the jobs they carry out.

   i Give the names of the three main types of blood vessels. (3 marks)

   ii For each of the vessels named in (i) give one adaptation which fits it so well for its function. (3 marks)

(Total 10 marks)

7 a How are red blood cells adapted for the carriage of oxygen? (3 marks)

b The graph shows the effect of an increased carbon dioxide concentration on the way haemoglobin carries oxygen.

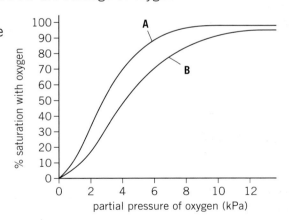

Key

A: haemoglobin under normal conditions

B: haemoglobin with a raised level of carbon dioxide

   i What is the percentage saturation of haemoglobin under normal conditions when the partial pressure of oxygen is 2 and 4? (2 marks)

   ii What is the percentage saturation of haemoglobin when the partial pressure of oxygen is 2 and 4 and the concentration of carbon dioxide is raised? (2 marks)

c What does this tell you about the way in which haemoglobin and oxygen interact

   i in the tissues of the body and

   ii in the lungs? (Think in terms of the carbon dioxide and oxygen concentrations in those two different areas.) (4 marks)

(Total 11 marks)

All living organisms need some awareness of their surroundings so they can avoid danger, find food and, in some cases, find a mate (Figure 1). They also need to be able to act on their awareness of their surroundings and this requires some co-ordination and control within the organism.

How do we know about our surroundings?

In human beings, our awareness of changes in our surroundings is due to our **nervous system**. This carries messages about our surroundings from the surface of our body where they are detected to other parts, usually the brain, which sends messages to other parts of the body to act on the information. The messages which travel in the nervous system are electrical messages.

Changes in our surroundings (known as **stimuli**) are picked up by cells called **receptors**. They *sense* stimuli. We have many different types of sensory receptors which respond to different stimuli. They are found in **sensory organs**. Some of the most important include:

Type of receptor	Sensory organs where the receptors are found
sensitive to light	eye
sensitive to sound	ear
sensitive to changes in position and help us to keep our balance	ear
sensitive to chemicals and enable us to taste and to smell	tongue and nose
sensitive to touch, pressure, temperature changes and pain	skin

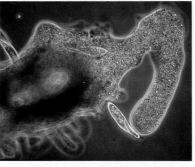

↑ **Figure 1:** Even relatively simple animals such as this amoeba are aware when food comes their way and can co-ordinate their actions to make sure they capture it.

How do we act on the information?

Once a stimulus is picked up by a sensory receptor, the information is passed along nerves to a **co-ordinator**, often the brain. The nerves which carry information from our receptors to the brain are made up of cells called **sensory neurones**.

In the brain the information is added to the vast amounts of other information arriving from different receptors. The brain co-ordinates all this information and then sends messages out along **motor neurones** to make the appropriate parts (the **effector**) **respond**.

↓ **Figure 2:** The rapid responses of the nervous system allow us to respond to immediate danger – and to plan ahead.

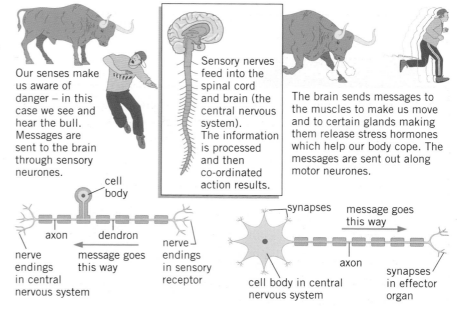

Our senses make us aware of danger – in this case we see and hear the bull. Messages are sent to the brain through sensory neurones.

Sensory nerves feed into the spinal cord and brain (the central nervous system). The information is processed and then co-ordinated action results.

The brain sends messages to the muscles to make us move and to certain glands making them release stress hormones which help our body cope. The messages are sent out along motor neurones.

cell body

axon   dendron

nerve endings in central nervous system   message goes this way   nerve endings in sensory receptor

synapses   message goes this way

axon

cell body in central nervous system   synapses in effector organ

Fast responses usually come from muscles moving but nerves can also trigger glands in the body (like the liver or pancreas) to release chemicals which the body needs.

Nervous control can be summed up as: **receptor → co-ordinator → effector.**

Ideas and Evidence

Evidence for the importance of being sensitive to the outside world is clearly visible in the bodies of many animals. For example, the American moon moth, with a wingspan of up to 11 cm, has enormous feathery antennae – but only in the males. The moths are relatively rare, so the males need to be able to detect females at great distances. The female produces a chemical scent which is very attractive to the males and which can be carried several kilometres away from her by diffusion in the air to be picked up by the huge antennae. However, the hearing and eyesight of these ghostly green insects seems normal for moths.

Many species of bats hunt insects at night. They cannot rely on vision to find their tiny prey, so they have to depend on picking up the slightest sounds. In addition, many bats have developed an extra sense – they can hunt using echo-location. They send out streams of high-pitched sound – beyond the range of human hearing – and they interpret the echoes which bounce back to them to help them find their prey. Many bats have very large ears, and some also have specially adapted noses with extra folds of skin almost like another ear.

← **Figure 4:** A Townsend's big-eared bat.

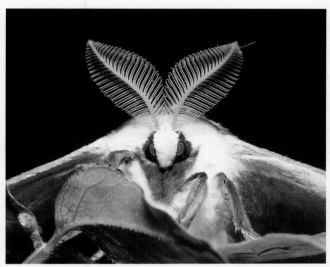

↑ **Figure 3:** A male American Moon moth with his amazing antennae.

Questions

1 Use the table showing the different types of sense receptors. For each type of receptor give an example of the sort of things it responds to, e.g. taste receptors respond to sweet tastes in the mouth.

2 Why are the brain, or spinal cord, called the co-ordinator?

3 **a** For each of the animals described in the box, explain

    i which of their sensory organs are the most important to them

    ii why that sense is so important

    iii what you would expect their other senses to be like.

  b Which senses do you think are most important to people? Explain your answer.

Key Ideas

⊙ The nervous system enables human beings to react to their surroundings and co-ordinate their behaviour.

⊙ Cells called receptors detect stimuli (changes in the environment).

⊙ Information from receptors passes along nerves to the brain which co-ordinates the response.

Sight is an important sense for human beings. The reason we can see so well is largely due to our complex eyes (Figure 1).

The human eye

The eye contains a large number of sensory receptor cells. All the light-sensitive cells are arranged together in a special light-sensitive layer inside and at the back of the eye known as the **retina**.

How the eye works

The white outer layer of the eye, the **sclera**, is very tough and strong so the eyeball is not easy to damage. It has a transparent area at the front known as the **cornea** which lets light in to the eye. The curved surface of the cornea is also very important for bending the light coming into the eye to make sure it enters the eye and is focused on the retina.

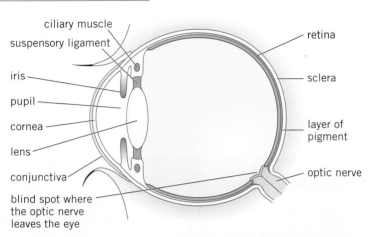

↑ **Figure 1:** The structure of the human eye – a very effective sense organ.

Once the light has travelled through the cornea it passes through the pupil in the centre of the iris. The **iris** is made up of muscles which contract or relax to control the size of the pupil and so control the amount of light reaching the retina. If the pupil is enlarged, lots of light can get into the eye. This is what happens when the light is relatively dim. In bright light, however, the iris makes the pupil very small. This reduces the amount of light which goes into the eye, so that the delicate light-sensitive cells are not damaged by too much bright light.

Once through the pupil, light passes through the **lens**, a clear disc. The lens is held in place by **suspensory ligaments** and the **ciliary muscles**. It is the lens of the eye which 'fine-tunes' the focusing of the light, bending it to make sure that it produces a clear image on the retina.

When the light hits the retina, the light-sensitive cells are stimulated. They send impulses to the brain along sensory neurones in the **optic nerve**. When the brain receives these messages it interprets them as a visual image – in other words, we see something!

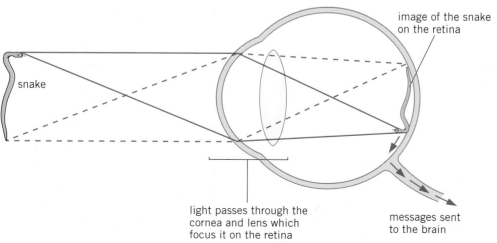

← **Figure 2:** When an image falls on the light-sensitive cells of the retina and a message is sent through the optic nerve to the brain, we can see.

Focusing the light

Sometimes we look at objects close to us – for example when we are reading or studying. At other times we are gazing into the distance looking at objects a long way away. The light arriving at our eyes in these circumstances is travelling differently. The light from a distant object reaching our eyes will be travelling in almost parallel rays, whilst the light from close objects will be spreading out or **diverging** very strongly.

The cornea bends all of the light entering the eyes towards the retina, but it is the lens which makes sure that we can see both close and distant objects equally well. It does this by changing shape. Light from distant objects needs little further bending once it has passed through the cornea, so the lens is long and thin and has little effect. However, light from close objects still needs some considerable bending to bring it into focus on the retina. The lens of the eye needs to be much thicker to focus light from near objects. These changes in the shape of the lens are brought about by the contraction and relaxation of the ciliary muscles which surround them.

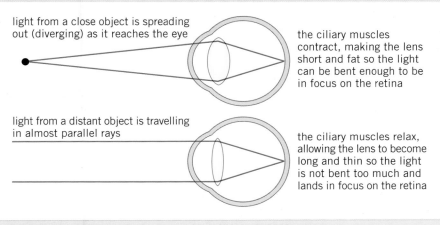

light from a close object is spreading out (diverging) as it reaches the eye

the ciliary muscles contract, making the lens short and fat so the light can be bent enough to be in focus on the retina

light from a distant object is travelling in almost parallel rays

the ciliary muscles relax, allowing the lens to become long and thin so the light is not bent too much and lands in focus on the retina

↑ **Figure 3:** It is the relaxation and contraction of the ciliary muscles which change the shape of the lens and allow distant and close objects to be focused equally clearly on the retina.

? Questions

1 Make a table to show the main components of the human eye and their functions.

2 Describe how the lens focuses light.

3 Why is your pupil more open in dim light than in bright light?

4 The image focused onto the retina is upside down but you 'see' it the right way up. What does this tell you about the importance of the brain in our ability to see?

5 People who do a lot of close work – reading or on computers – are advised to look up regularly and focus on things which are much further away.

   a Make a table to show the main differences in the eye when looking at objects which are close to the eye compared to objects a long way away.

   b Why do you think it might be good for the eye to look into the distance occasionally when doing close work?

⚷ Key Ideas

- ⊙ The human eye includes: sclera, cornea, iris, pupil, lens, ciliary muscle, suspensory ligament, retina and optic nerve.

- ⊙ The light-sensitive cells are found in the retina.

- ⊙ The iris controls the amount of light entering the eye.

- ⊙ The cornea bends the light entering the eye.

- ⊙ The lens controls the fine focus of the image onto the retina.

A reflex action

Some of our responses to stimuli are purely automatic. When we touch something very hot we withdraw our hand before we are consciously aware of the sensation of pain. If an object approaches our face we blink. Reactions such as these are known as **reflexes** (Figure 1).

Reflexes occur very fast. They often help us to avoid danger or damage. We also have lots of reflexes taking care of basic bodily functions. Breathing is a good example. You do not have to consciously make yourself breathe.

The way a reflex action happens is the same as all nervous reactions. An electrical impulse passes from the receptors along the sensory neurones to the spinal cord or brain and then along a motor neurone to a muscle or gland (Figure 2). The key point about a reflex action is that the messages do not reach a conscious area of the brain before instructions are sent out to take action. Many reflexes involve the spinal cord rather than the brain.

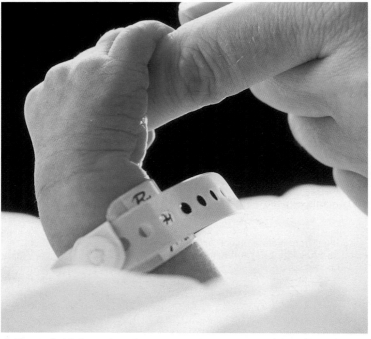

↑ **Figure 1:** If the palm of the hand of a new born baby is touched, the hand closes and grips in a reflex action. The grip is so tight that the baby can be lifted up by it.

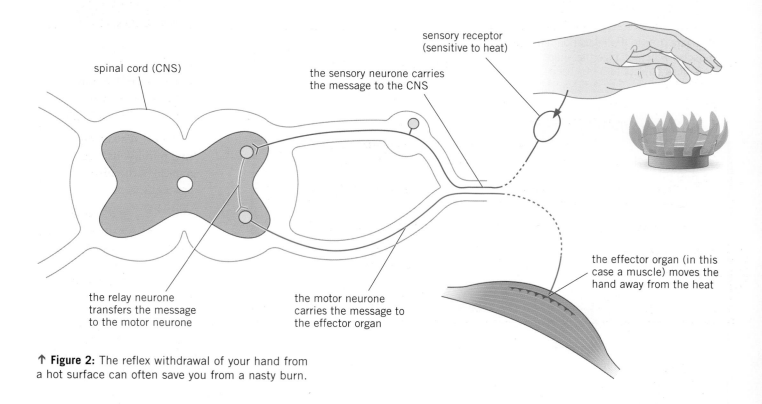

spinal cord (CNS)

sensory receptor (sensitive to heat)

the sensory neurone carries the message to the CNS

the relay neurone transfers the message to the motor neurone

the motor neurone carries the message to the effector organ

the effector organ (in this case a muscle) moves the hand away from the heat

↑ **Figure 2:** The reflex withdrawal of your hand from a hot surface can often save you from a nasty burn.

Connectors

The brain and spinal cord together form the **central nervous system** (**CNS**). These are co-ordinators which process the information coming from sensory receptors and neurones, and instruct motor neurones and effectors to react. They contain another type of neurone known as a **relay neurone**. This connects the sensory and motor neurones in the CNS.

The electrical impulses which carry messages travel across the three types of neurone at junctions called **synapses**. When an impulse arrives at the end of one neurone, chemicals are released which cross the synapse and start up an electrical impulse in the next neurone.

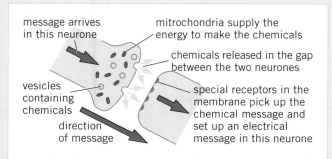

message arrives in this neurone

mitrochondria supply the energy to make the chemicals

chemicals released in the gap between the two neurones

vesicles containing chemicals

special receptors in the membrane pick up the chemical message and set up an electrical message in this neurone

direction of message

↑ **Figure 3:** Chemicals released at synapses such as this control the direction of impulses travelling all over the nervous system.

How reflexes work in detail

In the example shown in Figure 2 a person touches a very hot object:

⊙ Impulses from a receptor in the skin pass along a sensory neurone to the central nervous system – in this case the spinal cord.

⊙ When an impulse from the sensory neurone arrives at the synapse with a relay neurone, a chemical is released which causes an impulse to be sent along the relay neurone.

⊙ When the impulse reaches the synapse between the relay neurone and a motor neurone returning to the arm, again a chemical is released.

⊙ This starts impulses travelling along the motor neurone to the organ (effector) which brings about change. In this example the impulses arrive in the muscles of the arm, causing them to contract and move the hand rapidly away from the source of heat and pain.

Most reflex actions can be analysed as follows:

Stimulus → receptor → co-ordinator → effector → response

This is very similar to a normal conscious action, except that in a reflex the co-ordinator is a relay neurone either in the spinal cord or in the unconscious areas of the brain.

? Questions

1 Explain why certain actions, such as breathing and the squeezing of the gut, are the result of reflex actions whilst others, such as speaking and putting food in the mouth, are under voluntary control.

2 Many bodily functions are under reflex control. In what other circumstances are reflex actions very important? Explain why.

H 3 The nervous system is sometimes described as carrying electrical messages, but this is not a completely accurate picture. Explain why not.

4 For each of the following reflex actions, carry out an analysis to show the stimulus, receptor, co-ordinator, effector and response:

a knee jerk reflex

b stepping on a pin

c swallowing

d blinking when something approaches your face fast.

⚿ Key Ideas

⊙ Reflex actions run mundane bodily functions and help us to avoid danger – they avoid conscious thought.

⊙ In any nerve pathway the junctions between neurones are called synapses.

H ⊙ When an impulse arrives in one neurone chemicals are released in the synapse to trigger an impulse in the next neurone.

⊙ Reflex actions involve stimulus → receptor → co-ordinator → effector → response.

Many processes in the body are controlled by chemical substances known as **hormones**. Hormones act as chemical messages, produced in one part of the body but having an effect somewhere entirely different. Hormones are produced (**secreted**) by special **glands** found around the body and are carried in the bloodstream from the glands to their target organs. They can act very rapidly, but often their effects are slower and longer lasting than the results of nervous control.

Controlling sugar

Hormones control the levels of sugar in our blood. When we digest a meal, large amounts of glucose pass into our blood. Without a control mechanism these glucose levels would vary wildly – after a meal they would soar to a point where glucose would be removed from the body in the urine, but then a few hours later they would plummet and cells would not have enough glucose to respire.

This internal chaos is prevented by the actions of two hormones, **insulin** and **glucagon**, secreted by the **pancreas**. When blood glucose levels rise, insulin is released and this leads to glucose which is not needed at the time being taken out of the blood and stored. If the blood glucose level falls, glucagon releases stored glucose back into the blood. Between them they keep the blood glucose level fairly constant.

Diabetes

For some people life isn't quite this simple, because their pancreas does not make enough – or any – insulin. This is the disease known as diabetes, and it can affect anyone from young children through to very old people.

If you have a fairly mild form of diabetes, managing your diet carefully is enough to stay healthy. Avoiding carbohydrate-rich foods keeps the blood sugar levels relatively low so the reduced amount of insulin can cope with them. However, many diabetics also need to inject themselves with replacement insulin before meals to make sure that their blood glucose levels are kept as stable as possible.

Ideas and Evidence

(H) The treatment of diabetes has moved on over the years. For centuries nothing could be done. Then it was realised that extracts of animal pancreas could be used to keep diabetics alive and these were refined to give clean, reliable doses.

In recent years, genetic engineering has meant that bacteria can be used to produce pure human insulin, now injected by the majority of diabetics. Now scientists are trying to find easier ways for diabetics to give themselves the drugs and, most excitingly, to provide diabetics with new, functioning pancreas cells.

← **Figure 1:** Dorothy Hodgkin determined the structure of the insulin molecule and the way the protein is arranged. This understanding, with the work of other scientists, helped pave the way for the next step – genetically engineered insulin!

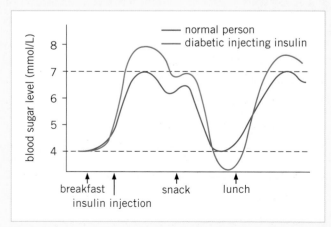

↑ **Figure 2:** Insulin injections keep the blood sugar level within safe limits – but cannot mimic the total control given by the natural production of the pancreas.

Insulin and glucagon

The pancreas does more than simply produce the hormones insulin and glucagon. It monitors the levels of sugar in the blood and balances the release of the two hormones. When blood glucose levels rise, the pancreas monitors this and releases insulin into the blood. As a result, the liver converts glucose into insoluble **glycogen** and stores it. Then when blood glucose levels drop, the pancreas is sensitive to the change and secretes glucagon. This causes the liver to break down glycogen, converting it back to glucose and releasing it into the blood. In this way, by using the glycogen store in the liver, the blood glucose is maintained at almost constant levels throughout the day.

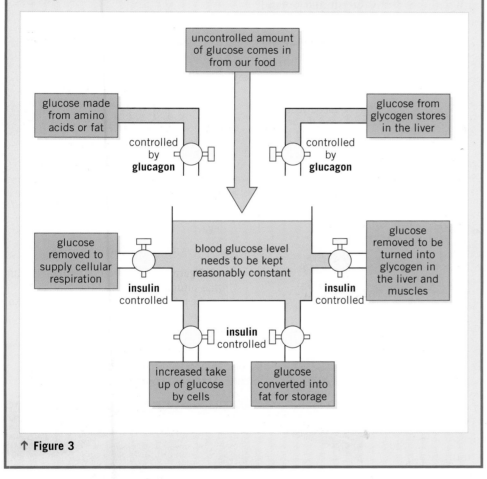

↑ **Figure 3**

Key Ideas

- Chemical co-ordination and control of the body is brought about by hormones secreted by special glands.

- Insulin and glucagon control blood glucose levels. They are secreted by the pancreas.

- In diabetes the blood glucose may rise to fatally high levels because the pancreas does not secrete enough insulin. Successful treatment involves diet management and regular injections of insulin.

? Questions

1 a What is a hormone?

b Where are hormones produced?

c How is control by hormones different from control by the nervous system?

2 a Explain how the level of glucose in the blood is controlled by hormones.

b Why is it so important to control the level of glucose in the blood?

c What is diabetes and how can it be treated?

d Look at Figure 2. Explain the differences in blood sugar levels between a normal individual and an injecting diabetic.

Chemical control by hormones is also vital in one of the most important bodily processes – reproduction. In girls and women hormones control the whole process of menstruation and pregnancy (Figure 1).

The menstrual cycle

A baby girl has ovaries full of immature eggs, but they do nothing until after puberty. Then, once a month, a surge of hormones from the pituitary gland in the brain starts a few of the eggs developing.

These hormones also affect the ovary itself which starts making the female hormone **oestrogen**. This stimulates the uterus to build up a spongy lining with lots of blood vessels ready to support a pregnancy (Figure 2).

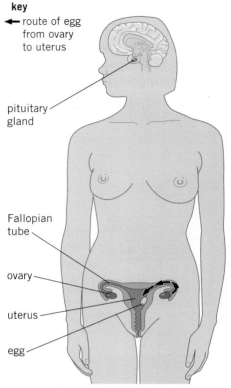

key
← route of egg from ovary to uterus

pituitary gland

Fallopian tube

ovary

uterus

egg

↑ **Figure 1:** The action of hormones from the pituitary gland and the ovaries makes it possible for women to produce fertile eggs and become pregnant.

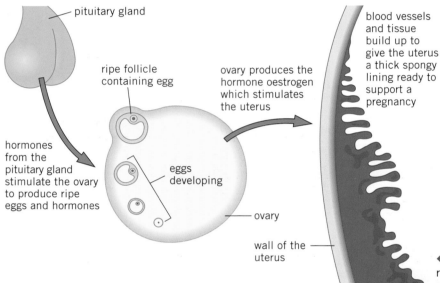

pituitary gland

ripe follicle containing egg

ovary produces the hormone oestrogen which stimulates the uterus

hormones from the pituitary gland stimulate the ovary to produce ripe eggs and hormones

eggs developing

ovary

blood vessels and tissue build up to give the uterus a thick spongy lining ready to support a pregnancy

wall of the uterus

← **Figure 2:** The ovary and the uterus respond to hormone messages to prepare for possible pregnancy.

About 14 days after the eggs start ripening, one of them bursts out of its follicle (Figure 3). This is called **ovulation** and when it happens the hormone levels from the pituitary and the ovary drop dramatically.

After ovulation, a different hormone makes sure that for some days the uterus lining stays thick and spongy, ready to receive a fertilised egg. However, in most months the egg is not fertilised and the woman does not become pregnant.

About 10 days after the egg is released the chemical messages change again and the blood vessels which are supplying the thick spongy lining of the uterus close down. The lining detaches from the wall of the uterus and is lost as the monthly period or bleeding. However, if the egg has been fertilised it will reach the uterus and sink into the thick, spongy lining, attach itself (**implant**) and start to develop.

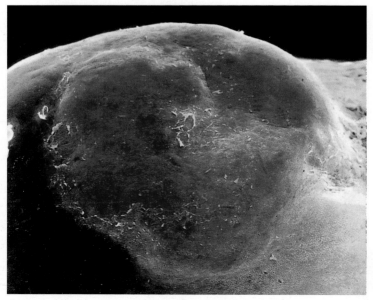

↑ **Figure 3:** As the egg ripens the follicle fills with fluid and finally bursts to release the egg.

The hormone factory

The pituitary gland produces two female sex hormones which are involved in the release of an egg in the middle of the menstrual cycle:

⊙ **FSH** (follicle stimulating hormone) stimulates the development of a follicle in the ovary, and within the follicle the egg matures and ripens. FSH also stimulates the ovaries to produce hormones, particularly oestrogen.

⊙ **LH** (luteinising hormone) stimulates the release of the egg from the ovary in the middle of the menstrual cycle and also affects the ovary so that it produces another hormone (progesterone) to keep the uterus lining in place.

The ovary itself also produces hormones which have a marked effect on the menstrual cycle:

⊙ **Oestrogen** stimulates the lining of the uterus to build up in preparation for pregnancy. It also affects the pituitary gland. As the oestrogen levels rise, the production of FSH by the pituitary gradually falls – which in turn means the oestrogen levels fall. The rise in oestrogen levels has the opposite effect on the levels of the other pituitary hormone, LH. As oestrogen rises, the production of LH goes up. When LH reaches its peak in the middle of the menstrual cycle it stimulates the release of a ripe egg from the ovary. By the end of the cycle, when the menstrual bleeding is about to start, all of the hormones are at a low ebb.

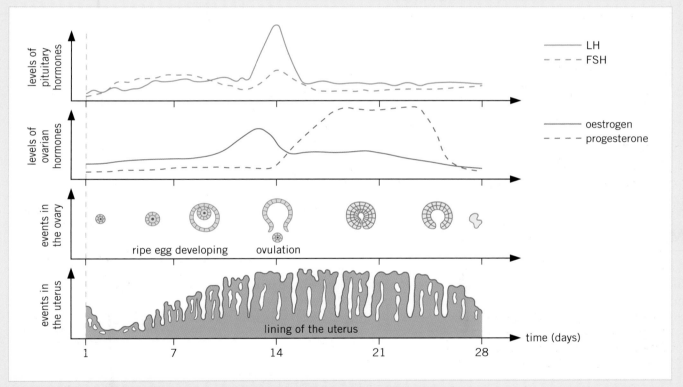

↑ **Figure 4:** The complex interactions of the different female hormones can clearly be seen in this diagram showing some of the events of the menstrual cycle.

? Questions

1 Give two effects of the hormones released from the pituitary gland.

2 Make a table to explain what happens to the ovary, the uterus and the hormones which control them during the menstrual cycle.

H 3 Explain the different ways in which oestrogen levels affect the levels of the pituitary hormones FSH and LH. Produce clear diagrams to help your explanation.

0ᴍ Key Ideas

⊙ Reproduction is controlled by hormones.

⊙ The menstrual cycle in women is controlled by hormones released from the pituitary gland and the ovaries.

Controlling fertility

People have tried for thousands of years to control their fertility and to have babies exactly when they wanted them. Methods of avoiding pregnancy have ranged from using camel dung or vinegar to avoiding sex completely, but most were unreliable!

Avoiding pregnancy

However, nowadays preventing unwanted pregnancies is possible. One of the most reliable methods is the contraceptive pill (Figure 1). The pill contains female hormones which give messages to the ovary to prevent the release of any eggs. The pill must be taken regularly – if the artificial hormone levels drop, the body's own hormones can take over and an egg can be released unexpectedly.

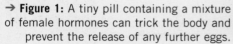

H Oral contraceptives contain oestrogen, which raises the level of oestrogen in the blood. This is detected by the pituitary gland which slows the production of FSH. Without rising FSH levels no follicles develop in the ovary and no eggs mature to be released.

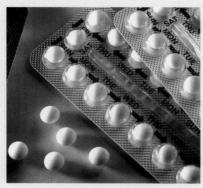

→ **Figure 1:** A tiny pill containing a mixture of female hormones can trick the body and prevent the release of any further eggs.

Making pregnancy possible

Sometimes the problem is not avoiding pregnancy but actually getting pregnant. In some women the levels of reproductive hormones produced by the pituitary gland are too low to stimulate the development of eggs in the ovary. Women with this problem can now be given hormones (as fertility drugs) which stimulate the release of eggs from the ovaries.

H Fertility drugs contain carefully calculated doses of FSH, triggering the normal responses in the ovary of egg development, oestrogen production and ovulation.

In the early days of fertility drugs it was difficult to judge the correct dosage and some women gave birth to up to eight babies at the same time. Sadly, some or all of these very tiny babies usually died. But now it is possible to calculate the dosage much more accurately, and large multiple births are mostly a thing of the past.

Fertility drugs are also used when a couple are trying to have a baby by IVF (in *vitro* fertilisation). If the Fallopian tubes are damaged, the egg cannot be fertilised naturally. Doctors can now remove eggs from the ovary, fertilise them with sperm outside the body and then place the tiny developing embryos into the uterus of the mother, bypassing the faulty tubes. To produce as many ripe eggs as possible for IVF the woman is given fertility drugs.

The use of hormones to control fertility has been a major scientific breakthrough. But it can be a mixed blessing.

In the developed world, using the pill has helped to make families much smaller than they used to be and so people are less likely to be poor because they have fewer mouths to feed.

↑ **Figure 3:** The contraceptive pill has helped to free women from repeated pregnancies and childbirth.

The pill also has also helped to control population growth in countries such as China, which find it difficult to feed all their people. But in many other countries of the developing world the pill is not available because of a lack of money, education and doctors.

However, taking the pill is not without risk. In some people the pill can cause blood clots or very high blood pressure, which can result in death. Less severely, the pill can cause headaches, and loss of interest in sex. Because of this the use of the pill is always overseen by a doctor.

The use of fertility drugs can also have some health risks for the mother and it can be expensive for society. A large multiple birth can be tragic for the parents if some or all of the babies die, and many resources in hospitals are needed to keep very small and premature babies alive.

Controlling fertility artificially also raises many ethical issues for society and individuals.

⊙ Many religious groups think that preventing conception is denying life and ban the use of the pill.

⊙ Fertility drugs can be used to make women produce as many as 15 mature eggs at once. These eggs may be stored until the women wants to get pregnant later. But what happens to these extra eggs if the woman dies, or does not want them any more?

? **Questions**

1 Hormones can be used to control fertility artificially. Explain:

   a how hormones in the contraceptive pill can be used to prevent pregnancy

   b how hormones can be used to help infertile couples become pregnant.

2 **a** What are the benefits of artificial fertility control? List the ones on these pages and add any others you can think of.

   b Summarise the problems which may arise from this form of artificial fertility control.

   c In your opinion, do the benefits outweigh the problems? Justify your answer.

Key Ideas

⊙ Hormones can be used to both prevent women getting pregnant and help them to get pregnant.

⊙ There are health and ethical issues linked to the use of both contraception and fertility drugs.

Homeostasis

For our bodies to work properly the conditions surrounding the millions of cells must stay as constant as possible. How do we achieve this? Many of the functions which go on in the human body are involved in keeping the internal environment as constant as possible. This is known as **homeostasis**.

↑ **Figure 1:** Wherever we go, whatever we decide to do, conditions inside our bodies must be kept stable if we are to survive.

Getting rid of waste

There are two main poisonous waste products which would cause major problems for the body if they built up:

⊙ **Carbon dioxide** is produced during cellular respiration. Almost all of it is removed from the body via the lungs when we breathe out (see page 20).

⊙ **Urea** is produced in the liver when excess amino acids are broken down. These excess amino acids come from protein in the food we have eaten and from the breakdown of worn out body tissue. The urea is filtered out of the blood by the kidneys and removed in the urine.

Controlling the internal concentration

If the concentration of the body fluids changes, water will move into or out of the cells by osmosis and they could be damaged or destroyed. How is the balance maintained?

Water

We gain water when we drink and eat, and from the breakdown of sugar in cellular respiration. We lose water constantly from the lungs when we breathe out – water evaporates into the air in the lungs and is breathed out. This water loss is constant. Whenever we exercise or get hot we sweat and lose more water.

The water balance is maintained by the kidneys (Figure 1). They remove any excess water and it leaves the body as urine. If we are short of water we produce very little urine and most water is saved for use in the body. If we have too much water then our kidneys produce lots of urine to get rid of the excess.

↓ **Figure 2:** The kidney is a very important organ of homeostasis, involved in controlling the loss of water and mineral ions from the body as well as getting rid of urea.

Ions

The ion concentration of the body is also important. We take in mineral ions with our food. Some are lost via our skin when we sweat. Again, the kidney is most important in keeping an ion balance. Excess mineral ions are removed by the kidneys and lost in the urine.

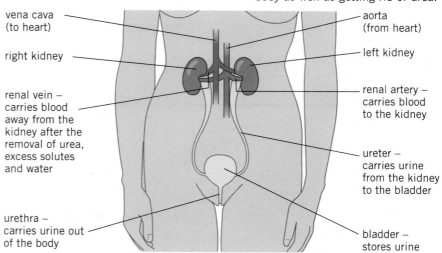

vena cava (to heart)

right kidney

renal vein – carries blood away from the kidney after the removal of urea, excess solutes and water

urethra – carries urine out of the body

aorta (from heart)

left kidney

renal artery – carries blood to the kidney

ureter – carries urine from the kidney to the bladder

bladder – stores urine

Controlling temperature

← **Figure 3:** People can live in conditions of extreme heat or extreme cold and still maintain a constant internal body temperature.

It is vitally important that wherever we go and whatever we do the body temperature is maintained at the temperature (around 37 °C) at which our enzymes work best. It is not the temperature at the surface of the body which matters – the skin temperature can vary enormously without causing harm. It is the temperature deep inside the body, known as the core body temperature, which must be kept stable. At only a few degrees above or below normal body temperature our enzymes cannot function properly. If this goes on for any length of time the reactions in our cells cannot continue and we die.

All sorts of things can affect internal body temperature, including heat generated in the muscles during exercise, fevers caused by disease and the external temperature rising or falling.

We can control our temperature in lots of ways. We can change our clothing, the way we behave and how active we are. But we also have an internal control mechanism: when we get too hot we start to sweat.

Sweat (made up mainly of water and salt) oozes out of the sweat glands and spreads over the surface of the skin. As the water evaporates it cools the skin, taking heat from the body, but this often affects our water and ion balance so we need to take more water and ions in through drink or food to replace the water which is lost.

? Questions

1 There are two main waste products which have to be removed from the human body – carbon dioxide and urea. For each waste product describe

  a how it is formed

  b why it has to be removed

  c how it is removed from the body.

2 Look at the marathon runners in Figure 1. List the ways in which the running is affecting their:

  a water balance

  b ion balance

  c internal temperature.

3 How can the people shown in Figure 3 maintain a constant internal environment? Include as many ways as possible in your answer.

4 Why is it so important to control the internal temperature and water balance of the body?

Key Ideas

- Humans need to maintain a constant internal environment.

- Waste products are removed from the body by the lungs and the kidneys.

- Water is lost through the lungs, the skin and the kidneys.

- The ion and water content of the body is controlled by the kidneys.

- Temperature is maintained in many ways including the loss of heat by sweating.

The kidney – superorgan!

How do the kidneys control the levels of water and ions in the body? They filter the blood and then take back (reabsorb) everything the body needs (Figure 1). So all of the sugar is reabsorbed, along with the mineral ions needed by the body. The amount of water reabsorbed depends on the needs of the body. The waste product urea, and excess ions and water not needed by the body are released as urine.

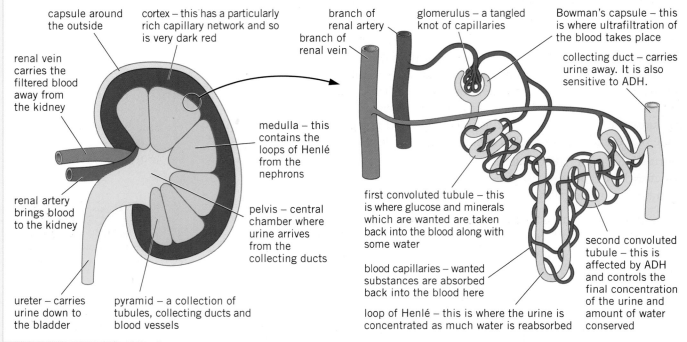

↑ **Figure 1:** The kidney filters the blood and removes materials which are not needed, to form the urine.

The amount of water lost from the kidneys in the urine is controlled by a sensitive feedback mechanism involving a hormone, **ADH** (anti-diuretic hormone). If the water content of the blood is too low, the pituitary gland in the brain (see page 42) senses this and releases ADH into the blood. This hormone affects the kidneys, causing them to reabsorb more water back into the blood. This means less water is left in the kidney tubules and so a more concentrated urine is formed.

If the water content of the blood is too high, the pituitary gland releases much less ADH into the blood. The kidney then reabsorbs less water back into the blood, producing a large volume of dilute urine (Figure 2).

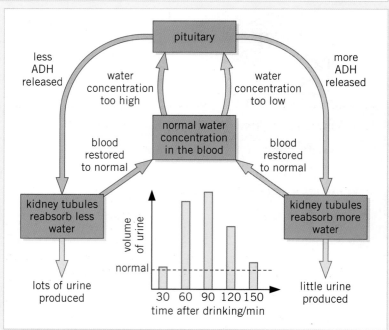

↑ **Figure 2:** The feedback system which operates to control the amount of water which the kidney removes from the blood means that we can cope with temporary shortages or loading of water surprisingly well.

Cooling down, warming up

Control of the temperature relies on the **thermoregulatory centre** in the brain. This centre contains receptors which are sensitive to the temperature of the blood flowing through the brain itself. Extra information comes from the temperature receptors in the skin, which send impulses to the thermoregulatory centre giving information about the skin temperature. These receptors are so sensitive they can detect a difference of as little as 0.5 °C!

If the core body temperature begins to rise and gets too high, impulses are sent from the thermoregulatory centre which cause:

⊙ blood vessels supplying the skin capillaries to dilate so that more blood flows through the capillaries – the skin flushes and more heat is lost

⊙ sweat glands to release more sweat which cools the body as it evaporates from the surface of the skin.

If, on the other hand, the core body temperature drops and gets too low, the thermoregulatory centre instructs the body to conserve heat:

⊙ The blood vessels which supply the skin capillaries constrict (close up) to reduce the flow of blood through the capillaries. This reduces the heat lost through the surface of the skin, and makes you look pale.

⊙ Shivering begins – the muscles contract rapidly which involves lots of cellular respiration. This releases some energy as heat which is used to raise the body temperature. As you warm up, shivering stops.

⊙ Sweat production is reduced.

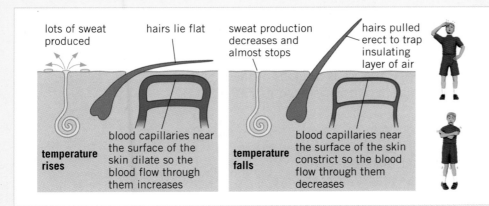

← **Figure 3:** Changes in the core body temperature set off both conscious and automatic responses to oppose the changes and maintain a steady internal environment.

? Questions

1 a Summarise the way in which the kidneys function.

   b Use the graph in Figure 2 to help you explain how the body responds to water loading.

2 a Why is it so serious if the kidneys fail?

   b What must an 'artificial kidney' or dialysis machine be able to do?

   c Most patients only receive dialysis three times a week. The food they eat and the amount they drink must be carefully controlled except for the first hour or two they are on dialysis. Explain why.

2 Homeostatic mechanisms in the body are closely linked and work together. If someone is working in very hot conditions, explain how both their temperature regulation and their water balance systems will be involved in maintaining a constant internal environment.

⊙━ Key Ideas

⊙ The kidney filters the blood and controls the amount of ions and water reabsorbed.

⊙ The amount of water reabsorbed is controlled by a feedback system involving the hormone ADH produced by the pituitary gland.

⊙ Core body temperature is controlled by the thermoregulatory centre in the brain. This affects the dilation of the blood vessels supplying skin capillaries and the amount of sweat produced.

1 The drawing shows an aardvark.

 a The aardvark has receptors which are sensitive to changes in the environment.
   Name one part of the aardvark's body where there are:
   i receptors sensitive to light
   ii receptors which help it to keep its balance
   iii receptors which are sensitive to chemicals. (3 marks)

 b The aardvark feeds mainly at night. It is hunted by several predators.
   Use the information from the drawing to give one feature of the
   aardvark which is an adaptation for sensing predators at night.
   (1 mark)
   (Total 4 marks)
   AQA specimen question

2 The diagram shows a
   cross section through
   the human eye.

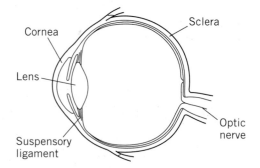

List **A** gives the names of five parts of the eye. List **B** gives the jobs of these parts
in a different order. Draw a straight line from each part in list A to its job in list B.

List A
Lens
Optic nerve
Sclera
Cornea
Suspensory ligament

List B
holds the lens in position
produces a clear image on the retina
allows light to enter the eye
is the tough, white outer layer of the eye
carries information about an image to the brain

(Total 5 marks)
AQA specimen question

H 3 When we touch something sharp with
   a finger we automatically pull the finger
   away in a reflex action. The diagram
   shows some parts of the nervous system
   which are involved in this reflex action.

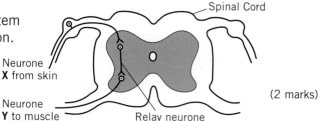

 a What type of neurone is
   i neurone X
   ii neurone Y? (2 marks)
 b In what form is information
   i passed along neurone X
   ii passed from neurone X to the relay neurone? (2 marks)
 c Copy and complete the following sentence.

   In this reflex action the spinal cord acts as the ....
   and the muscle acts as the .... (2 marks)
   (Total 6 marks)
   AQA specimen question

4 In women, two hormones control ovulation (the release of eggs from the ovaries). The drawing shows a monitoring machine which women can use to measure the amounts of the two hormones. A test stick is dipped in the woman's urine each morning, then placed in a slot in the machine.

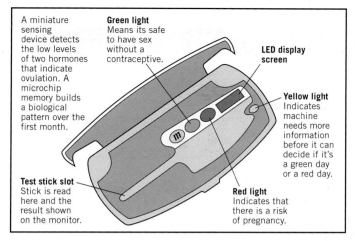

A miniature sensing device detects the low levels of two hormones that indicate ovulation. A microchip memory builds a biological pattern over the first month.

Green light Means its safe to have sex without a contraceptive.

LED display screen

Yellow light Indicates machine needs more information before it can decide if it's a green day or a red day.

Test stick slot Stick is read here and the result shown on the monitor.

Red light Indicates that there is a risk of pregnancy.

a The machine monitors the levels of two hormones.
  i What is a hormone? (1 mark)
  ii How is a hormone transported around the body? (1 mark)

b A woman is unlikely to become pregnant if she has sex on the days when the machine shows a green light during the test. Use information from the drawing to suggest why. (1 mark)

c Hormones can be used to control human fertility. Describe the benefits and problems which might arise from using hormones in this way. (4 marks)

(Total 7 marks)

AQA specimen question

5 The table shows four ways in which water leaves the body, and the amounts lost on a cool day.

Source of water loss	Water loss in cm³	
	Cool day	Hot day
Breath	400	The same
Skin	500	A
Urine	1500	B
Faeces	150	C

a **i** Write down whether, on a hot day, the amount of water lost in A, B and C would be **less, the same** or **more** than the amount of water lost on a cool day. (3 marks)
  ii Name the process by which we lose water from the skin. (1 mark)

b On a cool day the body gained 2550 cm³ of water; 1500 cm³ came directly from drinking. Give **two** other ways in which the body may gain water. (2 marks)

(Total 6 marks)

H 6 The diagram shows some of the processes which control the composition of the blood.

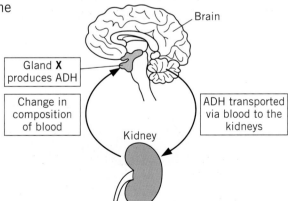

Brain

Gland **X** produces ADH

Change in composition of blood

ADH transported via blood to the kidneys

Kidney

a **i** Name gland **X**. (1 mark)
  ii What is the stimulus which causes gland **X** to produce ADH? (1 mark)
  iii What type of substance is ADH? (1 mark)

b Describe the effect of an increase in ADH production on the kidney and on the composition of the urine. (3 marks)

(Total 6 marks)

AQA specimen question

4.1 What *is* disease?

All over the world, in every country, disease attacks rich and poor alike. There are many different types of disease, but the most common world-wide are infectious diseases. These range from the common cold and tonsillitis to deadly killers such as tetanus, influenza, ebola virus, pneumonia, plague and malaria.

What causes infectious diseases?

An infectious disease is caused by a **microorganism** entering and attacking the body. The microorganism comes from another person or from unhygienic conditions such as dirty water. This is different to diseases like cancer or heart disease which are often caused by the body itself going wrong, not microorganisms. Common microorganisms include bacteria and viruses.

Bacteria are single-celled living organisms which are much smaller than the smallest animal and plant cells. A bacterial cell is made up of cytoplasm surrounded by a membrane and a cell wall. Inside the bacterial cell is the genetic material which carries the instructions for the cell, but this is not contained in a nucleus. The bacterial cell wall differs from a plant cell wall because it is not made of cellulose.

Some bacteria have additional features like flagella to help them move, or protective slime capsules. Bacteria also come in a variety of different shapes and sizes (Figure 1). Some are rod shaped, some are round, some are comma-shaped and some are spirals. Whilst some bacteria cause disease, many are harmless and some are actively useful to people.

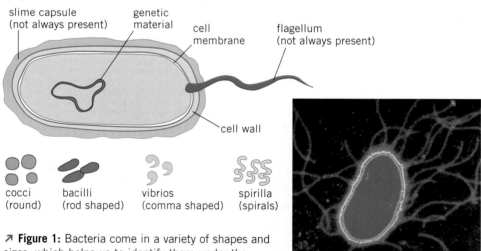

slime capsule (not always present) genetic material cell membrane flagellum (not always present)

cell wall

cocci (round) bacilli (rod shaped) vibrios (comma shaped) spirilla (spirals)

↗ **Figure 1:** Bacteria come in a variety of shapes and sizes, which helps us to identify them under the microscope, but they all have the same basic structure.

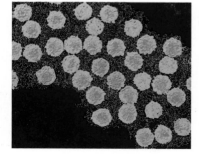

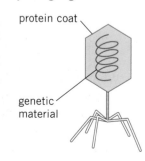

↓ **Figure 2:** Viruses are minute with a very simple structure. There is much argument about whether they are actually living organisms or not.

protein coat

genetic material

Viruses are even smaller than bacteria. They usually have regular geometric shapes, and they are made up of a protein coat surrounding genetic material containing relatively few genes (Figure 2). They do not carry out any of the functions of normal living organisms except reproduction, and they can only reproduce by taking over another living cell. So far as we know, all naturally occurring viruses cause disease.

What makes us ill?

Bacteria and viruses cause disease because once inside the body they reproduce rapidly. Bacteria simply split in two (Figure 3), whilst viruses take over the cells of the body and destroy them as they reproduce (Figure 4). Both types of microorganism cause tissue damage and it is the response of our bodies to this damage as well as the damage itself which cause the symptoms of disease. Sometimes, however, the microorganisms produce toxins and it is our reaction to these poisons which makes us feel ill.

↓ **Figure 3:** In ideal conditions bacteria are capable of growth like this – even though conditions are rarely ideal, it is no wonder they can make us feel so ill.

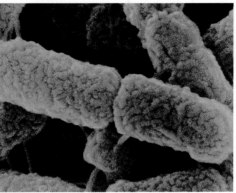

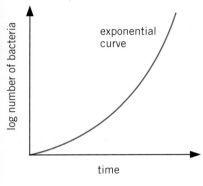

The germ theory of disease

The idea that microorganisms or 'germs' cause disease is generally accepted today, but this is a relatively recent development. For thousands of years people thought that disease was a sign of God's anger or the result of a curse. A look back in time can show us how people began to understand the true nature of infectious diseases, but also how difficult it was to overcome the prejudices of the time.

virus attaches
to host cell

genetic material injected into
host and attacks nucleus

cell used to make
new virus parts

viruses
assembled

new viruses free to
infect other cells

cell bursts open

↑ **Figure 4:** Viruses cannot reproduce without destroying the cells of their host – every time the cells burst more viruses are released to attack more cells and the body is once again under attack.

? Questions

1 How is an infectious disease different from a disease like lung cancer?

2 Bacteria and viruses can both cause disease. Make a table which shows how bacteria and viruses are different and how they are similar.

3 Some people say that viruses are living organisms. Others say they are non-living particles. Write two sentences, one supporting each point of view.

4 a If you are infected with one disease-causing bacterium which can split in two every 20 minutes, how many bacteria will you have in your body after 6 hours?

b Use the calculations you have carried out in part a, along with the graph in Figure 3 to explain why some infections cause symptoms within a day or two of contracting the bacterium.

c In most cases it is several days or even several weeks from when you are exposed to a bacterium before you develop disease. Why do you think this might be?

5 Use Figure 4 to help you explain why it is that in viral illnesses your temperature tends to shoot up for a time and then come down before shooting up again.

🔑 Key Ideas

⊙ Infectious diseases can be caused by the entry of microorganisms into the body.

⊙ Bacteria consist of cytoplasm and a membrane surrounded by a cell wall. The genetic material is not in a distinct nucleus.

⊙ Viruses are smaller than bacteria and consist only of a protein coat surrounding the genetic material. They can only reproduce inside living cells.

The germ theory of disease

The story of Ignaz Semmelweis

When most women had babies at home attended by their female relatives or midwives, serious infections after delivery were relatively rare. But in the late 18th and early 19th centuries doctors increasingly delivered babies, hospitals set up maternity wards and problems began. Soon after giving birth many women developed a range of symptoms including severe pain, high fever, inflammation of the womb, vomiting and convulsions. Death followed within five days. This dreadful illness, known as puerperal fever or childbed fever, killed about one woman in every five who had a baby (Figure 1). There were fierce debates about the causes of this mystery disease.

↑ **Figure 1:** In the worst hospitals the death rate from puerperal fever was as high as one new mother in every three.

Ignaz Semmelweiss was born in Hungary, in 1818. After qualifying as a doctor he worked at the maternity clinic of the Vienna General Hospital. The hospital had two delivery rooms, one staffed by female midwives and the other by medical students. Over 12% of the women delivered by the young doctors died of puerperal fever, which was more than three times as many as those delivered by midwives. Semmelweiss realised that the medical students often moved straight from dissecting a dead body to delivering a baby without washing their hands first. He wondered if they were carrying the cause of disease on their hands from the corpses to their patients.

Then another doctor cut himself whilst dissecting a body and died from symptoms identical to those of puerperal fever. Now Semmelweiss was sure that puerperal fever was caused by an infectious agent. He immediately insisted that his medical students wash their hands in chlorinated lime before they entered the maternity ward, and eventually he insisted that they should wash between each patient. Within 6 months the death rate of his patients had dropped to a quarter of the original figure, and after two years it was down to only 1.27%.

Semmelweiss presented his findings to other doctors, but his theory met with strong opposition. Even after he gathered more evidence his findings and publications were resisted, not just in Hungary but also abroad.

Why the opposition to Semmelweiss?

Pain and suffering during childbirth was an acceptable part of Christian doctrine at that time. Some European doctors and church men thought that puerperal fever showed God's wish to punish women by making birth dangerous and difficult. It was also hard for doctors to admit that they themselves had killed their patients instead of curing them.

We also need to remember that hand-washing was more difficult in the 19th century than in the 21st. There was no indoor plumbing, so getting water to wash in was not easy. Water brought in would have been cold, and the chemicals used to wash with (such as chlorinated lime) would have eventually damaged the skin of the hands.

Semmelweiss found the rejection of his work unbearable, because he knew that simple hygiene measures held the key to saving thousands of lives, and he suffered a major breakdown. In 1868, aged only 47, he died – by an ironic twist of fate from an infection picked up from a patient during an operation.

The battle continues

In the 21st century the germ theory of disease is generally accepted. Our behaviour and habits reflect it – we wash our hands after going to the toilet, we use disinfectants and doctors sterilise instruments between patients. Even so, it has recently been estimated that up to 5000 people die each year of infections picked up in UK hospitals – many of them contracted because staff fail to wash their hands between patients! But it can still be very hard for new ideas which fly in the face of the accepted science of the day to be taken seriously.

For example, for many years stomach ulcers were thought to be caused by stress. Then in the 1980s an Australian, Dr Barry Marshall (Figure 2), found the bacterium *Helicobacter pylori* living in the stomachs of all his patients with stomach ulcers. The accepted view was that bacteria could not live in the acidic conditions of the stomach, so this finding surprised Marshall. He devised a series of tests to find out whether the bacteria were causing the stomach ulcers. Eventually he developed a treatment using cheap antibiotics which cleared the ulcer symptoms in his patients, and because it destroyed the bacteria the ulcers did not return.

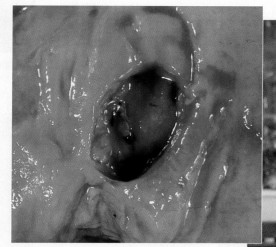

Figure 2: Dr Barry Marshall, the man who showed that the pain of a stomach ulcer was the result of a treatable bacterial infection rather than stress. →

This idea met with a great deal of resistance. In some countries doctors earned a lot of money treating long-term ulcer sufferers. Also, drugs to relieve ulcer pain and block acid production were among the best selling medicines in the world, so the drug companies were not happy. It took more than 10 years to convince people, but now most doctors accept Marshall's theory.

? Questions

1 Why did puerperal fever become more common when doctors started delivering babies rather than midwives, whose only job was helping with childbirth?

2 What made Semmelweiss suspect that puerperal fever was caused by infection from other places such as corpses?

3 Give three reasons why Semmelweiss's theory was not immediately accepted.

4 Give three examples of hygenic behaviour today which helps prevent the spread of infection.

5 Give three reasons why Barry Marshall's theory about stomach ulcers was not accepted for a long time.

Natural defences against disease

The key point about infectious diseases is that the microorganisms which cause the diseases can be spread from one person to another. The more microorganisms get into your body, the more likely it is that you will get a disease.

Spreading disease

Some common ways in which infections can be spread are:

- ⊙ **Droplet infection:** when we cough, sneeze or talk, tiny droplets are expelled from our breathing system (Figure 1). If we have an infection, those droplets will contain microorganisms. Other people breathe in the droplets, along with the viruses or bacteria they contain and so pick up the infection, e.g. 'flu (influenza), tuberculosis, the common cold.

- ⊙ **Direct contact:** some diseases are spread by direct contact of the skin, e.g. impetigo and some sexually transmitted diseases like genital herpes.

- ⊙ **Contaminated food and drink:** eating raw or undercooked food, or drinking water contaminated by sewage means we take large numbers of microorganisms straight into our gut, e.g. diarrhoea, salmonellosis.

- ⊙ **Through a break in the skin:** germs can enter the body through cuts, scratches and bites, as well as through needle punctures, e.g. AIDS, hepatitis.

Overcrowded and unhygienic conditions encourage the spread of disease. In the UK in the early 19th century, when the majority of people lived in squalid, overcrowded cities with no sewage or clean water systems and poor food, many diseases such as cholera were rife. As living conditions improved through the late 19th and the 20th centuries the incidence of these diseases fell dramatically. However, in the developing world many cities are getting larger and larger, with millions of poor people crowded together in dreadful conditions (Figure 2).

↑ **Figure 1:** Germ-filled droplets fly into the air at up to 100 miles an hour when we sneeze!

↑ **Figure 2:** When people live in crowded conditions with no sewage treatment, infectious diseases spread like wildfire.

Natural defences against disease 1 – Keep them out!

However hygienic and comfortable our living conditions, most of us will meet disease-causing microorganisms during our daily lives. However, the human body has a number of ways of defending itself.

The skin covers the body and acts as a barrier, preventing microorganisms from reaching the vulnerable tissues underneath. If the skin is damaged or broken in any way the blood forms **clots** which dry into scabs and seal over the cut (Figure 3).

The breathing system is vulnerable, because air is drawn right inside the body every time we breathe. However, the whole system produces a sticky liquid called **mucus** which covers the lining of the organs and the tubes and traps microorganisms. The mucus is then moved out of the body or swallowed down into the gut where the microbes are destroyed by the acid in the stomach.

← **Figure 3:** If the skin is damaged, the scabs which form rapidly protect against the entry of microorganisms while new skin grows.

Natural defences against disease 2 – the white blood cells

If microorganisms do manage to get through the body's defence system, the white blood cells help to defend us against them (Table 1). They make up the **immune system**.

Role of white blood cell	How it defends against disease
Ingesting microorganisms	Some white blood cells ingest (take in) microorganisms, destroying them and preventing them from causing disease.
Producing antibodies	Some white blood cells produce special chemicals called antibodies. These attack particular bacteria or viruses and destroy them. A unique antibody is needed for each type of bacterium or virus. Once they have produced antibodies against a particular bacterium or virus, the white blood cells can produce them again very rapidly if it invades again.
Producing antitoxins	There are some white blood cells which produce antitoxins capable of counteracting the toxins (poisons) released by some microorganisms.

← **Table 1:** The role of white blood cells.

? Questions

1 Explain the following in terms of disease prevention:

   a washing the hands before preparing food

   b disposing of tissues once we have blown our noses

   c ensuring that sewage does not contaminate drinking water

   d putting a hand in front of your mouth when you cough or sneeze.

2 Why do infectious diseases spread rapidly wherever people are crowded together, even if they are well fed and healthy?

3 Explain why the following symptoms mean that a person's ability to fight disease is reduced:

   a the blood won't clot properly

   b the number of white blood cells falls

   c the skin is damaged to expose the raw tissues underneath.

4 In the developing world very large 'supercities' have appeared. Millions of people move to live and work in these cities, living in shacks built of rubbish with no sewage provision. There is great concern about the spread of disease in these cities and the rapidly spiralling death rate. Explain why there are so many problems.

⊙m Key Ideas

- ⊙ Infectious diseases can be spread by droplet infection, direct contact, cuts in the skin or eating contaminated food.

- ⊙ The body's defences against the invasion of bacteria include the skin, mucus in the breathing system and blood clotting to seal cuts.

- ⊙ White blood cells attack invading microorganisms in a number of ways.

As scientific understanding of the causes of disease and the way the body fights disease has grown, so have the artificial defence mechanisms we can use to fight microorganisms.

A chemical approach

Microorganisms can be attacked chemically in a number of ways. Antiseptics and disinfectants kill microorganisms on the skin and in the environment around us, reducing the spread of disease and the infection of wounds. The other main line of attack is by antibiotic drugs. Developed in the mid-20th century, these drugs kill bacteria and so cure diseases caused by bacterial infections. Antibiotics have reduced many killer diseases – even the plague – to inconveniences. They have revolutionised medicine. However, they have no effect on diseases caused by viruses, so they are not always the answer.

Artificial immunity

Drugs can be used to treat an infection once we have it. An even better idea is to prevent us getting ill in the first place. When the body has come into contact with a microorganism, some of the white blood cells develop antibodies against that microorganism (see page 57). If that microorganism invades again it is destroyed before it can cause disease. We are **immune** to the disease. This immunity can be triggered artificially in the process known as **vaccination** (**immunisation**). When a disease is too serious to risk exposure to the real thing, vaccination gives people immunity (Figure 1).

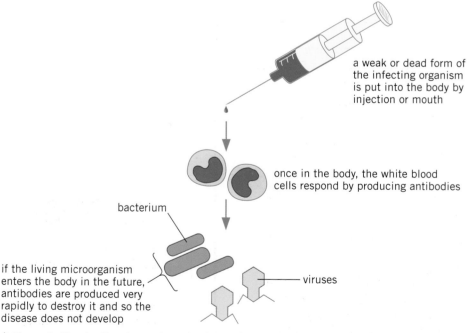

a weak or dead form of the infecting organism is put into the body by injection or mouth

once in the body, the white blood cells respond by producing antibodies

bacterium

if the living microorganism enters the body in the future, antibodies are produced very rapidly to destroy it and so the disease does not develop

viruses

↑ **Figure 1:** Vaccination is used to give immunity to a number of dangerous diseases.

In the UK, most people are vaccinated as babies or small children against diseases such as tetanus, diphtheria, whooping cough, polio, measles, mumps and rubella, meningitis and TB (Figure 2). At least in part as a result of these vaccination programmes, the number of children who die each year of infectious diseases is very low.

flu, hangover, or meningitis?

Look out for your mate

↑ **Figure 2:** Meningitis is an example of a disease which develops rapidly and can kill in hours. In recent years we have started using vaccines which can prevent some types of meningitis.

Pasteur and Lister

The French doctor Louis Pasteur (1822–1895) was broken-hearted when three of his five children died young of infectious diseases. He was determined to do something about it. He, more than anyone else, convinced people by his experiments that diseases were caused by microorganisms. He developed vaccines against some of them and by the end of his life was close to a vaccine against diphtheria, which had killed his little girls.

Joseph Lister was a young Scottish surgeon in the 19th century. He read Louis Pasteur's work and was convinced that the infections in his patients were caused by the microorganisms Pasteur described. Lister started washing surgical instruments and his hands before operating, and using phenol as an antiseptic in his operating theatres. As a result his patients lived – and antiseptics were born!

Questions

1 How do vaccines work?

2 Most vaccination programmes are aimed at babies and young children. Why do you think this might be?

3 Antibiotics will not cure a disease caused by a virus. Why not?

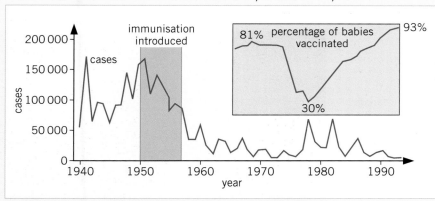

↑ **Figure 3:** Graph to show cases of whooping cough in the UK from 1940 onwards.

4 Whooping cough is a disease spread by droplet infection. It used to kill many children but there is now an effective vaccine against it. From the graph in Figure 3 explain:

  a what factors might have caused the drop in cases of the disease before the introduction of the vaccination programme

  b what factors might have caused the drop in cases of the disease after the introduction of the vaccination programme.

3 In the 1970s a link was suggested between whooping cough vaccine and serious brain damage in some children. It was later shown that the disease itself causes more damage to more children than any risk from the vaccine. Use the data in Figure 3 to explain what seems to have happened in response to these concerns.

4 Use a variety of resources to produce a summary of the work of Louis Pasteur and his influence on the germ theory of disease and vaccination.

Key Ideas

⊙ Antiseptics and antibiotics can destroy bacteria.

⊙ Vaccination exposes the body to a weak or dead strain of a dangerous microorganism so that the body can make antibodies to it.

What is a drug?

A drug is a substance which alters the way in which the body works. It can affect the mind, the body or both. In every society there are certain drugs which are used for medicine and others which are used for pleasure.

Usually some of the drugs used for pleasure are socially acceptable and others are illegal. In many countries such as the UK, Australia and the USA, caffeine (in coffee, tea and some soft drinks), nicotine (in cigarettes) and alcohol are the main legal recreational drugs (Figure 1). In other parts of the world, such as the Arab states, alcohol is illegal.

↑ **Figure 1:** Alcohol is highly intoxicating and extremely poisonous. If it was a newly discovered substance it would almost certainly be illegal and regarded as highly dangerous. But because in many countries alcohol has been used for centuries, the drug is widely accepted as part of normal social life.

Addiction

Drugs change the chemical processes in our bodies so that we may become **addicted** to them (dependent on them). If we are addicted to a drug we cannot manage or function properly without it. Once addicted to a drug, we generally need more and more of it to keep us feeling normal.

When addicts try to stop using their drug they will feel very unwell, often experiencing combinations of aches and pains, shaking, sweating, headaches, cravings for the drug and even fevers as the body reacts — these are known as **withdrawal symptoms**.

Solvent abuse

Solvent abuse, or 'glue-sniffing' as it is sometimes called, is very addictive (Figure 2). The solvents from glues and aerosols are inhaled and they change the behaviour by affecting the brain. They can also cause damage to the lungs, liver and brain. Very occasionally they cause instant death as the brain or heart fails completely. However, they are a relatively cheap way of getting high, and at one stage were very easy to obtain. It has since been made much more difficult to buy such solvents, and manufacturers often use alternative chemicals which do not have the same effect.

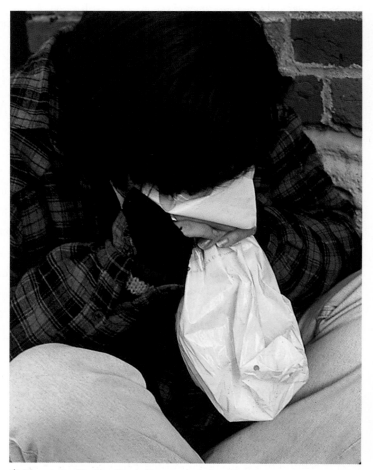

↑ **Figure 2:** During the latter part of the 20th century young people in particular discovered that the solvents used in some glues and aerosols would give them a 'high' if they inhaled them.

Alcohol

Alcohol is a commonly used social drug in many parts of the world. It is poisonous, but the liver in the human body can usually get rid of relatively large amounts of it by breaking it down before permanent damage or death results.

After an alcoholic drink the alcohol is absorbed into the bloodstream from the gut. Once the alcohol is in the blood it passes easily into nearly every tissue of the body, including the brain. It slows down thought processes and reflexes, so all the reactions are slower than normal (Figure 3). It also leads to lack of self control and lack of judgement. If the doses of the drug are too high it can lead to unconsciousness, coma and death.

Continued excessive alcohol use over a period of years causes long-term damage to the brain. The brains of dead alcoholics are sometimes so soft and pulpy that almost all the normal brain structures have been lost.

People who drink very large amounts of alcohol, or who drink heavily for a long time, are also at risk from potentially fatal liver diseases such as cirrhosis of the liver and liver cancer. The liver tissue is damaged by excess alcohol and replaced with scar tissue which cannot carry out the normal liver functions.

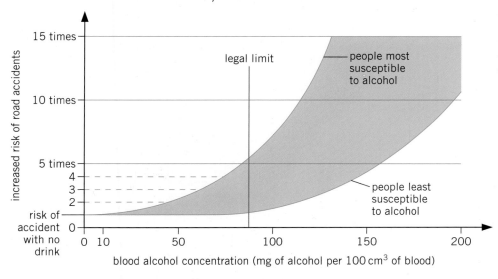

← **Figure 3:** Alcohol can cause direct damage to our body, and put us at risk because of the way we behave under the influence of the drug.

? Questions

1 What is meant by the term addiction?

2 Which two body organs are most affected by too much alcohol over a long period of time?

3 Why is it unsafe for someone to drive when they have been drinking alcohol? Use Figure 3 to help you.

4 Alcohol is the cause of a lot of violence between people, and many people who commit crime have been drinking. Why?

5 It is not always the most dangerous drugs which are illegal. Why do you think that alcohol is still legal in many parts of the world, despite the problems it causes?

6 Prepare a presentation on alcohol as a drug to be given to a group of 14 to 15-year-olds at a youth group. Balance information and warnings with a realistic sense of what will be relevant and useful to such a group. You might chose to do this using IT.

0🔑 Key Ideas

⊙ A drug is a substance which alters the way the body works.

⊙ Addiction to a drug means the body or mind do not function properly without it.

⊙ Solvents are inhaled – they affect behaviour and can damage the lungs, brain and liver.

⊙ Alcohol is very poisonous. It affects the nervous system and can damage the brain and the liver.

Look cool, die young? – tobacco and health

There are 1.1 billion smokers world-wide, smoking around 6000 billion cigarettes each year, so smoking is big business. Every cigarette smoked contains tobacco leaves which, as they burn, produce a smoke cocktail of around 4000 chemicals which are inhaled into the lungs. Some of those chemicals are absorbed into the bloodstream to be carried around the body to the brain.

Nicotine – a very addictive drug

Nicotine is the addictive drug found in tobacco smoke. It produces a sensation of calm, well-being and 'being able to cope'.

Some of the other chemicals in tobacco smoke cause lasting and often fatal damage to the body cells. Carbon monoxide is a very poisonous gas found in the smoke. It takes up some of the oxygen-carrying capacity of the blood – after smoking a cigarette up to 10% of a smoker's blood will be carrying carbon monoxide rather than oxygen. This can lead to a shortage of oxygen for the smoker which is why many smokers easily get breathless.

Smoking babies

Oxygen shortage is a particular problem in pregnant women who smoke (Figure 1). During pregnancy a woman is carrying oxygen not just for her own respiratory needs but for her developing fetus as well. If the mother's blood does not contain enough oxygen, the fetus is deprived of oxygen and does not grow as well as it should. This can lead to premature births, low birth-weight babies and even stillbirths where the baby is born dead.

← **Figure 1:** Pregnant women who smoke the most are most likely to have stillborn babies. The same pattern is there for low birth-weight babies.

H The haemoglobin in the blood picks up carbon monoxide more easily than it does oxygen. This means that carbon monoxide is picked up by the haemoglobin in the lungs in preference to oxygen. Once it has combined with carbon monoxide haemoglobin does not let it go – they combine *irreversibly*. This means that the haemoglobin in the blood which picks up carbon monoxide can never again pick up oxygen. Fortunately for smokers, red blood cells die and are replaced every 3 months or so by new cells full of new haemoglobin, but it still means that that smokers are continually short of oxygen.

Smoking-related diseases

In a non-smoker the ciliated epithelia of the breathing system (see page 00) are constantly active, moving mucus which has trapped dirt, dust and bacteria from the inhaled air up the respiratory tract away from the lungs. In a smoker, these cilia are anaesthetised by some of the chemicals in the tobacco smoke taken in with each cigarette and stop working for a time, allowing dirt down into the lungs.

Tar is a sticky, black chemical in tobacco smoke which accumulates in the lungs, turning them from pink to grey. Along with other chemicals from cigarette smoke it makes smokers considerably more likely to develop **bronchitis** – inflammation and infection of the bronchi (see page 00). Mucus builds up and causes coughing. The build up of tar in the delicate lung tissue can also lead to a breakdown in the alveolar structure. This is known as **emphysema** (Figure 2). Tar can also cause lung cancer.

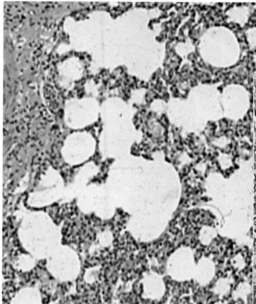
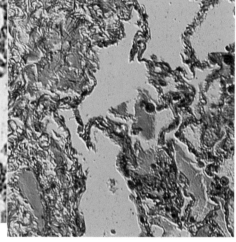

↙ **Figure 2:** In the lung with emphysema (on the right), large airspaces have developed instead of normal alveoli. The reduced surface area means gas exchange in the lungs is much less efficient.

The chemicals in tobacco smoke also affect the heart and blood vessels. Smoking raises the blood pressure and makes it more likely that blood vessels will become blocked, causing heart attacks, strokes and thrombosis.

? Questions

1 Make a table summarising the main components of tobacco smoke and their effects on the human body.

2 Smoking during pregnancy is potentially very damaging, yet many women continue to smoke when they are pregnant. Write a short article for a women's magazine explaining why smoking during pregnancy is so harmful.

3 a Smokers are more likely to get infections of their breathing system than non-smokers. Why do you think this might be?

   b In bronchitis, the tubes leading down to the lungs produce a lot of mucus. Compare the way the body of a non-smoker would deal with this mucus with the effect it would have on a smoker.

H 4 Explain why carbon monoxide is so poisonous.

0–m Key Ideas

- ⊙ Nicotine is the addictive drug found in tobacco.

- ⊙ Tobacco smoke also contains carbon monoxide which reduces the oxygen-carrying capacity of the blood.

- ⊙ In pregnant women carbon monoxide deprives the fetus of oxygen and can lead to low birth-weight babies and stillbirths.

- ⊙ Tobacco smoke contains tar and other chemicals which help to cause lung cancer, bronchitis, emphysema and disease of the heart and blood vessels.

H ⊙ Carbon monoxide combines irreversibly with haemoglobin.

Lung cancer and smoking

Not everyone who smokes will develop lung cancer, just as not all non-smokers will avoid lung cancer, but the evidence for the link is extremely strong – up to 90% of all lung cancers are thought to be due to smoking.

At one stage smoking was thought to be positively beneficial and very good for the nerves. Doctors even recommended smoking to their patients to help them cope with stressful situations! But through the 20th century evidence began to mount up that perhaps cigarettes were not so harmless after all.

Although they were widely used, the sale of cigarettes to children under the age of 16 was banned as early as 1908, four years before Dr I Adler suggested that there was a strong link between lung cancer and smoking. However, during the stresses of the First World war more people smoked than ever before and the habit continued when the fighting was over. By 1925 cigarette manufacturers were also specifically targeting women and in the 1930s Britain had the highest lung cancer rate in the world (Figure 1).

Also during the 1930s researchers in Germany found a strong statistical link between people who smoked and people who got lung cancer – but another war made sure that smoking continued to rise.

The first large-scale study into the relationship between smoking and lung cancer was carried out by Dr Richard Doll and Professor Austin Hill in 1951. They interviewed 1357 men with lung cancer and found that 99.5% of them were smokers. This was a very strong statistical link. Then in 1953 Dr Ernst Wynder painted cigarette tar on the backs of mice and they developed cancers, showing a biological link between the chemicals in cigarettes and cancer.

However, it has taken many years for the smoking public to accept the link between smoking and cancer – and even longer for the cigarette manufacturers. People did not – and still do not – want to accept that something which they enjoy could be damaging their health. Cigarette manufacturers did not want it recognised that their products caused millions of deaths each year – it might affect profits! In 1962 the Royal College of Physicians published a report suggesting the restriction of smoking, tax on tobacco products and warning of the dangers of smoking. For the first time in many years, cigarette sales fell.

In 1964 Doll and Hill published the results of a 10-year study into mortality (death rates) in relation to smoking, and showed that there was a dramatic fall in lung cancer cases in those who had given up smoking compared to those who still smoked.

All the time the cigarette manufacturers appeared to refuse to accept the evidence. It has now been shown that early on the manufacturers had evidence from their own scientists that not only did cigarettes cause cancer but that they were addictive, making it hard for people to give up. They responded by increasing the nicotine levels in the cigarettes, making them even more addictive and even harder to give up.

In recent years some people who have suffered from smoking-related lung cancer – and the families of people who have died of it – have successfully sued some of the big tobacco companies in America for damages from this type of deception.

↑ **Figure 1:** Cigarette advertising was everywhere. Some cigarette manufacturers even claimed their brand was positively healthy: '…Tests show three out of every four cases of smokers' cough cleared on changing to Philip Morris' ran one advertising campaign.

a) Deaths from lung cancer and smoking

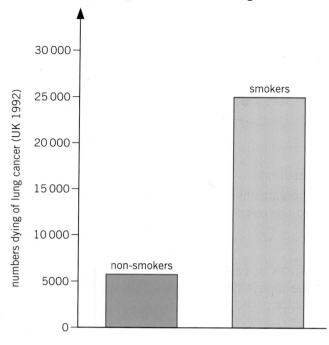

b) Cigarette consumption and risk of lung cancer death

Number of cigarettes smoked per day	Annual death rate per 100 000	Relative risk
0	14	–
1–14	105	8
15–24	208	15
25+	355	25

c) Death rates from lung cancer in men by age group: England and Wales 1974–92

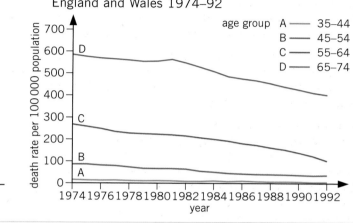

↑ **Figure 2:** Evidence like this gradually builds up a compelling picture showing that smoking is a major risk factor in the development of lung cancer.

? Questions

1 a Why might doctors have suggested that patients take up smoking in times of stress?

   b By the 1940s many doctors were trying to give up smoking at a time when many other people were still taking it up. Why do you think this was happening?

2 Produce a timeline showing the build-up of evidence for a link between smoking and lung cancer in the 20th century.

3 Look at the evidence produced by Doll and Hill in 1951.

   a Produce a pie chart to show the proportion of men suffering from lung cancer who were smokers and non-smokers.

   b How many of the men suffering from lung cancer were non-smokers?

4 The bar chart in Figure 2a shows all the people dying of lung cancer in 1992.

   a How many were there altogether?

   b What percentage were smokers?

   c What does this appear to show about the relationship between smoking and lung cancer?

5 Make a bar chart to display the data given in the table in Figure 2b in a way which makes clearer the link between the number of cigarettes smoked daily and the risk of death from lung cancer.

6 Given the link between smoking and lung cancer, what does the graph in Figure 2c tell you about the changes in smoking habits between 1974 and 1992?

0—m Key Ideas

⊙ Tobacco smoke contains substances which can help to cause lung cancer.

⊙ Evidence for the link between smoking and lung cancer took many years to build up and even longer before it was accepted by everyone.

1 The diagrams show a bacterium,
   a virus and an animal cell.

   a Give **two** features found in both
      bacteria and animal cells, and
      two features which are different
      in bacteria.   (2 marks)

   b List the three types of cell in order of size, with the **largest** first.   (1 mark)

   c There is some argument about whether viruses are living organisms or not.
      Give the evidence which suggests that they are living and the reasons
      why some people say they are not living organisms.   (3 marks)
                                                                  (Total 6 marks)

2 Cholera is a disease which causes severe diarrhoea and sickness. It can kill. Poor
   people living in overcrowded homes with poor sanitation have always been the worst
   affected. In 1884 during a cholera outbreak in London a doctor called John Snow
   recorded all the deaths. 500 people in one small area died in 10 days. Snow plotted
   the deaths on a map and found they all got their drinking water from the same place
   – the Broad street pump. Once the pump was put out of action the epidemic decreased.

   Outbreaks of cholera are still common in areas of the world where there is overcrowding
   and poverty, and after disasters when people have to live in make-shift camps.

   a Cholera is caused by a bacterium. From this evidence, how do you think it
      is spread?   (1 mark)

   b What is meant by 'the germ theory of disease'?   (2 marks)

   c How could this information about cholera be used to support the germ
      theory of disease?   (3 marks)
                                                                  (Total 6 marks)

3 In infectious diseases the microorganisms which cause disease are spread
   from one person to another. The following is a list of advice which might be
   given to people to help them avoid contracting infectious diseases:

   Always wash your hands before preparing food or eating.

   Put your hand in front of your mouth if you cough or sneeze.

   When travelling abroad, drink only bottled water in countries where the water
   supply is unreliable.

   Wash your hands after using the toilet.

   Cover a cut with antiseptic cream and a plaster.

   From what you know about the ways infectious diseases are spread,
   explain why each of these statements is good advice.   (2 marks each)
                                                                  (Total 10 marks)

4 **a** Give **two** ways in which the human body defends itself against the
      entry of disease-causing microorganisms.   (2 marks)

   b If disease-causing microorganisms do get into the body there
      is a special defence system which is ready to destroy them.
      Some white blood cells, like the one in the diagram, ingest
      and destroy microorganisms.

      i What is the internal body defence system called?   (1 mark)
      ii Give two other ways in which white blood cells can
         overcome the threat of invading microorganisms.   (2 marks)
                                                                  (Total 5 marks)

5 The graph shows the effect of
the introduction of the BCG
vaccination on cases of TB and
deaths from the disease.

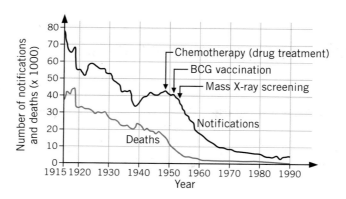

a What effect did the
introduction of the BCG
vaccination have on the
numbers of cases of TB and
the number of deaths from
the disease?

(1 mark)

b Explain how the vaccination would have this effect.

(2 marks)

c The numbers of cases of TB were dropping before the vaccination was
introduced. Suggest a reason for this drop.

(2 marks)

(Total 5 marks)

AQA specimen question

6 The diagram shows areas of lung tissue
from two people. One is a non-smoker,
the other is a long-term smoker who has
developed emphysema.

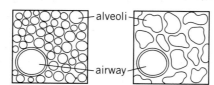

a Which sample of tissue is from the non-smoker?

(1 mark)

b What are the main symptoms of emphysema?

(2 marks)

c How does smoking cause emphysema?

(2 marks)

d The risk of having a number of diseases (like emphysema) increases with
the number of cigarettes smoked and the length of time someone has
been a smoker. Name **two** of these smoking-related diseases.

(2 marks)

(Total 7 marks)

7 The chart shows the
effect of smoking on
the annual death rate
in men.

a i What is the annual death rate per 100 000 of men aged 55–64 who
smoke 1–14 cigarettes a day?

(1 mark)

ii The death rate of men aged 45–54 who smoke more than 25 cigarettes
a day is higher than the death rate for non-smokers. How much higher
per 100 000 is it?

(1 mark)

b Explain, as fully as you can, why the death rate for smokers is higher
than the death rate for non-smokers in each age group.

(3 marks)

(Total 5 marks)

AQA specimen question

Like all living organisms plants need food to provide them with the energy they need for respiration, growth and reproduction. They do this in the process of **photosynthesis** which takes place in the green parts of plants, especially the leaves, when it is light.

What is photosynthesis?

Photosynthesis can be summed up in the following equation:

carbon dioxide + water (+ light energy) → glucose + oxygen

The chemical equation for the same process is:

$$6CO_2 + 6H_2O \ (+ \text{ light energy}) \rightarrow C_6H_{12}O_6 + 6O_2$$

During photosynthesis light energy is absorbed by a green substance called **chlorophyll** which is found in the chloroplasts of some plant cells. The energy which is captured is used to convert carbon dioxide from the air and water from the soil into a simple sugar, glucose, with oxygen as a by-product (Figure 1).

Some of the glucose produced during photosynthesis is used immediately by the cells of the plant for respiration, to provide energy for cell functions, growth and reproduction. However, much of the glucose produced is converted into starch for storage. This is because glucose is soluble and so could affect the water balance within the plant if allowed to build up. If the concentrations of glucose vary in different parts of the plant then osmosis takes place to correct this which could upset the whole organism (see pages 7 and 10). Starch is insoluble, which means that it has no effect on the concentration of solutions because it does not form a solution. This means that it can be moved around the plant and stored in different places without having any effect on the water balance of the plant (Figure 2).

↑ **Figure 1:** Oxygen is produced as a by-product of photosynthesis – about 368 000 000 000 tonnes every year! This oxygen is then used for respiration by plants and animals alike.

← **Figure 2:** We use the iodine test for the presence of starch to show us that photosynthesis has taken place. The leaf at the bottom has been deprived of light, so it has made no glucose to turn into starch, and has used up any starch stores it had for respiration. The leaf at the top has been in the light and been able to photosynthesise.
The glucose has been converted to starch which is clearly visible when it reacts with iodine.

A photosynthesising machine

The leaves of plants are perfectly adapted to allow the maximum possible amount of photosynthesis take place whenever there is light available (Figure 3).

↓ **Figure 3:** The leaves of plants are perfectly adapted to make the best possible use of the light which falls on them.

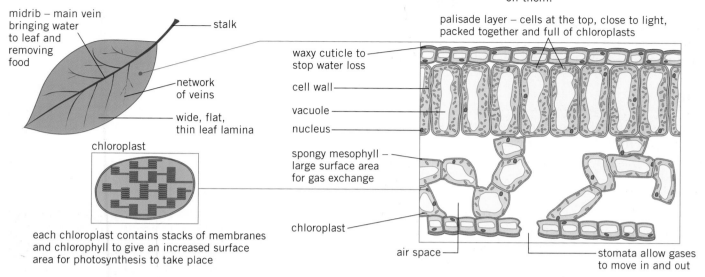

midrib – main vein bringing water to leaf and removing food

stalk

network of veins

wide, flat, thin leaf lamina

chloroplast

each chloroplast contains stacks of membranes and chlorophyll to give an increased surface area for photosynthesis to take place

palisade layer – cells at the top, close to light, packed together and full of chloroplasts

waxy cuticle to stop water loss

cell wall

vacuole

nucleus

spongy mesophyll – large surface area for gas exchange

chloroplast

air space

stomata allow gases to move in and out

H Using the products of photosynthesis

The glucose made during photosynthesis is used within the plant for respiration. The energy released in respiration is then used to build up smaller molecules into bigger molecules:

⊙ Sugars like glucose are built into starch for storage.

⊙ Sugars like glucose are built up into more complex carbohydrates like cellulose to make new plant cell walls.

⊙ Sugars, along with nitrates and other nutrients which the plant takes up from the soil, are used to make amino acids. These amino acids are then built up into proteins to act as enzymes and make up much of the cytoplasm of the cells.

⊙ Sugars may be built up into fats and oils (lipids) for storage in seeds and to make up part of the cell membranes.

? Questions

1 Where does a plant get the carbon dioxide, water and light that it needs for photosynthesis?

2 Figure 3 shows that a leaf has large surface areas both outside and inside. Describe three ways in which this helps it to photosynthesise effectively.

3 Design experiments to show that plants need

a water and

b light for photosynthesis to take place.

For each experiment, explain what your control would be and how you would show that photosynthesis has taken place.

4 Work out the path taken by a carbon molecule as it moves from being part of the carbon dioxide in the air to being part of a starch molecule in a plant.

5 Plants play a vital part in maintaining the balance of carbon dioxide and oxygen in the atmosphere. Explain why they are so important.

⊙━━ Key Ideas

⊙ Photosynthesis can be represented by: carbon dioxide + water (+ energy) → glucose + oxygen.

⊙ Some of the glucose made in photosynthesis is used in respiration to provide energy.

⊙ Some of the glucose made in photosynthesis may be converted to insoluble starch.

H ⊙ The energy released in the plant during respiration is used to build up smaller molecules into larger molecules.

Several different conditions affect the rate at which a plant can carry out photosynthesis. If they are in short supply they can limit the amount of photosynthesis a plant can manage, and so they are known as **limiting factors**.

Light

The most obvious factor which affects the rate of photosynthesis is light. If there is plenty of light, lots of photosynthesis can take place, but in the absence of light or very low light, photosynthesis will stop regardless of the other conditions around the plant. For most plants, the brighter the light, the greater the rate of photosynthesis.

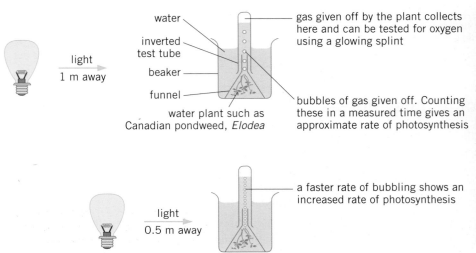

↑ **Figure 1**

The experiment in Figure 1 shows that when the light is moved away from a water plant, the rate of photosynthesis falls. This is shown by a slowing in the stream of oxygen bubbles being produced. If the light is moved closer (keeping the water temperature constant) the stream of bubbles becomes faster and faster, showing an increased rate of photosynthesis. The oxygen given off can be measured accurately using an oxygen sensor, or less accurately by just counting how many bubbles appear within a measured space of time.

Temperature

Temperature affects all chemical reactions and photosynthesis is no exception. As the temperature rises the rate of photosynthesis will increase as the reaction speeds up. However, because photosynthesis takes place in living organisms it is controlled by enzymes. Enzymes are proteins which denature after about 40 °C, so if the temperature goes too high the rate of photosynthesis will fall as the enzymes controlling it are destroyed (Figure 2).

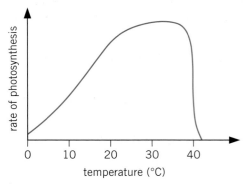

↑ **Figure 2:** The rate of photosynthesis increases steadily with a rise in temperature up to a certain point, after which the enzymes are destroyed and the reaction stops completely.

Carbon dioxide levels

The amount of carbon dioxide available limits the amount of photosynthesis which can take place – without carbon dioxide glucose cannot be made. In the natural environment of most plants carbon dioxide levels are often a limiting factor when there is plenty of light available. Carbon dioxide levels around the plant tend to rise in the night due to respiration, but as the light and temperature levels increase it all gets used up. However, in a laboratory or in a greenhouse environment the levels of carbon dioxide can be increased artificially so that they are no longer limiting, and the rate of photosynthesis increases with the rise in carbon dioxide (Figure 3).

In the laboratory we can isolate each factor and see how it limits the rate of photosynthesis. However, for most plants a mixture of these factors affects the photosynthetic rate. Early in the morning light levels and temperature probably limit the rate of photosynthesis, but as the level of light and the temperature rise then carbon dioxide becomes limiting. On a bright, cold, winter day temperature probably limits the rate of the process – there is a constant interaction between the different factors.

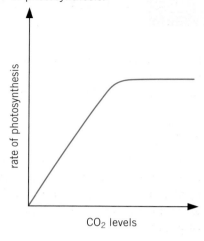
↓ **Figure 3:** The effect of increasing carbon dioxide levels on the rate of photosynthesis.

← **Figure 4:** Battery-reared plants? In greenhouses like this nothing is left to chance – the plants are even grown in nutritionally balanced water rather than soil to make sure nothing limits their rate of photosynthesis and growth.

? Questions

1 Why can you find the rate of photosynthesis in a plant by measuring the amount of oxygen given off?

2 **a** Using the same sort of apparatus as that shown in Figure 1, describe how you might demonstrate that temperature acts as a limiting factor for photosynthesis.

   b What variables would you need to control for such an experiment and why?

2 Which factors do you think would be limiting to photosynthesis in the following situations?

   a plants growing on a woodland floor in winter

   b plants growing on a woodland floor in summer

   c a field of barley first thing in the morning

   d the same field later on in the day.

O—ᴛ Key Ideas

⊙ There are three main factors which limit the rate of photosynthesis – light, temperature and carbon dioxide levels.

The need for minerals

Although plants can make their own food by photosynthesis, they do not survive for very long if they are only provided with water, carbon dioxide and light. Just as people need minerals and vitamins for healthy growth, so plants need more than simply the products of photosynthesis to survive.

The need for nitrates

The problem with the products of photosynthesis is that they are only carbohydrates. While carbohydrates are very useful for energy, for storage and even for structural features like cell walls, a plant cannot function without proteins to act as enzymes and to make up the bulk of the cytoplasm and the membranes.

Glucose and starch are made up of carbon, hydrogen and oxygen. Proteins are made up of amino acids which contain at the very least carbon, hydrogen, oxygen and **nitrogen**. So for a plant to make proteins it must obtain nitrogen in the form of nitrates from the soil. The nitrates dissolved in water are taken up from the soil by the roots. They are vital for healthy growth. When plants die and decay the minerals are returned to the soil to be used by other plants (Figure 1).

↑ **Figure1:** The crops grown by farmers are harvested – they are not left to die and decay naturally, returning minerals to the soil. So the farmer adds fertiliser to the soil to replace the minerals lost ready for the next crop he grows. The fertiliser may be a natural one like manure or an artificial mixture of the minerals plants need to grow.

 How to keep plants healthy

Plants need a number of different minerals to keep them healthy. Three of the major requirements are:

⊙ **Nitrate** which is needed for the synthesis of protein (see above)

⊙ **Phosphate** which has an important role in the reactions of photosynthesis and respiration – it is part of the energy-carrying molecule used in the cells.

⊙ **Potassium** helps the enzymes involved in photosynthesis and respiration to work.

If any of these minerals are missing the plants will begin to look decidedly sickly. This is true in the garden and for houseplants just as much as for crops in the farmer's field. If there are not enough mineral ions in the soil, the plants cannot grow properly and they begin to show the symptoms of mineral deficiencies.

↑ **Figure 2:** Plants A, B and C are suffering from a different mineral deficiency. Plant D is normal.

In Figure 2 plant A is suffering from a lack of nitrates in the growing medium. The yellow older leaves and stunted growth are typical symptoms of nitrate deficiency. Plant B has a lack of phosphate ions. As a result the roots don't grow very well and the younger leaves turn purple. Plant C has yellow leaves with dead spots on them. This is the result of a lack of potassium.

Plants with these problems will not flower properly and if they are crop plants they will give a much reduced yield, if any at all. However, the problems of these deficiencies can be overcome by supplying the plants with the mineral ions that they need. There is a wide range of plant feeds on the market for the home gardener, and for the farmer artificial fertilisers provide a well-balanced mixture of minerals (Figure 3).

↑ **Figure 3:** One of the most widely used artificial fertilisers is NPK, the chemical symbols which represent the three important minerals present in the powder. N = nitrogen, P = phosphorus and K = potassium.

1 a Why do plants need minerals?

   b Where do they get minerals from?

   c Which mineral is needed by plants to form proteins?

2 a Draw a diagram to show the cycle of nutrients between plants and the soil.

   b Farmers can add nutrients to the soil by spreading manure or artificial fertilisers. Suggest one advantage and one disadvantage of each method of adding minerals to the soil.

3 a Plants need a variety of minerals to keep them healthy. Devise a table which gardeners could use, giving the symptoms of various mineral deficiency diseases, which mineral is missing and why it is needed.

   b Magnesium is a mineral which is important in the formation of chlorophyll. What symptoms would you expect if a plant was magnesium deficient?

⊙━ Key Ideas

- ⊙ Plant roots absorb mineral salts including nitrate needed for healthy growth.

- ⊙ Nitrates, potassium and phosphorus are three important minerals for healthy plant growth.

- ⊙ If minerals are deficient, a plant develops symptoms because it cannot grow properly.

Plants are sensitive too!

It is very easy to assume that animals are the only members of the natural world with awareness of what is going on around them. However, although they often operate on a very different timescale to us, plants also show very clear sensitivity to light, gravity and moisture (water). Plant shoots move towards light (Figure 1) and against the force of gravity, while their roots grow towards moisture and in the direction of the force of gravity.

Why are plants sensitive?

When a seed leaves a parent plant it may fall any way up in the soil. However, it is very important when it germinates that its roots grow downwards into the soil. This means they can anchor the seedling and keep it stable, as well as take up the water and minerals needed for healthy growth.

At the same time the shoots grow upwards away from the soil and towards the light so that as much photosynthesis as possible can take place. Thus the sensitivity of the root to gravity and moisture and of the shoot to gravity and light make sure that whichever way up a seed may land, the plant never grows upside down.

How do plants respond?

This sensitivity is due to the action of **plant hormones**. Plant hormones encourage growth. The responses of plant roots and shoots to light, gravity and moisture are the result of an unequal distribution of hormones, which causes an unequal growth rate and so makes a root or shoot bend in the right direction. These responses are easy to see in young seedlings (Figure 2), but they also happen in adult plants – a houseplant left on the windowsill soon bends towards the light.

↑ **Figure 1:** When plants have been exposed to light coming from one side only for some time it is very easy to see how they have responded and grown towards the light.

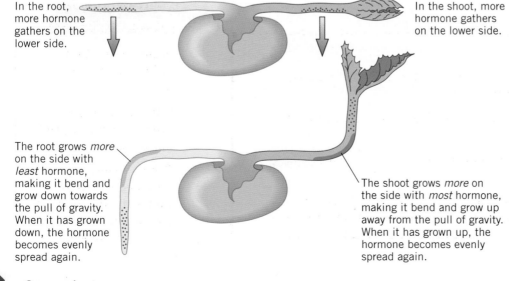

root · · · · · · · · · shoot · · · · · · · · ·

↓ gravity   ↓ gravity

A young bean plant is laid on its side in the dark. Hormone is equally spread through the tissues.

In the root, more hormone gathers on the lower side.

In the shoot, more hormone gathers on the lower side.

The root grows *more* on the side with *least* hormone, making it bend and grow down towards the pull of gravity. When it has grown down, the hormone becomes evenly spread again.

The shoot grows *more* on the side with *most* hormone, making it bend and grow up away from the pull of gravity. When it has grown up, the hormone becomes evenly spread again.

← **Figure 2:** The stimulus results in there being more hormone on one side of a plant root or shoot than the other. The uneven distribution of hormone has a different effect in the root and shoot causing bending in the right direction for the needs of the plant.

Darwin and son

When Francis Darwin was a child he loved to fiddle with his father's experiments. When he grew up, Charles found working with his son very rewarding and they made a lot of important discoveries together. Charles Darwin is so well known for his work on evolution that his other important contributions to biology are often forgotten. Whilst the battle over his book *The Origin of Species* was raging, Charles retreated to his home and family. He worked with his son, Francis, another keen biologist, and together they investigated the movements of plants. They carried out the first known work on plant movements in response to a particular stimulus. Together they showed that the shoot of a plant is sensitive to light from one direction.

↑ **Figure 3:** Down House – the home which Darwin loved and where he and Francis worked on plant sensitivity.

Using plant hormones

We put plant hormones to good use in the way we manage plants for our own needs (Table 1).

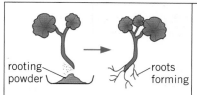 rooting powder → roots forming	Gardeners and horticulturists rely heavily on taking cuttings to produce lots of identical plants. A little plant growth hormone applied to the end of a cutting stimulates the growth of new roots and helps the cutting to take.
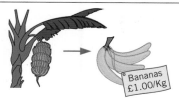 Bananas £1.00/Kg	Fruit ripens in response to a plant hormone. Much of the fruit we buy is harvested and transported to this country before it is ripe, because it is less likely to get damaged when it is unripe. The fruit is then exposed to the ripening hormone and ripens before it reaches the supermarket shelves.
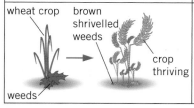 wheat crop, brown shrivelled weeds, crop thriving, weeds	We use high doses of plant hormones as weedkillers. Most weeds are broad-leaved plants which absorb a lot of hormone weedkiller and go into rapid uncontrolled growth which kills them. The narrower leaves of many grasses and cereal plants are not affected, so the crop or lawn grows on.

↑ **Table 1:** Human use of plant hormones.

? Questions

1 **a** What do plants respond to?

　b What feature of plant responses suggests that they are controlled by hormones rather than a nervous system?

2 Explain carefully how plant hormones work to make a root or shoot grow towards gravity or light.

3 Why are the responses of plant roots and shoots so important in the life of plants?

4 You are provided with some very young single shoots. Devise an experiment which would demonstrate that shoots grow towards the light.

Key Ideas

⊙ Plants are sensitive to light, moisture and gravity.

⊙ Plant responses are brought about by plant hormones.

⊙ The responses of plant roots and shoots to stimuli are the result of the unequal distribution of plant hormones.

Plants make food by photosynthesis in the leaves and other green parts, but it is needed all over the plant. Similarly, water and minerals move into the plant through the roots in the soil, but they are needed by every cell in the body of the plant. Plants need a transport system to move substances around their bodies (Figure 1).

A double transport system

There are two separate transport systems in plants. The **phloem** transports the nutrients made by photosynthesis from the leaves to the rest of the plant. It contains sugar and starch-rich liquid. These nutrients are carried to all the areas of the plant including the growing regions where they are needed for making new plant material, and the storage organs where they are needed to provide a store of food for the winter.

The **xylem** is the other transport tissue. It carries water and mineral ions from the soil around the plant (Figure 2).

In woody plants like trees the xylem tissue makes up the bulk of the wood, and the phloem is found in a ring just underneath the bark. This makes young trees in particular very vulnerable to damage by animals, because if a complete ring of bark is nibbled, transport in the phloem comes to a complete halt and the tree will die.

← **Figure 1:** Trees like this giant redwood can be up to 30 m tall – and then the roots go down under the ground as well. Plants need a very effective transport system to move substances distances like these.

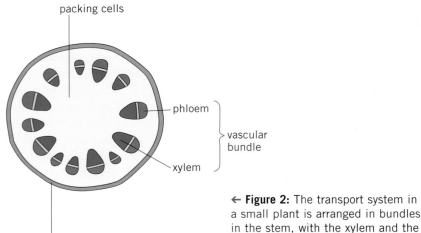

← **Figure 2:** The transport system in a small plant is arranged in bundles in the stem, with the xylem and the phloem arranged together.

Why is transport so important?

The importance of moving the food made by photosynthesis around the plant is obvious – all the cells need glucose for respiration as well as to supply materials for growth. The movement of water and minerals from the roots is equally valuable. The minerals are needed for the production of proteins and other molecules within the cells. The water is needed for two main reasons.

One reason is for photosynthesis. Less obviously, but just as important, water is needed to hold the plant upright. When a cell has enough water it makes the cytoplasm press against the cell walls. The pressure of the cytoplasm against the cell walls gives support for young plants. In fact for young plants and soft stemmed plants – not trees! – this is the main method of support (Figure 3).

H As we saw earlier in this book (Chapter 1, Section 1.5) water moves into plant cells by osmosis, increasing the pressure inside the cell as the cytoplasm swells and presses against the plant cell walls. The cell walls are strong enough to withstand the pressure which keeps the cells of the plant rigid and firm. When the pressure inside the cell is such that no more water can move in, the plant cell is said to be turgid. The pressure of the cell walls on the water which has moved into the cell maintains the turgor of the cell and this in turn supports the plant tissues (Figure 3).

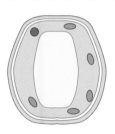

↑ **Figure 3:** The difference a good supply of water makes can be seen all too clearly here. Plant A has plenty of water, plant B has not. If the wilting is recent, plant B will recover once it is given water, but if the wilt lasts too long the plant will die.

? Questions

1 Why does a plant need a transport system?

2 Explain why a constant supply of

   a food and

   b water

   is so important to the cells of the plant.

3 Explain exactly how water helps to hold a plant upright.

4 A local woodland trust has set up a scheme to put protective plastic covers around the trunks of young trees. Some local residents are objecting to this, saying it spoils the look of the woodland. Write a letter to the local paper explaining exactly why this protection is necessary.

0ᴍ Key Ideas

⊙ Phloem carries the products of photosynthesis around the plant from the leaves to areas including the growing regions and the storage organs.

⊙ Xylem carries water and mineral ions from the soil up to the stems and leaves.

⊙ Water is vital to keep the cells firm and support the plant.

H ⊙ Water moves into cells by osmosis to maintain the water pressure inside them.

Water is moved from the roots of a plant up to the uppermost leaf, a distance which can be many metres, by a process known as **transpiration**.

The transpiration stream

Plants lose water vapour from the surface of their leaves. This loss of water vapour is an important part of the transpiration process. Most of the water loss takes place through tiny holes in the surface of the leaf known as **stomata**. These stomata are there to allow air containing carbon dioxide into the leaf for photosynthesis. Stomata can be opened and closed by the guard cells which surround tmhem. Losing water through the stomata is a side effect of opening them to let carbon dioxide in. Most of the stomata are found on the underside of the leaf (Figure 1).

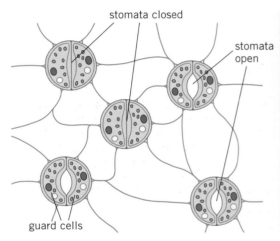

stomata closed

stomata open

guard cells

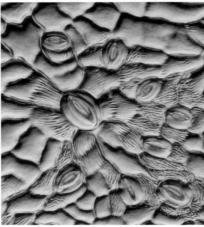

← **Figure 1:** Guards cells open and close the stomata to control both the carbon dioxide going into a cell and the water coming out of it.

As water evaporates from the surface of the leaves, water is pulled up through the xylem to take its place. This constant moving of water molecules through the xylem from the roots to the leaves is known as the transpiration stream (Figure 2). It is driven purely by the evaporation of water from the leaves – so anything which affects the rate of evaporation will affect transpiration.

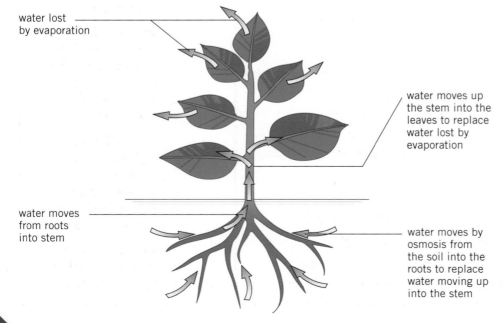

water lost by evaporation

water moves from roots into stem

water moves up the stem into the leaves to replace water lost by evaporation

water moves by osmosis from the soil into the roots to replace water moving up into the stem

← **Figure 2:** The transpiration stream – capable of pulling a column of water in the xylem up to 30 m above the surface of the Earth.

Conditions which increase the rate of evaporation also increase the rate of transpiration. Transpiration is more rapid in hot, dry and windy conditions than it is in still or humid conditions. Plenty of light also speeds up transpiration, because lots of photosynthesis takes place and so the stomata are opened to allow plenty of carbon dioxide in. When the stomata are open, lots more water can evaporate from the surface of the leaves.

Stopping water loss

If a plant begins to lose water faster than it is replaced by the roots, it runs the risk of wilting. The stomata in the leaves will close to stop this if possible. To make sure that water is not lost from the surface of the leaf generally, most leaves have a waxy, waterproof layer (known as the **cuticle**) to prevent uncontrolled water loss. In very hot environments the cuticle may be very thick and shiny. The fact that the stomata are on the underside of the leaf also helps because this means that they are not as exposed to the heat of the sun as they would be on the top of the leaf.

Evidence for transpiration

There are a number of experiments which can be carried out to investigate the movement of water in plants by transpiration. Many of them use a piece of apparatus known as a potometer (Figure 3). A potometer can be used to show how the uptake of water by the plant changes with different conditions, giving a good idea of the amount of water lost by the plant in transpiration.

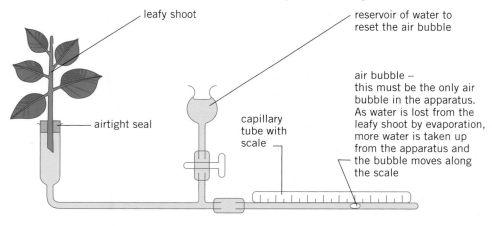

leafy shoot

reservoir of water to reset the air bubble

air bubble – this must be the only air bubble in the apparatus. As water is lost from the leafy shoot by evaporation, more water is taken up from the apparatus and the bubble moves along the scale

airtight seal

capillary tube with scale

← **Figure 3:** Using a potometer like this we can observe the effect of light, temperature and wind on the rate of water loss by a plant. We can even block up the stomata by covering the leaves with a film of Vaseline and see the effect on the movement of the air bubble.

Key Ideas

⊙ The loss of water vapour from the surface of plant leaves is known as transpiration.

⊙ Water is lost through the stomata which are opened and closed by guard cells to let in carbon dioxide for photosynthesis.

⊙ Water is pulled up through the xylem from the roots to replace the water lost from the leaves in the transpiration stream.

⊙ Transpiration is more rapid in hot, dry, windy or light conditions.

? Questions

1 a What are stomata?

  b What is their role in the plant?

  c How are they involved in transpiration?

2 Describe exactly how water moves up the plant in the transpiration stream.

3 What effect on the rate of transpiration would you expect if the leaves on the stem in a potometer were treated in the following ways. In each case explain your answer.

  a The top surfaces only have been covered in waterproof jelly.

  b The bottom surfaces only have been covered in waterproof jelly.

  c The whole leaves have been covered in waterproof jelly.

4 Suggest an investigation using a potometer to show the effect of either light or temperature on the rate of photosynthesis from a leafy stem.

1 The diagram shows a section through the leaf of a green plant.

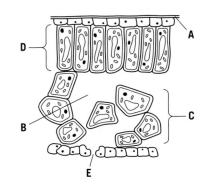

   a Use words from the list to name the parts labelled **A–E**.

stomata	spongy mesophyll
waxy cuticle	palisade layer
air spaces	epidermis

      (5 marks)

   b Name the **two** areas of the leaf where most photosynthesis takes place. (2 marks)

      (Total 7 marks)

2 Photosynthesis takes place in green plants. Variegated leaves have areas that are green and areas that are white. Some students used variegated leaves to investigate photosynthesis.

They covered part of a variegated leaf with a black paper shape.

The leaf was left in a sunny place. They tested the leaf for starch.

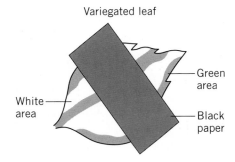

Variegated leaf

Area of leaf tested	Starch present after test	
	covered	uncovered
Green area	no	yes
White area	no	no

Explain why starch was not produced

   a in the covered green areas of the leaf (2 marks)

   b in the uncovered white areas of the leaf. (2 marks)

      (Total 6 marks)

      AQA specimen question

3 The diagram shows an experiment to investigate the effect of light on the rate of photosynthesis in a water plant.

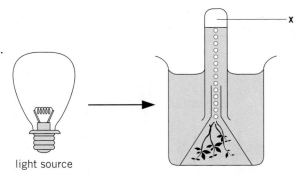

light source

   a What gas would you expect to collect at **X**? (1 mark)

   b What test would you carry out to show what gas has actually collected? (2 marks)

   c What would you expect to see if the light was moved closer to the beaker containing the pond weed? (1 mark)

   d Explain why you would expect this to happen. (2 marks)

   e What factors need to be kept constant in this experiment if it is to be a fair test of the effect of light? (2 marks)

      (Total 8 marks)

ⓗ 4 a Name **two** things that can happen in a plant to the glucose produced in photosynthesis. (2 marks)

b Plants need mineral ions.

　i Through which part of the plant are mineral ions absorbed? (1 mark)

　ii Explain why water is important in the absorption of mineral ions. (2 marks)

c Some students set up water cultures to find out if plants need nitrates. They had two sets of nutrient solutions. A full solution provided the plant with all the required ions.

The results table shows the average mass of the seedlings after 28 days of growth.

Culture solution	Average mass of seedling (g)
Distilled water	0.14
Full solution with no nitrates	0.29
Full solution	0.43

　i Give a conclusion from these results. (1 mark)

　ii What are nitrates used for in the seedling? (1 mark)

　iii How can you tell from its leaves that a plant is suffering from nitrate deficiency? (1 mark)

　iv Some factors need to be controlled to keep this test fair. Name **two** of them. (2 marks)

(Total 10 marks)

5 The diagram shows the results of an experiment to find the effect of light on the growth of seedlings.

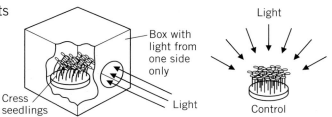

a Describe the results of the experiment. (2 marks)

b Name the type of substance that controls growth in plants. (1 mark)

c Copy and complete this sentence about growth in plant roots.

Plant roots grow towards ……. and in the direction of the force of ……… (2 marks)

(Total 5 marks)

AQA specimen question

6 A potted plant was left in a hot, brightly lit room for ten hours. The plant was not watered during this period. The drawings show how the mean width of stomata changed over the ten hour period.

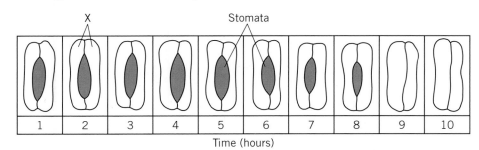

a Why do plants need stomata? (1 mark)

b Name the cells labelled **X** on the drawing. (1 mark)

c The width of the stomata changed over the ten hour period. Explain the advantage to the plant of this change. (2 marks)

(Total 4 marks)

AQA specimen question

Young animals and plants resemble their parents – cats have kittens, people have babies and tomato plants have baby tomato plants! Members of any species are similar to their parents and to all the other members of the species because of inherited characteristics which are passed on through the generations (Figure 1). This information is carried in the genes, units of inheritance that are carried on the chromosomes (see Chapter 1, Section 1.6). Genes are passed on from parents to offspring in special sex cells (**gametes**). In animals these are eggs and sperm, in plants, eggs and pollen.

↑ **Figure 1:** Both the parents and the puppies are individuals in their own rights – but they all have lots of inherited information in common.

 Science people

Gregor Mendel – the father of inheritance

Strange as it may seem, for many centuries people had no idea about how information moved from one generation to the next. For centuries the idea was that the characteristics of the parents blended together so that the distinct characteristics of each parent were lost.

The birth of Gregor Mendel in 1822 was the beginning of the end for those theories. Mendel was born into abject poverty and the only way for him to get an education was to join the church. As a monk at a monastery in Brunn, he became fascinated by the breeding patterns of the peas in the monastery gardens. He carefully bred different pure strains of peas – round peas, wrinkled peas, green peas, yellow peas – and then carried out breeding experiments with them. It might not sound exciting to us, but to this monk 150 years ago it was riveting! He developed a theory to explain his observations, based on independent particles of hereditary material, some of which had more influence on the offspring than others but which never mixed together. The Abbot of the monastery supported his work and built him a large greenhouse in which to carry it out.

← **Figure 2**

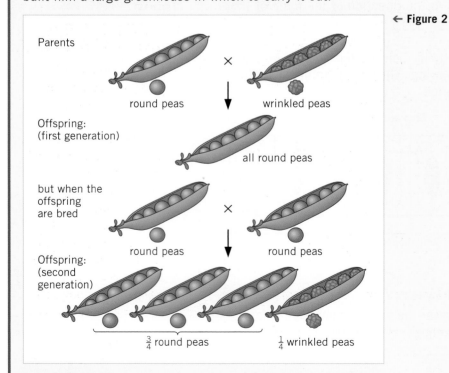

It was experiments like the one in Figure 2 that led Gregor Mendel to his ground-breaking conclusions. He saw that the round shape of peas seemed to emerge in offspring more than the wrinkled shape, but that the information for a wrinkled shape continued to be carried and could emerge again in later generations – in other words there were unique units of inheritance which were not blended together.

Mendel kept precise records of everything he did, and made a statistical analysis of his results – something almost unheard of in those times. Finally, in 1866, when he was 44 years old, Mendel published his findings which explained some of the basic laws of genetics in a way we still refer to today. Sadly no one believed him. He was ahead of his time – no one yet knew of the existence of chromosomes, let alone genes, so no one had a model on which to hang Mendel's new ideas. He died 20 years later with his ideas still ignored – but still sure that he was right.

Sixteen years after his death, Gregor Mendel's work was finally recognised. In 1900 chromosomes had been seen under a microscope. Three scientists, Hugo de Vries, Eric von Seysenegg and Karl Correns, discovered Mendel's papers and duplicated his experiments. To their eternal credit they acknowledged Mendel's ideas. From then on things snowballed – it was suggested that Mendel's units of inheritance might be carried on the chromosomes, and the science of genetics as we know it today began to emerge.

→ **Figure 3:** Gregor Mendel tending his pea plants. When he died in 1884 Mendel was still convinced that before long the whole world would acknowledge his discovery. From the 21st century we know just how right he was!

0—m **Key Ideas**

- Young animals and plants resemble their parents because of information in the form of genes passed on in the gametes from which they developed.

- Gregor Mendel, an Austrian monk in the 19th century, was the first person to recognise that individual units of information are inherited, although he did not call them genes.

? Questions

1 **a** What is the basic unit of inheritance?

  b Offspring inherit information from their parents but do not look exactly like their parents – why not?

2 How did Mendel's experiments with peas convince him that there were distinct 'units of inheritance' which were not blended together in offspring?

3 Advances in microscope technology finally helped to convince people that Mendel was right. How?

For genetic information to pass from one generation to another there has to be some type of reproduction. Two different types of reproduction have evolved over the millions of years life has existed on Earth – **asexual reproduction** and **sexual reproduction**.

Asexual reproduction

In asexual reproduction there is no joining of special sex cells and only one parent is needed for it to take place. It gives rise to offspring known as **clones** whose genetic material is identical to that of their parent and to each other. Bulbs, corms, tubers, runners and suckers are all ways in which plants reproduce themselves with only one parent, producing genetically identical offspring (Figure 1).

← **Figure 1:** Asexual reproduction leads to offspring which are genetically identical to their parents.

Sexual reproduction

Sexual reproduction involves the joining of two sex cells or gametes, usually – although not always – from different individuals. It gives rise to new individuals, each of which have a different mixture of genetic information from two parents. In plants the sex cells are ovules and pollen, in animals they are ova (eggs) and sperm.

Passing it on

The genetic information is passed from parent to offspring on the **chromosomes**. Human beings have 23 pairs of chromosomes. In 22 cases each chromosome in the pair is a similar shape and has genes carrying information about the same things. But one pair of chromosomes may be different – these are the **sex chromosomes**. Two X chromosomes mean the person is female but one X chromosome and one much smaller, known as the Y chromosome, give a male (Figure 2).

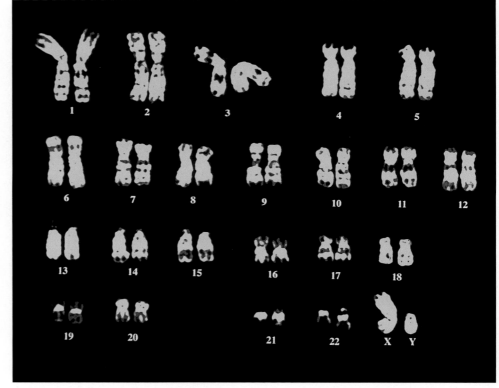

↑ **Figure 2:** The chromosomes of the human male. The X chromosome carries genes controlling lots of different features. The Y chromosome is much smaller than the X and carries information mainly about maleness!

Genes and alleles

The chromosomes we inherit carry our genetic information in the form of genes. Many of these genes have different forms, known as **alleles** (see page 86). A gene can be pictured as a position on a chromosome while an allele is the particular form of information in that position. For example, the gene for tongue rolling may have the rolling or the non-rolling allele in place (Figure 3). There may be only two possible alleles for a particular feature, but sometimes you could inherit one from a number of different possibilities.

DNA – the miracle molecule

Chromosomes are fundamental to successful reproduction. They are made up of long molecules of a chemical known as **DNA** (**d**eoxyribose **n**ucleic **a**cid). DNA carries the instructions to make the proteins which are the building blocks of life. Proteins form most of an organism's structure and make up the enzymes which control the cell chemistry. Genes are small sections of DNA.

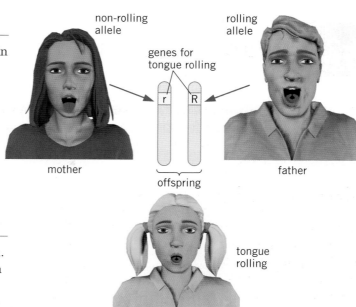

↑ **Figure 3:** You can inherit different alleles for the same characteristic from your parents. In the case of tongue rolling the 'roller gene' controls the characteristic.

H More about reproduction

The differences between asexual and sexual reproduction are a reflection of the different types of cell division involved in the two processes.

In asexual reproduction, the offspring are produced as a result of mitosis (see page 12) from the parent cells, so they contain exactly the same chromosomes and the same genes as their parents.

In sexual reproduction the gametes are produced by meiosis (see page 13) in the parental cells of the sex organs. When the gametes fuse, one of each pair of chromosomes and so one of each pair of genes comes from each parent. The combination of genes in the new pair may be different forms (alleles) from each parent and so they may well produce different characteristics in the offspring.

? Questions

1 What are the main similarities and differences between asexual and sexual reproduction?

2 a Every time a baby is conceived, there is a 50:50 chance that it will be either male or female. Why is this?

  b What is the main difference between the X and the Y chromosome?

3 a What is DNA?

  b What is a gene?

  c What is the difference between a gene and an allele?

H 3 Mitosis is the process which underpins asexual reproduction, while meiosis is vital for sexual reproduction. What are the main differences between these two processes and how do they affect reproduction so fundamentally?

0—π Key Ideas

- ⊙ Asexual reproduction involves one individual and the production of genetically identical offspring known as clones.
- ⊙ Sexual reproduction involves two gametes from different parents. When these sex cells fuse a new genetically unique individual is formed.
- ⊙ In humans sex is inherited by the sex chromosomes – females have two X chromosomes, males have an X and a Y.
- ⊙ Chromosomes are large molecules of DNA.
- ⊙ A gene is a small section of DNA.
- ⊙ Different alleles are different forms of a gene.

An introduction to genetics

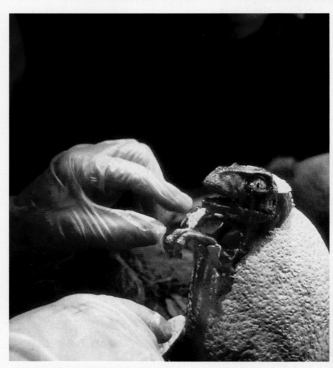

↑ **Figure 1:** Science fiction films, where dinosaurs were recreated from DNA fossilised in amber, helped make DNA and genes part of our everyday language – but the scientific discoveries behind the fiction are relatively recent.

Until the 1950s no one was really sure if DNA was actually the material involved in inheritance or not. Lots of people were trying to solve the riddle, especially two teams who were intense rivals. Maurice Wilkins and Rosalind Franklin in London were looking at the structure of DNA using X-rays, whilst James Watson and Francis Crick at Cambridge were trying to build a 3-D molecular model of it.

In the end it was the Cambridge team who came up with the now famous double helix structure for the DNA molecule using X-ray results from London. Once the structure was revealed, an enormous explosion in genetic research took place. Watson, Crick and Wilkins all received the Nobel prize for their work – Rosalind Franklin died of cancer before the prizes were awarded.

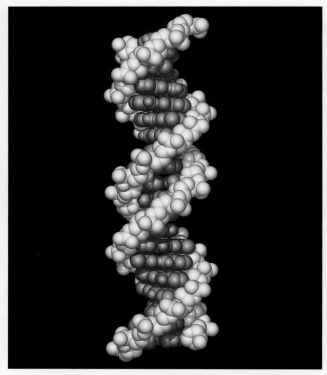

↑ **Figure 2:** An understanding of the double helix structure of DNA has made all of our modern work involving genetics possible.

Genes, alleles and genetics

Genes come in pairs which interact to determine what characteristics you will inherit.

Certain characteristics are controlled by one single pair of genes, although most of our features are controlled by many pairs. When studying genetics, we tend to stick to characteristics controlled by a single pair of genes, because they are much simpler to understand.

One of these is the way we inherit the ability to roll our tongues. There are two alleles which can control this characteristic – the allele to be a roller (R) or the allele to be a non-roller (r) (see page 85).

If we inherit a roller allele from both our parents (RR) or only from one (Rr), we will be able to roll our tongue. An allele like this which controls the development of a characteristic even when it is present on only one of the chromosomes is known as a **dominant allele**.

If we inherit a non-roller allele from both our parents (rr) we will not be able to roll our tongue. An allele like this which controls the development of characteristics only if the dominant allele is not present is known as a **recessive allele**.

Deeper into DNA

The long strands of DNA are made up of combinations of four different bases (see Figure 3). These are grouped into threes and each group of three codes for an amino acid. Different combinations of amino acids make different proteins. The order of the groups of three on the DNA determines which proteins are formed by deciding the order of the amino acids making up the protein.

A gene can be made up of hundreds or thousands of the bases on a strand of DNA. The order of the bases controls the order in which the amino acids are assembled so that they make a particular protein for use in the body cells.

A change or mutation in a single group of bases can be enough to change or disrupt the whole protein structure and the way it works.

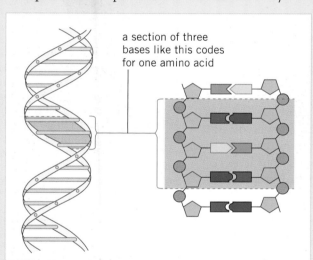

a section of three bases like this codes for one amino acid

← **Figure 3:** It is at this fundamental level of chemistry that your characteristics are determined. A small quirk of chemistry would have resulted in a very different you – a strange thought.

? Questions

1 What does a gene do?

2 a What is meant by a dominant allele?

  b What is meant by a recessive allele?

3 Explain why you always have two genes for each characteristic.

4 If neither of your parents can roll their tongue, is there any chance that you will be able to roll yours? Explain your answer.

H 4 a The DNA molecule is made up of a combination of four 'bases' arranged in groups of three. What does each group code for?

  b What does a gene consist of?

  c Each gene makes a very specific protein. Why?

6.4 Using genetics

When features are controlled by a single pair of genes we can use our knowledge of dominant and recessive alleles to predict what characteristics the offspring of certain parents are likely to have. One of the uses of this is in working out whether someone is at risk of inheriting a genetic disease.

Genetic diseases

Not all diseases are infectious. Sometimes diseases are the result of a problem in the genes and can be passed on from parent to child. They are known as **genetic diseases**.

Huntington's disease

One example of a very serious although very rare genetic disease is Huntington's disease (it used to be known as Huntington's chorea). This is a disorder of the nervous system and it can be inherited from one parent who has the disease because it is caused by a dominant allele of the gene.

Cystic fibrosis

Another genetic disease which has been studied in great detail is **cystic fibrosis**. This is a disorder of the cell membranes. They produce a very thick sticky mucus which clogs up the lungs and the gut and stops them from working properly (Figure 1).

Cystic fibrosis must be inherited from both parents because it is caused by a recessive allele. Children affected by cystic fibrosis are born to parents who do not suffer from the disease. They have a dominant healthy allele which means their bodies work normally. But they carry silently the cystic fibrosis allele, and have no idea it is there. People who carry a disease-causing allele like this that gives them no symptoms are known as **carriers**.

↑ **Figure 1:** 16-year-old Tom Watson who has cystic fibrosis, took part in a 4500 mile race around the British coastline. Modern medicine and determination means that many sufferers from cystic fibrosis manage to lead very full and active lives, but the cells in their bodies are still carrying the problem alleles and cannot function properly.

H When the genes from parents are combined it is called a genetic cross and we can show this using a genetic diagram. A genetic diagram like the one in Figure 2 shows us the alleles for a characteristic carried by the parents, the possible gametes which can be formed from these and how these could combine to form the characteristic in their offspring. Remember that a gamete is formed by meiosis and so only carries one gene not a pair.

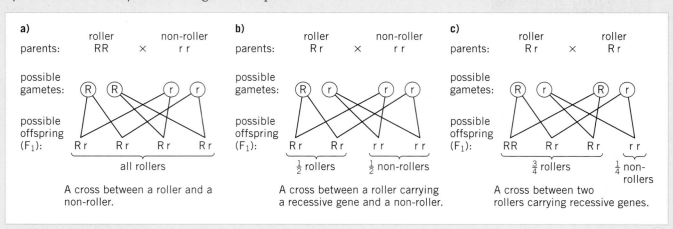

a)
parents: roller RR × non-roller r r
possible gametes: R R r r
possible offspring (F₁): R r R r R r R r
all rollers
A cross between a roller and a non-roller.

b)
parents: roller R r × non-roller r r
possible gametes: R r r r
possible offspring (F₁): R r R r r r r r
½ rollers ½ non-rollers
A cross between a roller carrying a recessive gene and a non-roller.

c)
parents: roller R r × roller R r
possible gametes: R r R r
possible offspring (F₁): RR R r R r r r
¾ rollers ¼ non-rollers
A cross between two rollers carrying recessive genes.

↑ **Figure 2:** Using genetic diagrams like this we can work out the possible offspring a couple might have.

A genetic diagram for Huntington's disease shows us how a dominant allele can affect offspring (Figure 3).

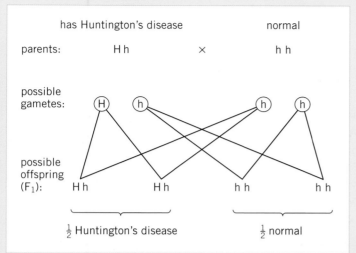

← **Figure 3**

has Huntington's disease   normal

parents: H h   ×   h h

possible gametes: (H) (h)   (h) (h)

possible offspring (F$_1$):   H h   H h   h h   h h

$\frac{1}{2}$ Huntington's disease $\frac{1}{2}$ normal

It is important to realise that Figure 3 shows that the chance of passing on the disease allele is 50%, but it cannot tell us which, if any, of the children will actually inherit the gene. The percentage chance is the same for each child. In reality, if this couple had children they might all avoid the disease, all inherit it, or be a mixture of the two.

? Questions

1 In cystic fibrosis, why must both parents have the allele for the disease to pass it on to their children?

2 Why are people who are carriers for cystic fibrosis unaffected by the disease themselves?

3 Why can one parent carrying the allele for Huntingdon's disease pass it on to their children even though the other parent is unaffected?

H 4 Gregor Mendel did his work on peas. Draw genetic diagrams showing the parents, the possible gametes and the possible offspring of a cross between

   a pure breeding round peas (RR) with pure breeding wrinkled peas (rr)

   b A round pea carrying a wrinkled gene (Rr) and a wrinkled pea (rr)

5 **a** Draw a genetic diagram for the inheritance of cystic fibrosis (C is dominant, c is recessive).

   b What is the chance that one of the children will inherit the disease?

O—π Key Ideas

⊙ Genetic diseases are caused by faulty genes and they can be inherited.

⊙ Huntington's disease is caused by a dominant allele.

⊙ Cystic fibrosis is the result of recessive alleles.

⊙ Healthy people who have a disease-causing recessive allele are known as carriers.

H ⊙ Genetic crosses can be represented by simple diagrams.

The way an organism develops will depend on its genetic information, but is there more to it than that?

Nature – the genetic element

The genes we inherit certainly determine a lot about us. An apple tree seedling will not develop into an oak tree, regardless of the soil and weather conditions it grows in. The basic characteristics of each species or breed is determined by the genes they inherit (Figure 1). Certain human features are clearly genetic. Eye colour, natural hair colour and texture, the shape of the nose and earlobes, sex, skin colour – all of these features are determined by our genes.

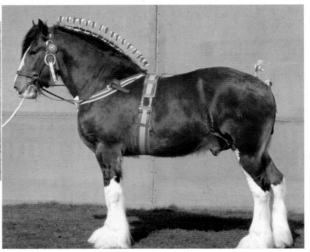

↗ **Figure 1:** No matter how much this Shetland pony eats, or how good the conditions in which it is kept, it will never attain the height of the giant Shire horse – it simply isn't in the genes.

Nurture – the environmental part

Whilst the genes undoubtedly play a major part in deciding how an organism will look, the conditions in which it grows and develops are also very important. Genetically identical plants can be grown under different conditions of light or soil nutrients, and the resulting plants look far from identical. Plants deprived of light or nutrients do not make as much food as plants with plenty of everything they need, so the deprived plants will be smaller and weaker – they will not have been able to fulfil their genetic potential (Figure 2).

← **Figure 2:** When plants like this *Pelargonium* (common name geranium) are grown in plenty of light they show attractive variegated patterns on the leaves. But when grown in low light levels, genetically identical plants lose the variegation and have green leaves to make the most of what little light there is for photosynthesis – the environment has a major effect on the appearance.

For organisms such as plants it is relatively easy to take genetically identical individuals and put them in different conditions to see how the environment affects the individual. To do the same experiments in humans is impossible! The only genetically identical humans are identical twins, because they come from the same fertilised egg (Figure 3).

It would be completely unethical to take such twins away from their parents by force and have them brought up in very different families to see if it made any difference to how they turned out. However, over the years there have been cases of identical twins who were adopted by different families. Some of them did not even realise that they had a twin until they were quite elderly.

Some scientists have researched this, tracing the twins after their very different lives and looking at the similarities and differences between them. The similarities in appearance at the first meeting of these twins, in their hairstyles and dress, were often quite astonishing. But the measurable facts – things like height, weight and IQ – showed that just like other organisms, some of the differences between humans are due to genetics and some are due to environment.

To see the effect of being brought up in different environments, scientists compared the average height, weight and IQ from a group of separated twins with a group of identical twins brought up together and a group of brothers and sisters (siblings) who were not twins. The table shows the results and indicates that environment certainly has an effect on how individuals develop.

↑ **Figure 3:** Identical twins are the only genetically identical humans. Even after years apart and very different environments the similarities between this pair of twins are striking.

Measured difference in	Identical twins brought up together	Identical twins brought up apart	Non-twin siblings
Height	1.7 cm	1.8 cm	4.5 cm
Weight	1.9 kg	4.5 kg	4.7 kg
IQ (a measure of intelligence)	5.9	8.2	9.8

1 Why can separated identical twins help to show us the effect which environment has on our development?

2 Display the data from the table above in the form of bar charts to make the information easier to understand.

3 Use the data from the table to answer the following:

   a In which characteristic are the differences between twins brought up separately and apart the greatest?

   b In which characteristic are the differences between the two the smallest?

   c Which characteristic do these results indicate is most influenced by environment, and which by genetic inheritance?

4 You are given a tray of identical cloned seedlings, all the same height and colour. Plan an investigation to show the differences which environmental factors such as light, temperature and water might have on them. Think about how many you will use and how you will work out your results.

⊙ Differences in the characteristics of different individuals are due in part to genetic differences.

⊙ Differences in the characteristics of different individuals are partly the result of the conditions in which they have developed.

6.6 Mutation!

Mutation has a bad name. In horror movies mutation is seen as a dramatic event which brings about enormous – and often revolting – changes (Figure 1). The truth is much less exciting, but much more important. All of us are here on Earth now as a result of millions of mutations which have taken place in our DNA since the earliest days of life on Earth.

What is mutation?

New forms of genes result from changes in existing genes. These changes are known as **mutations**. They are tiny changes in the long strands of DNA. Mutations occur quite naturally through mistakes made in copying the DNA for new cells as cells reproduce.

Certain things also increase the likelihood of mutation taking place. If cells are exposed to ionising radiation, such as ultraviolet light, X-rays and radiation from radioactive substances, mutations in the DNA are more likely. Certain chemicals, such as some of those found in cigarette smoke, also cause mutations.

↑ **Figure 1:** Mutation in fiction tends to be a long way from the real facts!

H More about mutation

Many mutations are neutral in their effects – they take place in a part of the DNA which has no effect on the characteristics of the organism. However, some mutations are harmful.

If they take place in the reproductive cells, they can cause the young to develop abnormally, or to die at an early stage of their development. Many couples suffer from the early miscarriage of at least one baby, and it is thought that many of these early miscarriages are due to abnormalities in the fetus caused by genetic mutation. This is why your abdomen is shielded with lead sheets if you need an X-ray, to protect your ovaries or testes from the ionising radiation.

If a mutation takes place in the normal body cells it can trigger the cells into uncontrolled growth. The cells multiply rapidly, and may break off and invade other parts of the body. This is cancer and it is a major killer in the developed world. This is probably partly because people in the developed world are much more likely to be exposed to ionising radiation or chemicals which cause mutations.

It is why you are advised to avoid spending too long in the sun – the ionising ultraviolet radiation can cause skin cancer (Figure 2).

↑ **Figure 2:** Sunscreens are made with chemicals which can absorb the ionising radiation from the sun and prevent it damaging our skin.

However, in rare cases a mutation increases the chances of survival of an organism. It may make it capable of surviving a few more degrees of frost, or a longer time without water, or make it that little bit faster or taller. If this advantage enables to organism to survive and reproduce and pass on the mutation, those individuals which inherit the mutant gene will gradually become more and more common in the population. In this way mutation brings benefits and causes a species to **evolve**, a tiny amount at a time (Figure 3).

↑ **Figure 3:** Peppered moths are usually light and well camouflaged against the tree trunks where they live. A rare mutation throws up the occasional dark form.

The dark mutation of the peppered moth makes it very visible on pale tree trunks, and these dark moths are rapidly eaten by birds. However, when tree trunks became darkened with pollution during the industrial revolution, it was the light moths which stood out clearly and got eaten, and more dark moths survived to breed. The dark form became increasingly common, until pollution control resulted in paler tree trunks returning. Now the paler version of the moth is becoming common again and the dark mutation is getting rarer.

? **Questions**

1 **a** What is a mutation?

   b How are new genes made by mutation?

   c Why is the 'horror movie' version of mutation wrong?

2 Describe three things which might cause a mutation.

H 3 **a** Explain when mutation is likely to happen in the reproductive organs.

   b What might increase the risk of mutation in the reproductive organs?

   c How do the chemicals in tobacco smoke cause cancer?

4 Describe how a mutation might be useful.

5 Some mutations have no effect whatsoever. Why?

Key Ideas

- New forms of genes result from mutations (changes) in existing genes.
- The chance of mutations occurring is increased by ionising radiation and certain chemicals.

H - Mutations are often neutral, but they can be harmful – causing abnormalities in babies and cancer – or beneficial, giving an individual an advantage in the race for survival.

6.7 A deadly advantage

It is easy when looking at genetic disease to think of all mutations as bad and harmful. However, occasionally something that is a disadvantage under some circumstances may become a positive advantage in other circumstances. A good example of this is the genetic disease known as **sickle cell anaemia**.

Sickle cell anaemia

This disease is the result of a single mutation which affects the red blood cells. It changes their shape from the usual discs to shrunken sickle shapes (Figure 1). These sickle shaped red blood cells give the disease its name. The problem is that they cannot carry oxygen properly which means that without treatment affected children die whilst they are still very young.

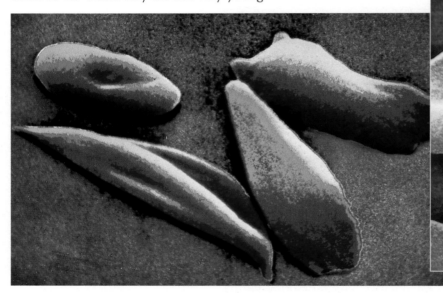

▲ **Figure 1:** It is astonishing that a simple change of shape in the red blood cells has caused the death of hundreds of thousands of children over the years.

So far it might seem that the mutation which causes this disease is all bad. However, the mutated allele responsible for sickle cell anaemia has another effect. An individual with two normal alleles has normal blood. An individual with two mutant alleles has sickle cell anaemia and is very ill. But people who are carriers, who have one normal allele and one sickle cell allele, show an amazing effect. They have a touch of anaemia, it is true, but far more importantly they are resistant to malaria.

Malaria is an infectious disease carried by the bite of mosquitoes, and it causes death and illness to millions of people every year across the world. Sickle cell anaemia is particularly common in those areas of the world which are badly affected by malaria – and although it causes serious illness for those unfortunate enough to be born with two copies of the sickle cell allele, it saves the lives of many thousands more who are carriers of the allele and so are saved from the horrors of malaria.

The maps in Figure 2 show that the sickle cell mutation is found where malaria is rife. This is because people without the mutation are more likely to die from malaria than those with one allele for the sickle cell. So people with the sickle cell anaemia allele have a better chance of surviving malaria and having children, and the mutation is passed on. Over hundreds of years it has become common.

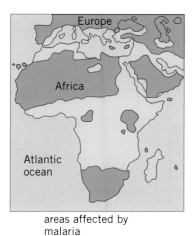

areas affected by malaria

areas where the sickle cell anaemia is relatively common

← **Figure 2:** As these maps clearly show, the sickle cell mutation is found where malaria is rife and the advantages outweigh the disadvantages.

H More genetic crosses

If both of the chromosomes in a pair contain the same allele of a gene, the person is said to be **homozygous** for that gene. So someone with two tongue rolling alleles is homozygous for the dominant allele, while with two non-rolling genes they are homozygous for the recessive allele.

If, on the other hand, the chromosomes in a pair contain different alleles of a gene the individual is said to be **heterozygous** for that gene. For example, if they have a rolling and a non-rolling gene they are said to be heterozygous for tongue rolling.

In the case of genetic diseases, carriers are always heterozygotes. Figure 3 shows a genetic cross for two parents who are heterozygous for sickle cell anaemia.

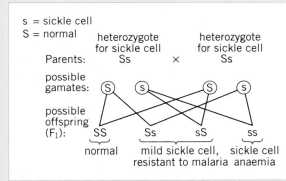

s = sickle cell
S = normal

	heterozygote for sickle cell	heterozygote for sickle cell
Parents:	Ss	×	Ss

possible gamates: Ⓢ ⓢ Ⓢ ⓢ

possible offspring (F₁): SS   Ss   sS   ss

normal   mild sickle cell, resistant to malaria   sickle cell anaemia

Figure 3 →

? Questions

1 Explain why inheriting one allele for sickle cell and one for normal red blood cells can be an advantage in areas which suffer from malaria.

2 What happens to people who inherit two sickle cell alleles?

3 With global warming it seems possible that malaria might spread into Europe, where at present the allele for sickle cell anaemia is rarely found. What would you expect to happen if malaria spreads? Explain your answer.

H 3 a The allele for normal red blood cells can be shown as **S**. The allele for sickle cell anaemia can be shown as **s**. Construct a genetic diagram for a cross between one person who is heterozygous for the sickle cell gene and one who is homozygous for normal blood cells.

b What are the chances are of them having **i** a normal child, **ii** a child with sickle cell anaemia, **iii** a child who is resistant to malaria?

Key Ideas

⊙ Mutations which seem harmful can have unexpected benefits.

⊙ Sickle cell anaemia is a genetic disease which kills those people who inherit two sickle cell alleles, but which gives resistance to malaria to people who have one sickle cell and one normal allele.

1 a Copy and complete the following sentences using words from the list

   alleles   chromosomes   gametes   genes   mutations

   The nucleus of a cell contains thread-like structures called ....

   The characteristics of a person are controlled by .... which may
   exist in different forms called ....   (3 marks)

   b The drawing shows some of the
      stages of reproduction in horses.

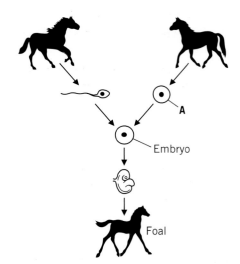

Embryo

Foal

      i Name this type of reproduction.   (1 mark)
      ii name the type of cell labelled **A**.   (1 mark)

   c When the foal grows up it will look similar to its parents but it will not
      be identical to either parent. Explain why it will not be identical to either
      of its parents.   (2 marks)
                                                                      (Total 7 marks)
                                                                 AQA specimen question

2 The diagram shows the sex chromosomes
   of two cells, **A** and **B**.

   a Which of these cells comes from
      a male and which from a female?   (1 mark)

   b How can you tell which is which?   (2 marks)

   c The information on the sex chromosomes, like all other chromosomes,
      is carried on the genes.
      i What is a gene?   (1 marks)
      ii What is an allele?   (1 marks)
                                                                    (Total 5 marks)

3 A child suffers from cystic fibrosis. Neither parent has cystic fibrosis.

   a Explain how it is possible for a child to be born with cystic fibrosis, even
      though neither parent has the disorder. Use a genetic diagram to help
      explain your answer.   (3 marks)

   b The DNA in the genes of people who suffer from cystic fibrosis differs from
      the DNA of people who do not have the disorder. As a result a different
      protein is made in the cells of sufferers. It stops chloride ions leaving cells,
      so the concentration inside the cells rises. Explain why the protein made
      in the cells of sufferers is different.   (2 marks)
                                                                    (Total 5 marks)

H **4** The diagram shows a cross between a heterozygous tongue roller and a non-roller. The allele for tongue rolling is dominant over the allele for non-rolling.

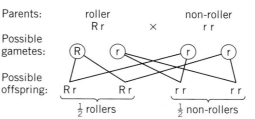

Parents: roller R r × non-roller r r

Possible gametes: (R) (r) (r) (r)

Possible offspring: R r   R r   r r   r r
½ rollers   ½ non-rollers

a What are the possible offspring in the genetic cross shown here? (2 marks)

b Draw a diagram to show the cross between two people who can roll their tongue, both of whom have one rolling and one non-rolling allele. (4 marks)

c Use your answer to (b) above to explain how children with cystic fibrosis can be born to carriers who show no sign of the disease themselves. (2 marks)
(Total 8 marks)

5 Huntington's disease is a rare genetic disorder which can be inherited even if only one parent carries the allele because it is a dominant allele.

a What is a **genetic disorder**? (2 marks)

b What is a **dominant allele**? (1 mark)

c What is a **recessive allele**? (1 mark)

d What is the difference between a disease caused by a dominant allele like Huntington's disease and a disease caused by a recessive allele like cystic fibrosis? (3 marks)
(Total 7 marks)

6 a What is a mutation? (1 mark)

b Name **three** factors which can increase the chances of mutations taking place. (3 marks)

The diagram compares the red blood cells of normal people and people with sickle cell anaemia.

c Sickle cell anaemia is the result of a single mutation which affects the red blood cells.

normal blood   sickle cell mutation

i Use the information from the diagram to explain the difference in the red blood of people with normal alleles, those with one sickle cell allele and those with two sickle cell alleles. (3 marks)

ii Why is sickle cell anaemia so serious? (1 mark)

iii In parts of the world where there is a lot of malaria the sickle cell allele is very common. Why is this? (3 marks)
(Total 11 marks)

H **7 a** Many mutations have no effect on the organism. Why is this? (1 mark)

b A mutation in a normal body cell, such as a cell in lung or skin tissue, can sometimes cause serious problems. Why? (2 marks)

A mutation in the peppered moth affects the colour of the wings. The normal colour is a speckled cream, but the mutation gives dark, almost black wings. Both forms have advantages and disadvantages.

The diagram shows both forms of the peppered moth on light and dark tree bark.

c Use the diagram to help you explain the value of both the normal colouring and the black mutation to the peppered moth. (6 marks)
(Total 9 marks)

Up to the 18th century most people in Europe believed that the world and all living creatures had been created by God as described in the Book of Genesis in the Bible, and that the world was very young. This view was strongly defended by the Church. However, by the beginning of the 19th century some scientists were coming up with revolutionary new ideas. Jean-Baptiste Lamarck, a French biologist, suggested that all life sprang from simple worms, and had evolved into more complex organisms, such as mammals and even people.

H Jean-Baptiste Lamarck

Lamarck thought that all organisms were linked by a fountain of life, and that every type of organism evolved from primitive worms. He argued that this evolution happened because of the **inheritance of acquired characteristics**. Organisms change during their lives as they struggle to meet the demands of their environment. Lamarck believed that these changes are passed on from parents to their offspring. For example, giraffes have long necks because each generation stretched up to reach the highest leaves and so each new generation had a slightly longer neck (Figure 1). This theory fell down because there was no evidence for Lamarck's fountain of life, and because people could observe that acquired characteristics were not passed on.

↑ **Figure 1:** In Lamarck's model of evolution, giraffes have long necks because each generation stretched up to reach the highest leaves and so each new generation had a slightly longer neck.

Charles Darwin and the origin of species

Charles Darwin set out in 1831 at the age of 22 as the ship's naturalist on *HMS Beagle*. It was a five year voyage to South America and the South Sea Islands. Darwin planned to study geology on the trip but as the voyage progressed he became as excited by his collection of animals and plants as by his rocks and fossils.

On the Galapagos Islands Darwin was amazed by the variety of species and the way they differed from island to island. For example, he found strong similarities between types of tortoises and mockingbirds on the various islands, yet each was different and adapted to make the most of the local conditions. To his surprise, he also found marine iguanas which were very similar to land iguanas but with differences which enabled them to live in the sea (Figure 2).

Darwin collected huge numbers of specimens of animals and plants during the explorations of the *Beagle*, as well as making detailed drawings and written observations. After he returned to England he worked on his ideas for the next 20 years, building up evidence from experiments to support his theory. In 1859 he published his masterpiece *On the Origin of Species by Natural Selection*.

↑ **Figure 2:** The marine iguanas of the Galapagos made a great impression on Darwin.

Darwin's central theory was that all living organisms have resulted from a long process of **natural selection**. Reproduction always produces more offspring than the environment can support, for example with food, water or breeding grounds. Only those which are most suited to their environment – the 'fittest' – will survive long enough to breed themselves. His idea was that all the species on Earth were the result of this gradual process of evolution which we know as 'survival of the fittest'. Species developed, or evolved, to deal with the conditions in their environments.

Origin of Species sold out on the first day it was published and caused uproar. Lots of people, including many other scientists, were hugely excited by the ideas Darwin proposed and supported them enthusiastically. Others, particularly in the Church, were shocked and horrified at the suggestion that they had evolved from 'primitive' organisms rather than being directly created by God.

The Church fought a long and heated battle against the theory of evolution by natural selection but a growing weight of evidence finally convinced most other scientists that it was correct.

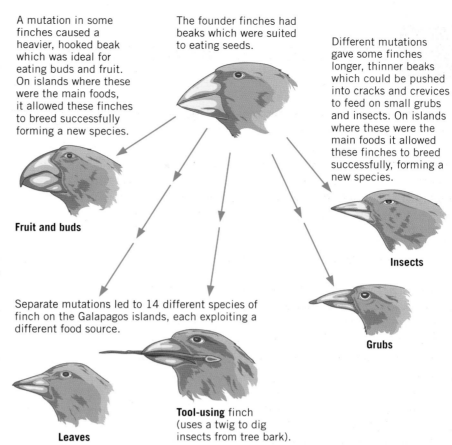

A mutation in some finches caused a heavier, hooked beak which was ideal for eating buds and fruit. On islands where these were the main foods, it allowed these finches to breed successfully forming a new species.

Fruit and buds

The founder finches had beaks which were suited to eating seeds.

Different mutations gave some finches longer, thinner beaks which could be pushed into cracks and crevices to feed on small grubs and insects. On islands where these were the main foods it allowed these finches to breed successfully, forming a new species.

Insects

Grubs

Separate mutations led to 14 different species of finch on the Galapagos islands, each exploiting a different food source.

Tool-using finch (uses a twig to dig insects from tree bark).

Leaves

↑ **Figure 3:** On the Galapagos Islands Darwin collected 12 different species of finches which all seem to have evolved from a single original type by natural selection as shown here. Their beaks were shaped to deal with the type of food on the island where they lived. Although Darwin's finches are well known today, they do not appear in the *Origin of Species* as an example of his theory.

? Questions

1 a What does 'survival of the fittest' mean?

   b Why did Darwin call this 'natural selection'?

2 Explain how the finches on the Galapagos islands provide evidence for Darwin's theory of natural selection.

3 How does natural selection lead to the evolution of new species?

4 Why were many people reluctant to accept Darwin's theory of natural selection?

5 What was the importance of the following in the development of Darwin's ideas:

   a Galapagos tortoises, iguanas and finches

   b the long voyage of the *Beagle*

   c the 20 years from his return to the publication of the book *Origin of Species*?

H 6 a Summarise the similarities and differences between Darwin's theory of evolution and Lamarck's theory.

   b Why do you think Lamarck's theory was so important to the way Darwin's theory was received?

⊙—ᴍ Key Ideas

- ⊙ Darwin's theory of natural selection was the result of his voyage on the Beagle and many years of study.

- ⊙ Darwin's theory is that evolution takes place through natural selection or survival of the fittest.

H ⊙ Lamarck thought evolution took place by the inheritance of acquired characteristics.

Some of the most convincing evidence in support of Darwin's theory came from the work of other 19th century scientists on fossils.

The fossil record

Fossils are the remains of plants or animals from many thousands or millions of years ago which are found in rocks. The fossil record is often fragmented and incomplete, but it can give us a fascinating glimpse into life millions of years before we were born.

Fossils can be formed in a number of ways:

- ⊙ They may be formed from the hard parts of an animal which do not decay easily, such as the bones, teeth, claws or shells (Figure 1).

- ⊙ They may be formed from parts of animals or plants which have not decayed because conditions were not right for decay to take place. This often means there was little or no oxygen present, or maybe poisonous gases killed off the bacteria needed for decay to take place. Sometimes the lack of decay is because the temperature was too low and the animals and plants are preserved in ice. These ice fossils are very rare but can give us an amazing insight into what an animal looked like, what it had been eating, or even the colour of a long-extinct flower.

- ⊙ Many fossils are formed when parts of the animal or plant are replaced by other minerals as they decay – these are some of the most common fossils.

- ⊙ Some fossils are not of actual animals or plants, but rather of traces they have left behind – footprints, droppings, burrows or traces where roots have been.

↓ **Figure 1:** Fossils are formed over long periods of time, but the record they give us of life millions of years ago is priceless.

A reptile dies and falls to the ground.

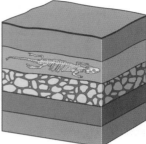

The flesh rots, leaving the skeleton to be covered in sand or soil and clay before it is damaged.

Protected, over millions of years the skeleton becomes mineralised and turns to rock.

The fossil emerges as the rocks move and erosion takes place.

← **Figure 2:** These amazing fossils show us traces of an animal in the form of the dinosaur eggs. Fossils are always tantalising – we will never know exactly what calamity prevented these eggs hatching millions of years ago.

The story of the horse

Very often the fossil record, exciting and valuable as it is, can be very limited. But for one animal in particular we have a very complete fossil record (Figure 3).

The age of the Earth

For evolution to be possible, and for fossils to provide evidence that animals and plants have indeed changed and developed over time, the Earth must have existed for a very long time. However, in the 17th century the Bible was still largely unquestioned and Archbishop Usher used it to calculate that the Earth was less than 6000 years old.

By the beginning of the 19th century the evidence was building up that the Earth was much older than this. Sir Charles Lyell, a British geologist, showed that the Earth was very ancient, shaped by rivers and 'subterranean fires'. He estimated that the Earth was several hundred million years old and published these ideas from 1830 onwards. Lyell's work was important to Darwin, because if all living organisms have arisen from evolution by natural selection it would have taken many millions of years. Fossils also helped to confirm Darwin's ideas, because they showed some of the stages by which the evolutionary process had happened.

By the 1890s, Arthur Holmes was using radioactivity to date rocks, establishing the age of the Earth as around 4.6 billion years old and giving plenty of time for evolution to have happened.

Equus – the modern horse is a fast runner on hard ground with only one toe forming the hoof.

about 12 million years ago

Merychippus – bigger again, walking mainly on one enlarged toe for speed.

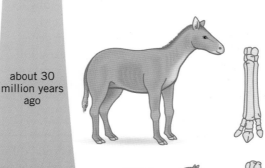

about 30 million years ago

Mesohippus – bigger, only three toes on the ground for moving fast on drier ground.

about 60 million years ago

Hyracotherium – small, swamp-dwelling with well-spread toes for walking on soft ground.

↑ **Figure 3:** The horse as we know it today has evolved from some very different animals. We know of their existence from the very clear record left in the fossils.

The mechanism of evolution

If Lamarck's ideas were wrong, how do species change and evolve?

As we saw in Chapter 6, the individual organisms within a particular species show a wide range of variation because of differences in their genes. Large numbers of them die before they reproduce because of disease, starvation or being eaten by a predator. Some of the survivors will not reproduce because they fail to find a mate.

The individuals which survive and breed successfully will be the ones with the characteristics most suited to the environment in which they live (they are the best fitted to survive or the 'fittest'). The genes which have made those characteristics are then passed on to the next generation. This is what we mean by natural selection or 'survival of the fittest'.

In Figure 1 only the cheetahs with the genes for the longest legs, the sharpest claws and teeth and the best developed hunting skills will catch enough prey to feed their cubs. Those cubs will survive, carrying on the genes into another generation. Fewer of the cubs born to less well adapted animals will survive to adulthood and breed themselves. Prey animals are similarly affected by their genes. Only those with the best hearing and the fastest escape reflexes will survive to breed successfully – this is how natural selection works throughout the living world.

↑ **Figure 1:** Natural selection in action, red in tooth and claw – only the best adapted predators capture prey – and only the best adapted prey animals escape!

Evolution in action

Another example of evolution is the Arctic hare. There are several different alleles for coat colour but the two most common ones are white and light brown. For Arctic hares which live in the most northern snowy climates, a white coat is a distinct advantage. A pure white hare sitting on the snow is much less visible to a fox or owl than a light brown hare, and so white hares are much more likely to survive and breed successfully. In northern areas, the great majority of the hares are white. On the other hand, further south where the hares live in coniferous forests, a brown coat is an advantage among the pine needles. Here it is the white hares that are very visible to predators, and so in these areas it is the brown form of the hare which is successful (Figure 2).

Evolution is happening all around us today. Sometimes the effects of evolution are very clear to see, and sometimes they can cause us unexpected problems.

↖ **Figure 2:** Evolution in action – the white fur which gives Arctic hares such good camouflage in the snow makes them easy prey in warmer regions.

As we saw in Chapter 4, antibiotics are chemicals which kill bacteria. When they were first developed their effect was nothing short of miraculous and they saved millions of lives. They still save many, many lives, but some problems have arisen. Each time an antibiotic is used, most of the bacteria are wiped out. However there are almost always a few bacteria which carry a mutant gene which makes them resistant to the effect of the antibiotic – they are not killed by it. These few that remain – the fittest – survive and reproduce their resistant genes. This means that a resistant strain of bacteria evolves. A small number of resistant bacteria left by an antibiotic can usually be dealt with by the body's defences but antibiotics have been used so widely for even very minor infections that resistant strains are becoming more common.

When the next new antibiotic is tried the whole evolutionary process is repeated again, until eventually some strains of bacteria end up resistant to all antibiotics – superbugs which kill anyone who catches them! (Figure 3.)

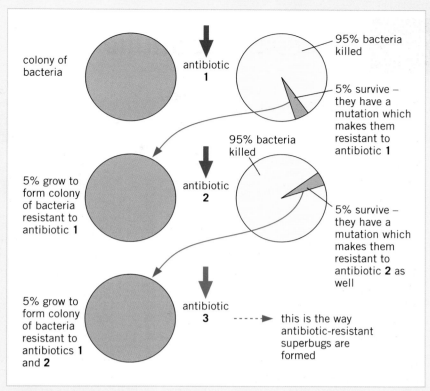

↑ **Figure 3:** It really is important to complete a course of antibiotics – the bacteria with some resistance will be the last ones to be killed by the drug. If they are not destroyed they may go on to breed, passing on their mutation and forming a resistant strain.

? Questions

1 Explain, using the examples of cheetahs and Arctic hares, how evolution is brought about by the 'survival of the fittest'.

2 Explain how the following characteristics of animals and plants help them survive successfully:

  a male peacocks have large and brightly coloured tails

  b cacti have spines instead of leaves

  c a large proportion of the mussels found in the sea off Long Island in the USA have a gene which helps them cope with the osmotic effects of sea water; while a similarly large proportion of the mussels growing near the mouth of the river do not have this gene.

3 **a** How is the development of antibiotic-resistant bacteria an example of evolution in action?

  b Why are you always advised to finish a course of antibiotics, even after you've started feeling better?

🔑 Key Ideas

⊙ Predation, disease and competition cause large numbers of individuals to die.

⊙ Individuals with characteristics most suited to the environment are more likely to survive and breed successfully.

⊙ The genes which enabled these individuals to survive are then passed on to the next generation.

⊙ Over-exposure to antibiotics has lead to the evolution of antibiotic-resistant bacteria.

For centuries people have attempted to speed up evolution to get the characteristics of animals and plants they wanted. This happened long before any scientific idea of evolution was developed. In earliest times farmers bred from the plants which produced the biggest grain or the animals which produced the most milk, to get plants which all had bigger grain and animals which all produced a lot of milk. This is called **selective breeding**.

→ **Figure 1:** Pictures like this, showing agricultural work in ancient times, provide evidence that plants and animals had been changed dramatically in appearance and nature from their wild ancestors.

How does selective breeding work?

We can change animals and plants by artificially selecting which members of the group are allowed to breed. Farmers and breeders select animals and plants which have a particularly useful or desirable characteristic, and use those organisms as their breeding stock. They then select from the offspring and only breed again from the ones that show the desired characteristic. This process can be used to select for a whole range of features (Figure 2).

Parents:

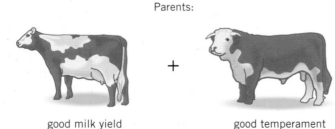

good milk yield   good temperament

← **Figure 2:** Sometimes animals or plants with one desirable trait will be cross-bred with organisms showing another desirable trait. Only the offspring showing both of the favoured features will be used for further breeding.

possible offspring:

good milk yield, average temperament

good milk yield, good temperament

average milk yield, average temperament

average milk yield, good temperament

this is the cow which will be selected for further breeding

The results of centuries of selective breeding have been dramatic. Our placid dairy cows which produce litres and litres of milk a day are a far cry from their aggressive wild ancestors which produced enough milk for their single calf and little more. The fields of corn with their large and heavy heads of grain bear little resemblance to the wild grasses which were their ancestors. So genetic manipulation by selective breeding has resulted in animals and plants with strange mixtures of genes which would never have occurred naturally, but which have produced organisms which are either useful or simply enjoyable (Figure 3).

The limitations

Selective breeding has been responsible for much of the agricultural progress that has been made over the centuries, but there is a major drawback. Selective breeding greatly reduces the number of alleles in the population – because only individuals with the chosen alleles are allowed to breed. This reduces not only the variety of individuals but also the variety of the alleles for characteristics.

This is not a problem when conditions are stable, but as soon as there is a problem – the climate changes or a new disease appears – then the lack of variety can mean that none of the animals or plants in a population can cope with it and the whole lot die out.

↑ **Figure 3:** Not all selective breeding is to produce useful organisms – this chihuahua is very far removed from its ancestor, the wolf! Most of our pets are the result of years of selective breeding for largely cosmetic reasons.

Ideas and Evidence

Gene banks for the future

Selective breeding has steadily reduced the genetic variety of our agricultural crops, and cloning (see next page) has made things even worse. On top of this, species of plants are becoming extinct all over the world due to changing environments. The loss of all this plant genetic material could be dramatic. We need to preserve as much genetic variety as possible for cross-breeding if modern varieties of crop plants begin to struggle.

Seeds are a perfect way of preserving plant genetic material. They are small and as plants make huge numbers of seeds, collecting some of them does not damage the natural population. Once they have been dried and stored at low temperatures they should survive for up to 200 years, providing a source of genetic variety for use all over the world.

The aim of the Royal Botanic Gardens at Kew is to preserve the seeds of all the native UK plants and those of at least 10% of the plants from the rest of the world by the year 2010 (Figure 4).

↑ **Figure 4:** This seed bank at Wakehurst Place in Sussex should be a treasure-house of plant DNA for many years to come.

Questions

1 **a** What is selective breeding?

   b Why have people bred animals and plants selectively through the centuries?

2 **a** How does selective breeding work?

   b What are the advantages of selective breeding?

3 **a** Why does selective breeding cut down the variety of alleles in a species?

   b Why can variety be useful in helping a species survive?

   c What are the dangers of reducing the amount of variety?

Key Ideas

⊙ Selective breeding (artificial selection) can be used to produce new varieties of organisms.

⊙ Only individuals with useful characteristics are used for breeding.

⊙ Selective breeding reduces genetic variety.

A clone is an individual which has been produced asexually from its parent and is therefore genetically identical to the parent. Many plants reproduce naturally by cloning and this has been used in agriculture and horticulture for many years. The bulbs which produce daffodils, snowdrops and tulips, the runners which produce new strawberry plants and the tubers from which new potato plants are grown are all examples of the use of natural cloning (Figure 1).

↑ **Figure 1:** These wild daffodils in Farndale, North Yorkshire, are a stunning example of natural plant cloning.

Taking cuttings

Another way of making new plants by cloning is taking cuttings. This is not a natural method because it is done by people, but it uses natural plant responses. If a small piece of a plant is removed – part of the stem or sometimes just part of the leaf – and grown in the right conditions, new roots and shoots will form to give a small, complete new plant. Using this method new plants can be formed quickly and cheaply from old plants, and the cuttings will be genetically identical to the parents. Many growers now use hormone rooting powders (see page 75) to encourage the cuttings to grow, and they are most likely to develop successfully if they are kept in a moist atmosphere until roots develop. Plants such as orchids and many fruit trees are produced commercially by cloning in this way (Figure 2).

← **Figure 2:** Orchids have become a relatively common sight in garden centres around Britain. They are produced from cuttings to give plants which are reliably the same.

Cloning tissue

The most modern way to clone plants involves much more human intervention. Using a mixture of plant hormones, a single plant cell from a particularly desirable plant can be used to produce a mass of identical plant cells. Then, using a different combination of hormones and conditions, each of these cells can be stimulated to form a tiny new plant. This type of technology ensures that the crops or trees that are grown will have guaranteed characteristics.

Cloning animals

In recent years cloning technology has moved forward even further and cloning animals is now becoming a relatively common agricultural practice, particularly the cloning of embryos in cattle. Early embryos are formed in the laboratory using eggs and sperm from the best possible breeding stock. As they start to develop they are divided to produce many more identical embryos in an exaggerated version of the natural process which results in identical twins. Each one is transplanted into the uterus of an ordinary cow, which acts as a host mother. The host mother gives birth to a calf which is not biologically hers at all (Figure 3).

Cloning embryos in this way has enabled high-quality embryos to be taken around the world, to places where cattle with a high milk yield or lots of meat are badly needed for breeding with the local stock.

True cloning of animals, without sexual reproduction being involved at all, only started in 1997 when a team of scientists in Edinburgh produced Dolly the sheep from the adult cell of another sheep. This type of cloning is still relatively rare.

The problem with cloning of species of plants or animals is that it produces lots of individuals with identical genes, so it reduces variety within a population. This means the population is less able to survive any changes in their environment which might happen in the future, because if one of them does not contain a useful mutation, none of them will. In a more natural population, at least a few individuals can usually survive change and live to reproduce and restock.

Human clones

There has been a lot of speculation about the possible cloning of humans. Perhaps people will have clones made of all their embryos, so that if a child dies, they will have a replacement. On the other hand some people will want to clone themselves, to make sure that they will go on for ever. The big question is – should it be done?

↑ **Figure 3:** Embryo cloning takes selective breeding one step further, by producing far more identical offspring than would ever be possible using a cow, a bull and normal reproduction.

Key Ideas

- Many plants form natural clones.

- Artificial cloning of plants may involve taking cuttings, or tissue culture when single cells are used to clone whole plants.

- Animals can now be cloned. The most common way is the cloning of embryos.

One of the new technologies which has caused more controversy than most is genetic engineering.

What is genetic engineering?

Genetic engineering involves changing the genetic material of an organism. It usually involves taking a small piece of DNA – a gene – from one organism and transferring it to the genetic material of an entirely different organism. So, for example, genes from the chromosomes of a person, or other living organism, can be 'cut out' using enzymes and transferred to bacterial cells. The gene that has been transferred continues to control the production of the same protein as it did in the organism it came from, even though it is now in a bacterial cell.

If the genetically engineered bacteria are cultured on a large scale they will make huge quantities of protein from other organisms (Figure 1). This is now used in the manufacture of a number of drugs and of hormones including human insulin (see page 40).

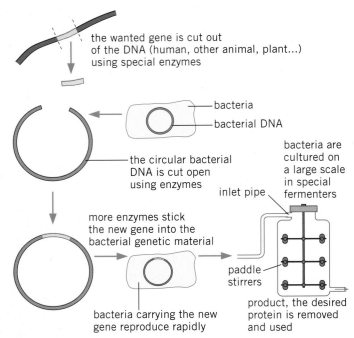

the wanted gene is cut out of the DNA (human, other animal, plant...) using special enzymes

bacteria
bacterial DNA
the circular bacterial DNA is cut open using enzymes
bacteria are cultured on a large scale in special fermenters
inlet pipe
more enzymes stick the new gene into the bacterial genetic material
paddle stirrers
bacteria carrying the new gene reproduce rapidly
product, the desired protein is removed and used

↑ **Figure 1:** Genetic engineering and the way it can move from the laboratory to an industrial process.

What are the benefits?

One of the biggest advantages is that genetically engineered bacteria can make exactly the protein needed, in exactly the amounts needed and in a very pure form. For example, when insulin was extracted from the pancreases of pigs and cattle, the supplies were not quite the same chemically as human insulin, and the amounts available depended on how many animals were slaughtered for meat rather than how many diabetics needed insulin. Both of those problems have been solved by the introduction of genetically engineered human insulin.

More engineering

There is a limit to the types of proteins bacteria are capable of making. So for this reason amongst others, genetic engineering has moved on. It has been found that genes from one organism can be transferred to the cells of another type of animal or plant at an early stage of their development. As the animal or plant grows it develops with the new desired characteristics from the other organism.

For example, engineered genes can be used to improve the growth rates of plants and animals. They can be used to improve the protein yield of crops or to reduce the fat levels in meat. They have even been used to produce plants which make their own pesticide chemicals.

A number of sheep and other mammals have also been engineered to produce life-saving human proteins in their milk. These are much more complex proteins than the ones produced by bacteria, and they have the potential to save many lives.

↓ **Figure 2:** Engineered genes have been put into plants to improve the flavour of the fruit, and to prevent it going bad so quickly. However, because there are still concerns about their safety, food containing genetically modified material (GM food) has to be clearly labelled.

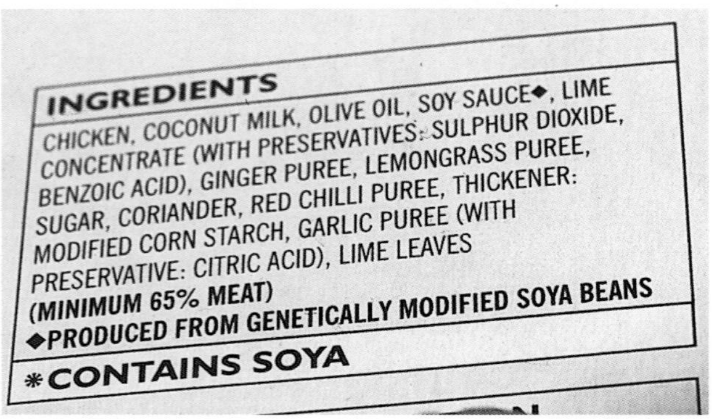

INGREDIENTS
CHICKEN, COCONUT MILK, OLIVE OIL, SOY SAUCE◆, LIME CONCENTRATE (WITH PRESERVATIVES: SULPHUR DIOXIDE, BENZOIC ACID), GINGER PUREE, LEMONGRASS PUREE, SUGAR, CORIANDER, RED CHILLI PUREE, THICKENER: MODIFIED CORN STARCH, GARLIC PUREE (WITH PRESERVATIVE: CITRIC ACID), LIME LEAVES (MINIMUM 65% MEAT)
◆PRODUCED FROM GENETICALLY MODIFIED SOYA BEANS
✳**CONTAINS SOYA**

Human engineering

Many hope that genetic engineering will hold the key to solving the problem of genetic diseases which bring great misery to people all over the world. If the affected cells can have 'healthy' DNA inserted by genetic engineering, or if the cells of an early embryo can be engineered so that the individual develops to be a healthy person, then many people would have new hope of a normal life for themselves or their children. The disease which is closest to being treated in this way at the moment is cystic fibrosis (see page 88). Scientists are working on the theory that if healthy DNA is inserted into the cells of the lungs and the gut, those cells will take over from the diseased cells and make normal mucus. Unfortunately progress on this treatment is still very slow.

The disadvantages

There are many concerns about genetic engineering as no one can be completely sure what all the effects might be. There are fears that insects may become pesticide resistant as a result of a constant diet of pesticide-forming plants. Many people are concerned about the effect on human health of eating genetically modified DNA. And perhaps most frightening, people may want to manipulate the genes of their future children, not to make sure they are born healthy, but to have a child who is clever, or good-looking, or sporty, or good-tempered (Figure 3).

← **Figure 3:** Designer babies? Tampering with the DNA for vanity's sake would surely lead to catastrophe, yet because everyone wants the perfect baby, such genetic engineering would equally surely be in demand.

? Questions

1 How can genes from one organism be inserted into the DNA of another organism?

2 a Why are genes from human beings or other organisms inserted into bacteria?

   b What are the advantages of this type of genetic engineering?

   c What disadvantages might there be with the genetic engineering of bacteria?

3 a What are the potential advantages of genetic engineering in plants?

   b Suggest at least one possible disadvantage of genetically engineering plants.

4 Genetic engineering in humans is a very controversial subject. Write a piece for the science page of your local newspaper explaining both the reasons why work on human genetic engineering is being carried out (the potential benefits) and also the concerns of people who feel it should not be done (the possible disadvantages).

0⏌ Key Ideas

⊙ Genes from many organisms can be inserted into bacteria.

⊙ The bacteria then make human or other proteins.

⊙ Genes can be transferred to the cells of animals and plants at an early stage of development so they develop with certain desired characteristics.

1 Giraffes feed on the leaves and other plants in areas of Africa. They are adapted, through evolution, to survive in their environment.

To gain full marks in this question you should write your ideas in good English. Put them into a sensible order and use the correct scientific words.

   a Explain how Jean-Baptiste Lamarck (1744–1829) accounted for the evolution of the long neck in giraffes.

(3 marks)

   b Another scientist, August Weismann (1834–1914) wanted to check Lamarck's explanation. To do this he cut off the tails of a number of generations of mice and looked at the offspring.

   His results did not support Lamarck's theory. Explain why.

(2 marks)
(Total 5 marks)
AQA specimen question

2 Fossil evidence is very important in helping us to understand how life has evolved.

   a Name **three** different ways in which fossils can be formed. (3 marks)

   b Why is the fossil record so important? (1 mark)

The diagram shows part of the evolution of the horse.

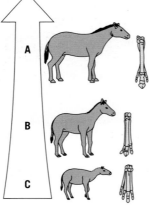

   c What does the evidence tell you about animals **A**, **B** and **C** and the conditions in which they lived?

(6 marks)

H 3 Modern humans belong to the species *Homo sapiens*. Many people think that modern humans evolved from more primitive species. Three of these primitive species were *Australopithecus*, *Homo habilis* and *Homo erectus*. These three species are now extinct. The graph shows the brain size of several specimens from each of the species.

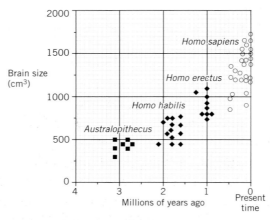

a Estimate the mean brain size of *Homo habilis* (1 mark)

b Suggest how we know about the brain size of *Australopithecus*. (2 marks)

To gain full marks in this question you must write down your ideas in good English. Put them in a sensible order and use the correct scientific terms.

c Suggest an explanation, in terms of natural selection, for the change in brain size during the evolution of *Homo sapiens*. (3 marks)

(Total 6 marks)
AQA specimen question

5 The diagram shows how the number of groups of animals has changed during the history of life on Earth.

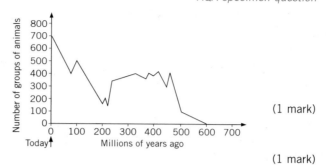

a **i** How many million years ago did the first living animals appear on Earth? (1 mark)

ii How many million years did it take for the number of groups to rise to 400? (1 mark)

b **i** Calculate the proportion of groups which disappeared between 100 million years and 80 million years ago. Show your working. (2 marks)

ii Give **two** reasons why some groups of animals disappeared during the history of life on Earth. (2 marks)

(Total 6 marks)
AQA specimen question

6 The original wild breed of sheep looked very much like the Soay sheep shown in the diagram. However, most of the sheep raised commercially today look much more like the Suffolk.

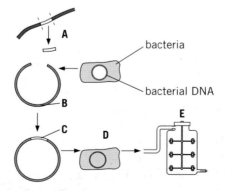
Soay   Suffolk

a By what process have modern sheep been obtained from the original wild types of sheep? (1 mark)

b Suggest **three** features which have been bred for in modern sheep to make them more useful to us. (3 marks)

c Explain how the process of improving a breed of animals works. (3 marks)

(Total 7 marks)

7 The diagram shows the steps involved in genetic engineering.

a Chose from the following list to complete the labelling on the diagram.

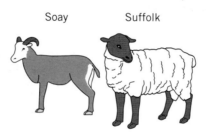

Bacteria carrying the new gene reproduce rapidly.

The circular bacterial DNA is cut open using enzymes.

The wanted gene is cut out of the DNA using special enzymes.

The new gene is joined into the bacterial genetic material. (4 marks)

b What is the advantage of using genetically engineered microorganisms? (2 marks)

c Sometimes animals such as sheep are genetically engineered to make particular human proteins in their milk. Why are mammals used instead of bacteria? (2 marks)

(Total 8 marks)

Words like ecosystem and environment are commonly used in everyday life in the media, by journalists and by advertisers. But what do they actually mean?

An **ecosystem** is an environment where living organisms can survive. The **environment** describes the physical features and conditions of the place where they live. These can include:

⊙ the temperature and how it changes

⊙ the amount of light

⊙ the availability of water

⊙ the availability of oxygen and carbon dioxide.

All of these factors can vary according to the time of day and the time of year, and this affects which organisms can live there and when. This is why you find different organisms in different places and sometimes at different times (Figure 1).

← **Figure 1:** These swallows are summer visitors in the UK. They arrive, breed and then fly away to somewhere warmer for the winter.

Habitats and how they change

The **habitat** of an animal or plant is its home – the little bit of the environment where it lives. The conditions in some environments are very stable, even if they are difficult. For example, conditions in a salt marsh are usually salty, whilst in Greenland it is usually cold and icy, and in a tropical rain forest it is very hot and humid almost all the time.

In many other environments conditions can change dramatically. In the UK, for example, the winter can be very cold compared to the summer. Also, particular places and areas have their own environments. For example, organisms which live on a seashore have to cope with conditions which range from cold, salty water to hot dry rocks or warm, very salty rock pools over a matter of hours (Figure 2).

↗ **Figure 2:** At high tide these rocks are covered in water, and animals like these limpets can move around and feed. But when the water goes, survival is difficult – limpets cling tightly to the rocks, trapping a little sea water inside their shell until the tide returns.

Adapted for the environment?

The conditions in different environments can be very stable or very changeable. Whatever they are like, living organisms have special features which enable them to survive in the conditions in which they normally live. These special features are adaptations which have arisen over the years through natural selection (Figure 3).

← **Figure 3:** The high temperatures in the hot springs of Yellowstone Park in the USA would kill most living organisms, but the bacteria which live here are adapted to survive and thrive in these extreme conditions.

In the UK we have many examples of organisms which are adapted to survive in the conditions of the country. Some birds migrate to the UK for the summer, others for the winter. They have evolved both the strength and stamina to make long flights, and internal navigation systems which allow them to fly from one continent to another, sometimes over thousands of miles.

Other organisms, like squirrels, dormice and hedgehogs, are active and breed during the warm summer months when the food they eat is in plentiful supply. Then over the winter they hibernate, until spring and food returns. Plants such as the insectivorous sundew and the Venus fly trap have evolved a way of getting nitrates from insects instead of the soil, allowing them to survive and grow on very poor soil (Figure 4).

↑ **Figure 5:** Carnivorous plants use a very successful adaptation to help them cope with living on soil which contains little nitrate – they 'eat' nitrate-rich animals!

If we compare the animals and plants which are found on a cold, high and windy Scottish mountainside with those on the low-lying fenlands of Lincolnshire we find that they are often very different. What is more, in many cases they cannot survive in different conditions. If a plant from a Scottish peat bog is planted in the rich and fertile soil of the fens it will die, whilst some plants found in the south of England would not survive in the harsher conditions of a Scottish winter.

? Questions

1. What is the difference between the environment and an ecosystem?
2. Give three examples of a habitat from these pages.
3. Describe three ways in which animals in the UK adapt to winter.
4. Explain how 'eating' insects can help some plants survive in very poor soil.
5. What different types of conditions do you think organisms would need to be adapted for on a Scottish mountain or the Lincolnshire fenlands?

Key Ideas

⊙ Physical conditions within an environment affect the organisms which can survive there.

⊙ Organisms become adapted to survive in the conditions in which they live.

8.2 Surviving the heat

More than a fifth of the land surface of the Earth is covered by desert or very hot, dry conditions. Deserts are very difficult environments for animals and plants – scorching heat during the day is often followed by bitter cold at night, whilst water is constantly in short supply (Figure 1).

The heat and water problem

The biggest challenges for organisms living in deserts are coping with the lack of water and preventing their body temperature from getting too high. Many desert animals are adapted to need little or no fluid – they get the water they need from the food they eat.

Warm-blooded mammals maintain a more or less steady body temperature so as the environment gets hotter they have to find ways of keeping cool. Many mammals in the world rely on sweating to help them cool down. Unfortunately, this means they lose water through their skin and it's not easy to replace this in the desert.

So desert animals have evolved other ways of cooling down. Desert mammals tend to be most active in the early morning and late evening, when the temperature is moderate. During the cold nights and the heat of the day they often rest in burrows well below the surface, where the temperature varies very little.

Many desert animals tend to be quite small, so their surface area is large compared to their volume. Other animals have large, thin ears which increase the surface area for losing heat (Figure 2). The classic example is an elephant – a very large animal which lives in hot climates. An elephant is big, but its huge wrinkled skin would cover an animal which was much bigger still. The wrinkles in the skin increase the surface area through which heat can be lost.

↑ **Figure 1:** What types of adaptations make it possible for living organisms to survive in conditions such as these?

sa:vol ratio = 6:1

sa:vol ratio = 54:27 = 2:1

Another feature of many desert animals is that they have relatively little fur, and what they have is fine and silky. They also tend to have relatively little body fat stored under the skin. Both of these features make it easier to lose heat through the surface of the skin. The animals keep warm during the cold nights by retreating into their burrows.

↖ **Figure 2:** The ratio of surface area to volume makes a big difference to how much heat can be lost from the skin. The Saharan fennec fox has these massive ears to help with heat loss – they increase the surface area of its body considerably. The large size of the elephant seal means it has a smaller surface area to volume ratio, helping it to conserve heat in the cold conditions in which it lives.

The camel – adaptation in action

Camels are the classic desert animal, but they certainly don't hide in a burrow in the heat of the day! They have wide feet so they do not sink into the sand. They can close their nostrils to avoid inhaling sand during sandstorms. They cannot retreat to a burrow at night to keep warm either, so they need thick coats to prevent them from losing heat during the cold nights. This insulating layer also helps to prevent them from getting too hot in the day, protecting their skin from the heat of the sun (Figure 3).

The fat stored in their humps provides enough water as it is digested to allow them to go without drinking for days at a time, but when they do drink they also have an enormous capacity for liquid.

↑ **Figure 3:** Although the camel is large, with a thick coat and lots of fat, it is perfectly adapted to life in the desert.

Hot plants

Plants grow in hot and arid areas – without them there would be no food for many of the animals. They have several ways of surviving the drought conditions. Some plants exist as dormant seeds for years until a rare desert rain stimulates them to grow, flower and set seeds again in the space of two or three weeks. Some trees, like the acacia, have roots that will reach down as far as 30 metres to underground water sources.

Many desert plants are succulents – they have small leaves with a thick cuticle and ways of storing water in the leaves, stems or roots. Some plants have broad leaves which catch the dew and funnel it towards their shallow roots. However, the best-known desert plants are the cacti, which store water in their fleshy stems and have reduced their leaves to spines to reduce water loss (Figure 4).

↑ **Figure 4:** Cacti are so well adapted to desert life that they can survive where no other large plants are seen.

8.3 Coping with cold

The Arctic is one example of an extremely cold environment which is a real challenge to survival for all organisms. The other problem with the Arctic is that it changes considerably throughout the year. Although it is still cold in summer it is much greener, while in winter it is totally bleak. The photos in Figures 1 and 2 show how different the Arctic looks in summer and winter. How do animals cope with this?

↓ **Figure 1** The Arctic is a cold and bleak environment.

↑ **Figure 2:** As water, warmth and light become available in the Arctic tundra the frozen wastes bloom.

Warmth equals survival

Some animals such as reindeer and caribou just leave and move south for the winter. Those who stay must concentrate on keeping warm. They need to reduce the heat lost from their bodies in as many ways as possible. The amount of body heat lost is related to the surface area:volume ratio (see page 114) so many Arctic mammals, such as seals, walruses, whales, and polar bears, are relatively large. In all Arctic mammals the area of thin-skinned parts of the body like ears is as small as possible. This is one way to reduce heat loss (Figure 3).

Many Arctic mammals also have plenty of insulation, both inside and out. Mammals like seals have blubber – a thick layer of fat which is built up under the skin and which insulates the animal very effectively against the cold, reducing the amount of heat lost through the skin. An added advantage of the fat layer is that it also provides a food supply. Animals often build up their blubber before the winter months so that they can live off their body fat through the winter when there is almost no food.

Jack rabbit   Arctic hare

↑ **Figure 3:** Adaptation in action! The ears of the Arctic hare are clearly smaller than those of the jack rabbit (actually a hare) which lives much further south.

Additional insulation is often provided by an extremely thick fur coat. This fur will thicken up even more as winter approaches. We see the same sort of thing in the UK, where wild ponies in places like the New Forest and Dartmoor grow thick, shaggy coats to insulate them from the chill of a British winter. Imagine how much thicker the fur of a polar bear might need to be, to survive the winter on Arctic ice floes.

The camouflage game

Another problem of living in the Arctic is the change in the colour of the background environment. In the summer the tundra is green, but in the winter the whole Arctic becomes a world of swirling white. Camouflage is important both to predators so their prey doesn't see them coming, and to prey so they can't be seen. Unfortunately the colours which would camouflage an animal in summer would stand out against the snow in winter, whilst winter white would show up against the summer vegetation. So many animals change the colour of their coat or plumage with the season of the year. The Arctic fox, the Arctic hare, the stoat and the ptarmigan (a type of bird) all exchange their greys and browns of summer for pure white in the winter (Figure 4).

← **Figure 4:** The white winter coat of this Arctic hunter means it can get close to its prey without being seen.

The polar bear remains white all year round, although the coat gets more yellowy in the summer. This is because polar bears fear no predators on the land, and they hunt their prey in the sea amongst the ice all year round, so the white colour makes them much less visible to the seals and penguins they hunt in the water.

Key Ideas

⊙ Animals must keep warm to survive – they have a small surface area:volume ratio and thick, insulating layers of fat and fur.

⊙ Fat layers help many animals survive the lack of food in the winter.

⊙ Changing coat colour in the different seasons allows animals to be camouflaged all year round.

All around the world there are many unique environments, and in each of these we find animals and plants which are perfectly adapted to survive there.

The walrus

Walruses are mammals found in the very cold northern parts of the Atlantic and Pacific oceans (Figure 1). Walruses are huge, and up to a third of their weight is blubber, a thick layer of fat which insulates them against the cold. Yet they also have a very good blood supply to the skin, so when they bask in the (relatively) hot summer sun they turn rose pink and lose the excess heat. They have a pair of massive tusks which can be over a metre long. They use these tusks to drag themselves out of the sea onto Arctic ice, to open breathing holes in the ice when they are swimming underneath it, and to scrape up shellfish from the seabed for food. They have giant hind flippers which make them excellent swimmers.

↑ **Figure 1:** Walruses display some astonishing adaptations to their way of life.

Deadly beauty

Tropical rain forests provide a warm, humid atmosphere, ideal conditions for insects. We will probably never know exactly how many species of insect live in this abundant environment. Insects are major consumers of the forest vegetation, and in turn they are an important source of food for mammals, birds, reptiles and amphibians. Not surprisingly, one of the major adaptations found in insects in the tropical forests is camouflage. A particularly striking example is the orchid mantises (Figure 2). They are hunters, preying on insects which are active during the day. They are themselves eaten by birds. They look amazingly like flowers, and butterflies and other insects approach the bright coloured 'petals' in search of nectar, only to be grabbed by the spiny forelegs of the mantis and eaten. The flower camouflage also protects the mantis from birds, which are often deceived by the apparent petals and ignore the mantis as possible food.

Plumbing the depths

The deep ocean starts at about 1.8 km below the surface and reaches to the ocean floor which can be about 10 km down. The organisms which live in these areas have to withstand enormous pressures from the weight of water above them, and they are adapted to cope with this by maintaining enormous internal pressures in their bodies. This makes bringing them up to sea level very difficult, because they can explode as the water pressure gets less.

↑ **Figure 2:** The adaptations of the orchid mantis to its environment leave it looking much more like a flower than an insect – but in spite of its delicate appearance it is a deadly hunter.

There is no plant life in the deep ocean, so the animals which live there rely on the remains of dead animals and plants dropping down from the higher regions and on each other for food. Most deep sea animals are small – there isn't enough food to sustain large organisms. One example is the deep sea angler fish. It can withstand the great pressures of the depths and it attracts prey by a lure which is luminous and dangles over its head (Figure 3). The light in this black environment attracts other curious fish, which find themselves literally swimming into the jaws of the angler. Because prey is so rare, nothing which approaches can be ignored. The angler has enormously wide jaws and a highly elastic stomach which mean it can swallow prey which is larger than itself.

← **Figure 3:** The deep sea angler fish is adapted to be a successful hunter in one of the most extreme environments on Earth.

↑ **Figure 4:** Plants such as these which grow without soil seem to defy all our expectations, but they are well adapted to the environment in which they live.

Seeking the light

Epiphytes are plants that need a lot of light, but they do not grow in the soil.

They get to the light by growing on other plants. Epiphytes will grow in cracks or crevices on a large plant like a tree, taking nutrients from any decaying plant material wedged there. They photosynthesise in the light they receive near the top of the tree, and many of them have dangling aerial roots which absorb moisture from the air. They are often found in tropical rain forests, where the very tall trees take much of the light and the air is always moist. Orchids are a very beautiful example of these strange plants (Figure 4).

? Questions

1 List the adaptations a walrus has to its way of life and explain how each one helps it to survive.

2 Describe two ways in which the appearance of the orchid mantis helps it to survive.

3 a Why are epiphytes often found at the tops of tall trees in the rain forest?

   b Where do epiphytes get their water from?

4 Why do you think there is no plant life in the deep ocean?

5 Explain why an animal like the angler fish might explode if brought to the surface of the sea too quickly.

Key Ideas

⊙ Successful organisms are always adapted to their environment.

Competition

The ways organisms are adapted are important in helping them to survive the environment in their habitat. But they are also important in helping them to compete against other organisms for the things they need to survive such as food, water and light (Figure 1). The best adapted organisms are the most successful – that is they survive to produce healthy offspring.

Competition in plants

Plants compete with each other for space, for light, for water and for nutrients from the soil. When seeds of different plants land on the soil and start to grow, those plants which grow fastest will compete successfully against slower growing plants. The plants which get their roots into the soil first will get most of the available water and nutrients. The plants which open their leaves up fastest will be able to photosynthesise and grow faster still, and then they will also be shading the seedlings which grow up more slowly, depriving them of light (Figure 2).

If the seeds of a plant land close to it, the parent plant will be in direct competition with it's own seedlings. Because the adult plant is large and well established, it will take water, minerals and light, depriving its own offspring of the resources they need. To prevent this happening, most plants have successful dispersal mechanisms which carry the seeds as far as possible from the parent plant (Figure 3).

↑ **Figure 1:** Idyllic scenes like this are actually the site of cut-throat competition between the plants and the animals for the resources they need to survive.

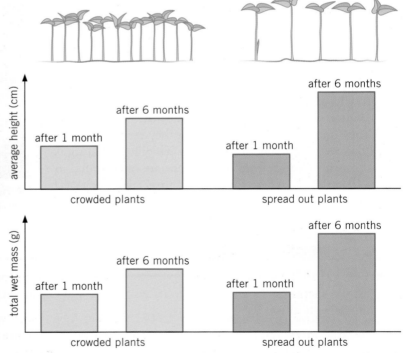

↑ **Figure 2:** Experiments like this can be carried out to show the effect of competition on seedlings. All the other conditions – light level, temperature, amount of water, etc. – are kept identical for both sets of plants, so the differences between them are the result of overcrowding and competition for the resources available.

← **Figure 3:** Dandelion seeds, with their light, fluffy 'parachutes', can travel great distances from their parent plant on air currents and the wind.

Competition in animals

Animals compete for water, food and space. They also compete for mates and for breeding sites.

Competition for food is very common. Herbivores eat plants, and often different species will all eat the same plants. Those which eat a wide range of plants are most likely to be successful. A picky eater risks extinction if other animals in the area eat its only food source (Figure 4). An animal with wider tastes will just eat something else for a while.

Similarly, carnivores compete for prey. Small mammals like mice are food for foxes, owls, hawks and domestic cats. Rabbits too will be eaten by at least some of these predators, together with small birds, large slugs and snails, frogs and voles. Not all of the predators will eat all of these prey animals, but if one is in short supply the carnivore will eat more of a different prey.

Carnivores will compete with other members of their own species for the prey as well as members of different species. For many animals, setting up and defending a territory against their own kind is vital for finding enough food both for themselves and their young when they breed.

Competition for mates can be fierce. The female often selects her mate, and the males compete in different ways to win the privilege of mating with her. In some species the males fight between themselves and the winner gets the females. This may be mostly a ritual fight or it may be life-threatening. Sometimes males rely on spectacular displays to win a mate. This is particularly true in the bird world, where the peacock with its large and brilliantly coloured tail is one of the best examples.

← **Figure 4:** Some herbivores, like the giant panda eating bamboo, only thrive on one particular plant. They are especially vulnerable to competition, or to anything that damages their food plant, like disease.

? Questions

1 How does marking out and defending a territory help an animal to breed successfully?

2 Some plants in deciduous woodland (where trees lose their leaves in winter) flower and make seeds very early in the year before the trees have regrown all their leaves. How does this help them to survive?

3 Look at the graphs in Figure 2. Explain:

   a why average height and average mass were used as measures

   b the results seen in the graphs after 1 month and 6 months.

4 What message does a male's fine body display give a female, which would encourage her to mate with him?

🔑 Key Ideas

⊙ Plants often compete with each other for space, light, water and nutrients.

⊙ Animals compete with each other for space, food and water as well as for mates and breeding sites.

A **population** is a group of organisms all of the same species which are living together in a particular habitat, for example frogs in a local pond. A **community** is the total of all the different populations of animals and plants living together in a habitat at any one time. So all the different populations in the local pond, not just the frogs but the fish, insects and plants, would make up the pond community (Figure 1).

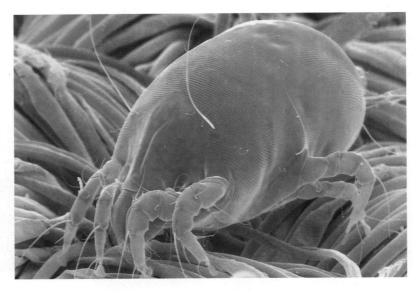

← **Figure 1:** The dust mites which live in your mattress eating your dead skin cells make up one population out of the community of bacteria, fungi and arthropods which share your bed!

A changing population

In any population of plants or animals the numbers will decrease as organisms die and increase as new organisms come into being. If the population is stable these losses and gains will more or less balance out. The size of a population is dependent on a number of things:

⊙ The total amount of food or nutrients available – when they are plentiful the population grows; when they are in short supply populations will get smaller as more organisms die and fewer new ones are created.

⊙ Competition for food and nutrients – if there is competition between species for a resource, then populations will be kept smaller; if there is no competition and plenty of resources then populations can grow unchecked.

⊙ With plants, competition for light will have a big effect on the size of a population. With plenty of light, plants will grow and reproduce, making thousands of seeds; without enough light, fewer plants will grow or reproduce successfully so the population will shrink.

⊙ Disease can have a major effect on populations. A new disease can wipe out the vast majority of a population. When myxomatosis was introduced into the UK rabbit population to control its numbers, it wiped out more than 90% of the population in just a few years!

⊙ Predation can have a major effect on a population, particularly if a new and successful predator moves into an area. When hedgehogs were introduced onto some Scottish islands with large colonies of wading birds breeding on the beaches, they ate the eggs and young of the birds. With a massive supply of food, and no predators to hold them in check, the hedgehog population exploded and almost wiped out the birds (Figure 2).

⊙ If the grazing pattern changes, plant populations can be strongly affected. When rabbits were almost wiped out by myxomatosis, a lot of farm grazing land was lost. Rabbits ate all the young seedlings which sheep and cattle avoided. As a result of the lack of rabbits, young shrubs and bushes grew up, forming scrubland which was not so suitable for grazing domestic animals.

↑ **Figure 2:** Hedgehogs may look endearing but they have wreaked havoc on the populations of breeding birds on the Scottish islands where they were introduced.

A community effect

All populations interact as part of a community, and what happens to one population has a knock-on effect on others. This can be seen in the way the population of a predator and its prey are linked. If there is plenty of plant food, prey numbers increase. This means there is more food for the predators, so more of their offspring survive and their numbers go up. But more predators eat more prey, and the extra prey also overgraze the food, so the prey population falls. In turn this means there is less food for the predators, so their population falls allowing prey numbers to rise again, and so on (Figure 3).

↘ **Figure 3:** Predator and prey populations – from tiny mites through to large animals like the fox and the grouse shown here – are linked together in cycles like this.

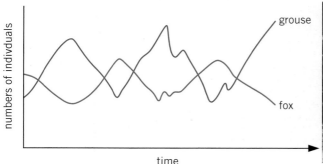

However, this model is oversimplified. Other herbivores may eat more of the plant food so that a prey population crashes and the predator population then falls. Many predators feed off a variety of prey so fewer of one type might not affect the size of the predator population but might mean that it eats more of a different type of prey. So population numbers of the different species depend both on environmental conditions and on the fortunes of other populations within the community (Figure 4).

↓ **Figure 4:** If anything major happens to affect the numbers of one part of the predator–prey equation, numbers on the other side are always affected. The gamekeeper on moor B was ill for 6 months and so predators were not controlled – with a dramatic effect on grouse numbers.

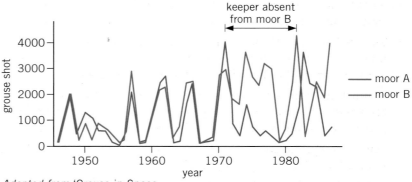

Adapted from 'Grouse in Space and Time' by Hudson, by kind permission of the Game Conservancy Trust.

Adapted from 'Grouse in Space and Time' by Hudson, by kind permission of the Game Conservancy Trust.

? Questions

1 What is the difference between a population and a community?

2 Make a table to summarise the factors which can affect the numbers in a population.

3 **a** The preferred food of the Arctic fox is a small mammal called a lemming. Draw a graph to show what you would expect the pattern of the population numbers of the lemming and the Arctic fox to look like.

   b Lemming numbers tend to crash every two years – but when this happens the Arctic foxes switch to eating Brent geese instead. Draw a graph with three lines to show what you would now expect, on the basis of this information, the population patterns of lemmings, Arctic foxes and Brent geese to look like.

⊙ᴛᴍ Key Ideas

- ⊙ The size of an animal population may be affected by the amount of food available, competition for food, predation or grazing and disease.

- ⊙ The size of a plant population may be affected by the amount of light, water and nutrients available and grazing by animals.

1 **a** Explain what is meant by each of the following terms:

    i environment

    ii ecosystem

    iii habitat. (3 marks)

  b Give an example of two common British habitats. (2 marks)

     (Total 5 marks)

2 The graph shows the change in the daylight hours and average temperature in the UK through the year.

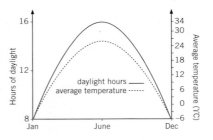

  a Using information from the graph, what is the difference between the average number of hours of daylight in the UK in the summer and in the winter? Show your working. (2 marks)

  b What is the difference in the average temperature in the summer and the winter? Show your working. (2 marks)

  c Give an example of the way an animal or plant deals with changes in environmental conditions like these. (2 marks)

     (Total 6 marks)

3 The gemsbok is a large herbivore that lives in herds in desert areas of South Africa. Gemsboks feed on plants that are adapted to living in dry conditions. There are not many rivers, lakes or ponds that can provide drinking water for the animals. The desert areas are hot during the day but cool at night. As the air cools it becomes moist, and the plants absorb the moisture.

  a A few lions live in the desert areas. They hunt and feed on the gemsboks. Use information from the drawing of the gemsbok to suggest **two** ways in which it could avoid being killed by lions. (2 marks)

  b The graphs show the water content of the desert grass and the times of day gemsboks feed.

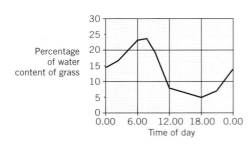

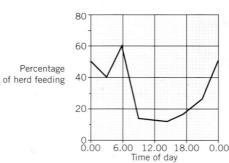

    i Describe how the water content of the grass changes during the day. (1 mark)

    ii Suggest why the water content of the grass changes. (1 mark)

  c **i** Between which times of the day are more than 25% of the herd feeding? (1 mark)

    ii Suggest an advantage to the gemsbok of feeding mainly at these times. (2 marks)

     (Total 7 marks)

     AQA specimen question

4 Emperor penguins feed and get as fat as possible during the Antarctic summer. They then lay their eggs as the Antarctic winter sets in and the females swim off out to sea to feed for several months, leaving the male penguins to incubate the eggs. The incubating males huddle together in big groups with their feathers fluffed out. The eggs are tucked up close to their bodies in a special flap of skin, completely hidden from the winter weather. Once the worst of the winter has passed and the very fluffy chicks hatch, the female penguins return loaded with fish which they regurgitate to feed the young.

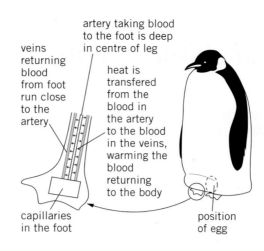

artery taking blood to the foot is deep in centre of leg

veins returning blood from foot run close to the artery

heat is transfered from the blood in the artery to the blood in the veins, warming the blood returning to the body

capillaries in the foot

position of egg

a Explain how the blood flow into the feet of the Emperor penguin helps prevent heat loss as the bird stands on the ice. (2 marks)

b List **three** other adaptations of the Emperor penguins described above and explain how each helps them to survive and breed in the extreme cold conditions. (6 marks)

(Total 8 marks)

5 a Competition between plants for different resources is often fierce. Give **three** different resources for which plants might compete. (3 marks)

b In this experiment, tree seedling were allowed to grow very close together or spaced apart. After one year the difference in their average heights was as shown on the graph.

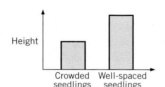

Height

Crowded seedlings

Well-spaced seedlings

i Explain the differences you can see on the graph. (3 marks)

ii Sketch a graph to show what the heights might have looked like after only one month's growth. (1 mark)

iii Explain the appearance of the graph you have just drawn. (2 marks)

c Use this information to explain why most plants have effective dispersal mechanisms for their seeds. (3 marks)

(Total 12 marks)

6 A population of rabbits lived on a small island. The graph shows their population over the last 50 years.

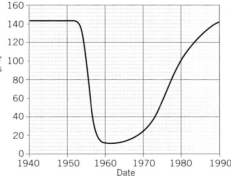

Number of rabbits

160
140
120
100
80
60
40
20
0

1940   1950   1960   1970   1980   1990

Date

a i How many rabbits were there on the island in 1950? (1 mark)

ii Give one year when there were 88 rabbits on the island. (1 mark)

b i Calculate the decrease in the rabbit population between 1950 and 1960. (1 mark)

ii Suggest **one** reason why the rabbit population fell in these years. (1 mark)

c The most rabbits on the island is always about 140. Suggest one reason for this. (1 mark)

(Total 5 marks)

AQA specimen question

Science people

In the 1920s a young biologist at Oxford University called Charles Elton travelled to Bear Island off the northern coast of Norway (Figure 1). The island is part of the Arctic tundra, so he made his trips in summer when there was some plant life to observe and conditions were not too uncomfortable. He wanted to see how the animals which live in this tough environment divided up the scarce resources between them.

← **Figure 1:** Bear Island is a very stark environment. It was here that Charles Elton first observed food chains in action.

Bear Island only supports a few hardy grasses and small scrubby plants so it was relatively easy for Elton to observe the animals which fed on the plants and each other. Arctic foxes were the main large carnivores. During the summer months they fed largely on birds like ptarmigan and sandpipers which were summer visitors only – rather like the biologist watching them! The birds in turn fed on the leaves and berries of the tundra plants, or on plant-eating insects. Elton described the links between plants, insects, birds and fox as a food chain (Figure 2), and defined the first link of the chain as the trapping of energy from the sun by photosynthesis in plants.

He devised the term **producer** for plants, and defined animals as **primary consumers** if they ate plants, **secondary consumers** if they ate the animals which eat plants, and so on.

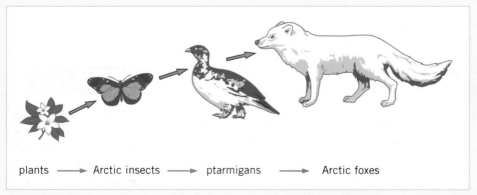

plants ⟶ Arctic insects ⟶ ptarmigans ⟶ Arctic foxes

↑ **Figure 2:** This was the food chain which Charles Elton first observed. His ideas have underpinned much of our study of ecology ever since.

Charles Elton recognised that a food chain was a great simplification. He saw that Arctic foxes actually ate a wide range of animals, and that polar bears were also large predators on the island. Many different types of plants fed the herbivores. ↓

He built these complex interactions up into what he called a **food web**, another term we still use today (Figure 3).

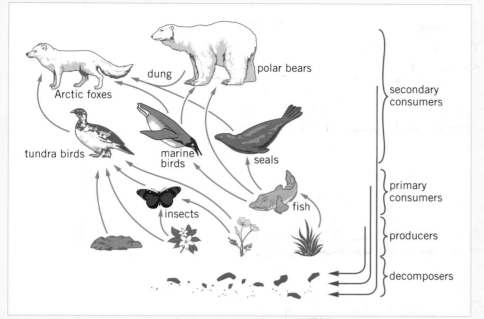

↑ **Figure 3:** Even though a food web like the one Charles Elton produced is still a simplification of the real situation, it gives us a much better picture of the complex interactions between living organisms than a simple food chain.

Energy for life

As Charles Elton showed, radiation from the sun is the source of energy for all communities of living organisms. Solar energy pours out continually onto the surface of the Earth and a small part of it is captured by the chlorophyll in plants. It is used in photosynthesis and the energy from the sun is stored in the substances which make up the cells of the plant. This new plant material adds to the **biomass**. Biomass is a term which describes all the material produced by living organisms, plant or animal. Biomass all comes originally from plants as they make new material by photosynthesis at the beginning of all food chains.

This biomass is then passed on through the food chain or web into the animals which eat the plants and then on into the animals which eat other animals. However long the food chain or complex the food web, the original source of all the energy and biomass involved is the sun.

? **Questions**

1 Draw all the different food chains which you can see in the food web in Figure 3.

2 **a** What are the differences between a food chain and a food web?

   b Which do you think is the most useful to us? Explain your answer.

3 Make a table to show which organisms in the food web shown in Figure 3 are producers, primary consumers and secondary consumers.

4 What is biomass?

0—π **Key Ideas**

⊙ Radiation from the sun is the source of energy for all communities of living organisms. It is captured by green plants in photosynthesis.

⊙ Food chains and food webs show the feeding relationships between animals and plants.

Biomass and energy

When we look at a food chain, there are usually more producers than primary consumers, and more primary consumers than secondary consumers. This can be shown as a **pyramid of numbers** (Figure 1).

However, in many cases a pyramid of numbers does not accurately reflect what is happening. For example, the caterpillar of the oak beauty moth feeds on the leaves of an oak tree, and some of the birds such as the great tits which visit the tree then feed on the caterpillars. However, the pyramid of numbers for a common food chain such as this does not look like a pyramid at all (Figure 2).

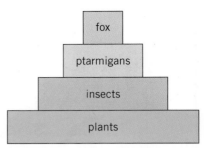

↑ **Figure 1:** A pyramid of numbers like this seems a sensible way to represent a food chain.

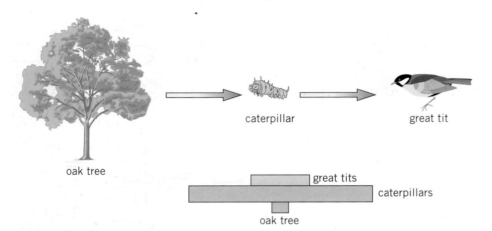

← **Figure 2:** This food chain cannot be accurately represented using a pyramid of numbers.

Pyramids of biomass

To represent what is happening in food chains more accurately we can use **biomass**. Biomass is the mass of living material in an animal or plant and ultimately all biomass is built up using energy from the sun. The total amount of biomass in the living organisms at each stage of the food chain can be drawn to scale and shown as a pyramid of biomass (Figure 3).

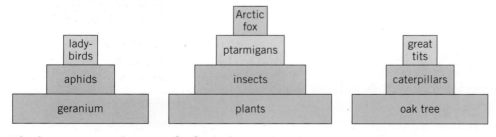

← **Figure 3:** Regardless of the numbers of organisms involved in a food chain, when the biomass of the different feeding levels is considered a pyramid of biomass always results.

The biomass at each stage of a food chain is less than it was at the previous stage. This is because:

⊙ not all organisms at one stage are eaten by the stage above

⊙ when a herbivore eats a plant, it turns some of the plant material into new herbivore material. However, much of the biomass from the plant is used by the herbivore to release energy for living and so does not get passed on to the carnivore when the herbivore is eaten.

So at each stage of a food chain the amount of biomass which is passed on is less – a large amount of plant biomass supports a smaller amount of herbivore biomass, which in turn supports an even smaller amount of carnivore biomass.

What can we learn?

As pyramids of biomass clearly show us, at each stage of the food chain less material and therefore less energy are contained in the biomass of the organisms. This has some major implications for the way we humans feed ourselves.

In the developed world much of our diet consists of meat or other animal products such as eggs, cheese and milk. To get those animal products, plant material is eaten by the animals and a large amount of energy from the plant is used before it gets to us. In some cases we even feed animals to animals – ground-up fish, for example, is often part of commercial pig and chicken feed. This means we have put another extra layer into the food chain – plant to fish, fish to pig, pig to people. What could have been biomass for us has been used as energy by other animals in the chain.

There is only a limited amount of the surface of the Earth which can be used to grow food. The most efficient way to use this food is to grow plants and eat them directly. If this was the case, then in theory at least there would be more than enough food for everyone on the Earth to eat their fill. But every extra stage we introduce – feeding plants to animals before we eat the food ourselves – the more biomass and energy is lost to humans and the less food there is to go round the human population (Figure 4).

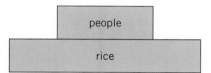

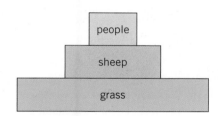

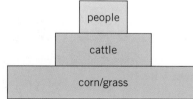

↖ **Figure 4:** Reducing the number of stages in food chains could dramatically increase the efficiency of our food production. Eating less meat would probably be better for our health and mean there would be more food for everyone all over the world.

? Questions

1 a Draw a pyramid of numbers for the following food chains

    i grass → sheep → people

    ii rosebush → greenfly → ladybirds → birds

    iii marine plants → small fish → large fish → seals → polar bears

  b Why is a pyramid of numbers not always a useful way to represent a food chain?

2 a Using the food chains **i** to **iii** above, draw pyramids of biomass for each chain.

  b What do these pyramids show about the effect of the number of stages in a food chain on the amount of biomass which is available at the end of the chain?

3 Explain why the biomass from one stage of a pyramid of biomass does not all become biomass for the next stage when it is eaten.

⊙ Key Ideas

- ⊙ The mass of living material (biomass) at each stage of a food chain is always less than it was at the previous stage.

- ⊙ The biomass at each stage of a food chain can be drawn to scale and shown as a pyramid of biomass.

- ⊙ The efficiency of food production can be improved by reducing the number of stages in food chains.

A budget for living

An animal like a zebra eats grass and other small plants. It takes in a large amount of plant biomass, and converts it into a smaller amount of zebra biomass. What happens to the rest?

Firstly, not all of the plant material can be digested by the animal, so it is passed out of the body in the faeces (Figure 2). Excess protein which is eaten but not needed in the body is broken down and passed out as urea in the urine. The same is true for carnivores – they often cannot digest hooves, claws and teeth, so some of the biomass which is eaten is always lost in their waste.

Part of the biomass which is eaten by an animal is used for cellular respiration. This supplies all the energy needs for the living processes taking place within the body, including movement which uses a great deal of energy. The muscles use energy to contract, and the more an animal moves about the more energy (and biomass) it uses from its food.

Much of the energy produced in cellular respiration is eventually lost as heat to the surroundings. These losses are particularly large in mammals and birds, because they are warm-blooded. This means their bodies are kept at a constant temperature regardless of the temperature of the surroundings. They use up energy all the time to keep warm when it's cold or to cool down when it's hot. Because of this, warm-blooded animals need to eat far more food than cold-blooded animals like fish and reptiles to get the same increase in biomass.

↑ **Figure 1:** The amount of biomass in a lion is substantially less than the amount of biomass in the grass which feeds the zebra which the lion preys on. But where does it all go?

↑ **Figure 2:** Animals like elephants eat vast amounts of biomass, but they also produce very large quantities of dung containing all the material they cannot digest.

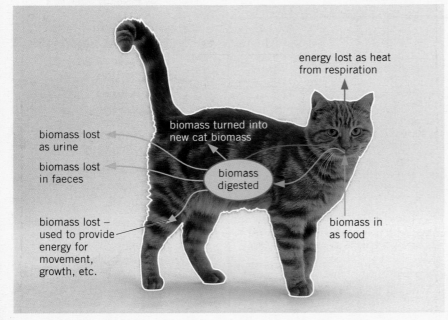

← **Figure 3:** Only about 2% of the biomass eaten by an animal such as this cat will get turned into new cat – the rest will be used or lost in other ways.

Farms or factories?

Farmers apply these ideas to the production of food to get the maximum possible increase in biomass from animals without feeding them any more. There are two ways of doing this:

⊙ Limiting the movement of food animals so that they lose a lot less energy in moving their muscles and so will have more biomass available from their food for growth.

⊙ Controlling the temperature of their surroundings so that the animals will not have to use too much energy keeping warm. Again this leaves more biomass spare for growth.

This means keeping the animals inside with restricted room to move and a constant temperature. This is exactly what happens in the massive poultry rearing sheds which produce the majority of the chickens that we eat. Keeping chickens in these conditions means relatively large birds can be reared for the table in a matter of weeks. When animals are reared in this way they can appear more like factory products than farm animals and these intensive regimes are sometimes referred to as factory farming (Figure 4).

← **Figure 4:** Intensively reared pigs live in small stalls in a warm building with carefully measured amounts of food delivered at regular intervals for maximum growth.

Improving the efficiency of farming applies to plants as well. Most fruit is picked and transported unripe, with plant hormones used to control the time and amount of ripening (see page 75). This means that far less produce is bruised, damaged or becomes over-ripe before going on sale, and makes the yield of biomass from the plant far higher.

Intensive farming methods are used because there has been a steadily increasing demand for cheap meat and animal products (such as eggs and milk) from consumers. On the other hand there has been a backlash against the conditions in which intensively reared animals live. Many people now say they would be willing to eat meat less often and pay more if the animals they eat are raised naturally.

❓ Questions

1 Explain why so much of the energy from the sun which lands on the surface of the Earth is not turned into biomass in animals.

2 Why do warm-blooded animals need more food than cold-blooded ones to put on the same amount of weight?

3 Why are animals restricted in their movement and kept indoors in intensive farming?

4 Prepare a presentation either explaining and defending intensive farming methods or explaining and criticising intensive farming methods.

9.4 The decomposers

Living things are constantly removing materials from the environment. Plants take minerals from the soil and these minerals are then passed on into animals through the food chains and food webs which link all living organisms. If this was a one way process then the resources of the Earth would have been exhausted long ago. Fortunately, however, the materials are eventually returned to the environment from the waste products of animals and the dead bodies of plants and animals.

The role of the decomposers

The nutrients held in the bodies of dead animals and plants, and in animal droppings, are released back into the soil by the action of a group of organisms known as the **decomposers**. These are microorganisms such as bacteria and fungi. They feed on waste droppings and dead organisms. They digest them and use some of the nutrients. They also release waste products which are nutrients broken down into a form that plants can use. When we say that things decay they are actually being broken down and digested by these microorganisms (Figure 1).

The chemical reactions which take place in microorganisms, like those in most other living things, work faster in warm conditions. But as in other organisms, these reactions are controlled by enzymes, and if the temperature gets too hot the reactions stop altogether as the enzymes denature. They also stop if conditions are too cold (Figure 2).

↑ **Figure 1:** The dead body of this tree is slowly being broken down by the action of decomposers. The fungi are clearly visible, whilst the bacteria are too small to be seen.

← **Figure 2:** Sometimes when an organism dies it is frozen rapidly. The decomposers cannot function at these low temperatures and so the organism – like this baby mammoth – is preserved with very little decay. Once it begins to warm up, however, the rot will rapidly set in.

Most microorganisms also grow better in moist conditions which make it easier to dissolve their food and also prevent them from drying out (Figure 3). So the decay of dead plants and animals – and dung – takes place far more rapidly in warm, moist conditions than it does in cold, dry ones.

The majority of decomposers respire like any other organism to release energy to feed and reproduce as rapidly as possible. This means that decay takes place more rapidly when there is plenty of oxygen available.

As people have developed an understanding of decomposers they have also developed ways of using them in artificial situations.

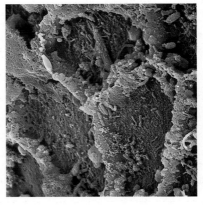

← **Figure 3:** The decomposers are all microorganisms and so they are vulnerable to drying out – moisture is vital for decay.

The sewage story

As the human population has grown, so has the amount of human waste (sewage) produced. Not only is this material unpleasant to live with, it also carries disease. Sewage treatment plants use microorganisms to break down the sewage and make it harmless enough to be released into rivers or the sea for the breakdown to be completed. They have been designed to provide the bacteria and other microorganisms with the conditions they need, particularly a good supply of oxygen (Figure 4).

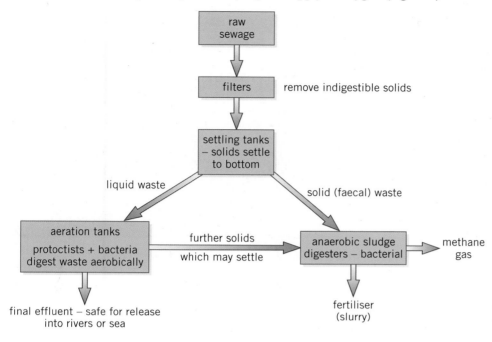

← **Figure 4:** The breakdown of human sewage using microorganisms is an important process in removing human waste – and the products of the sewage farm can be used to fertilise the soil!

The gardener's friend

Another place where the decomposers are useful is in the garden. Many gardeners have a compost heap. This is where they place grass cuttings, sometimes vegetable peelings and bits they cut off plants, and then leave it to let decomposing microorganisms break all the plant material down to a fine, rich, powdery substance known as compost. This process takes at least a year, and the compost produced is full of mineral nutrients released by the decomposers. This compost is then dug into the soil to act as a valuable and completely natural fertiliser.

? Questions

1 The following methods are all ways of preserving foods to prevent them from decaying. Use your knowledge of the decomposing microorganisms to explain how each method works:

a food may be frozen

b food may be cooked – cooked food keeps longer than fresh food

c food may be stored in a vacuum pack – with all the air sucked out

d food may be tinned, when it is heated and sealed in an airtight container.

2 a Make a list of the main stages in the process of sewage treatment. Indicate which stages rely on the action of microorganisms.

b Compare and contrast the process of sewage formation with the formation of garden compost. Explain the value of each process.

0━ Key Ideas

⊙ Living organisms remove materials from the environment as they grow and return them when they die through the action of the decomposers.

⊙ Dead materials decay because they are broken down by microorganisms.

⊙ Decomposers are used in the treatment of human sewage and in the formation of compost.

In a stable community of plants and animals living in an environment, the processes which remove materials from the soil are balanced by processes which return materials. In other words, the materials are constantly cycled through the environment (Figure 1).

The carbon cycle

The element carbon is vital for living organisms because all of the main molecules of life – carbohydrates, proteins, fats and DNA – are based on carbon atoms in combination with other elements. There is a vast pool of carbon in the form of carbon dioxide, both in the air and dissolved in the water of rivers, lakes and seas. At the same time carbon is constantly recycled between living things and the environment. This is known as the **carbon cycle**.

Carbon dioxide is removed from the air by green plants in the process of photosynthesis. It is used to make the carbohydrates, proteins and fats which make up the body of the plant. Then when the plants are eaten by animals, and those animals are eaten by predators, the carbon is passed on and becomes part of the animal bodies. This is how carbon is taken out of the environment. How is it returned?

When green plants themselves respire, some carbon dioxide is returned to the atmosphere. Similarly, when animals respire they release carbon dioxide as a waste product into the air. Finally, when both plants and animals die their bodies are broken down by the action of decomposers and when these microbes respire they release carbon into the atmosphere as carbon dioxide, ready to be taken up again by plants in photosynthesis. This cycling of carbon can be summarised in a diagram (Figure 2).

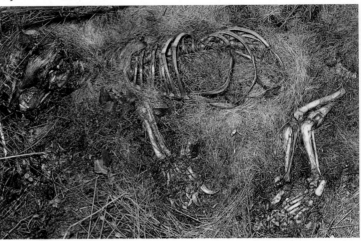

↓ **Figure 1:** Within the natural cycle of life and death in the living world mineral nutrients are cycled between living organisms and the physical environment.

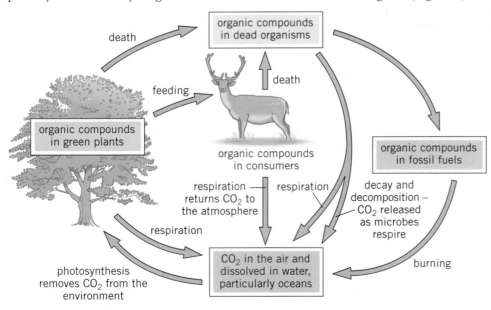

← **Figure 2:** The carbon cycle in nature.

In a natural situation the carbon cycle regulates itself. However, as human activities pour increasing amounts of carbon dioxide into the atmosphere there are fears that this cycle may become distorted.

H The nitrogen cycle

The carbon cycle is not the only example of the way minerals are cycled through living organisms and their environment. Another important example is the constant cycling of nitrogen in the nitrogen cycle.

Green plants absorb nitrogen in the form of nitrates dissolved in the soil water. They use these nitrates to make proteins, and then this protein is passed along the food chain as herbivores eat plants and are then themselves eaten by carnivores. In this way the nitrogen taken from the soil becomes incorporated into the bodies of all types of living organisms.

The nitrates are returned to the soil in a number of ways. Urine contains urea, a breakdown product of proteins, and proteins are also passed out in the faeces, so the waste passed out of animals' bodies contains many nitrogen-rich compounds. Similarly, when animals and plants die their bodies contain a large proportion of protein. Some of the decomposing or **putrefying** bacteria and fungi which break down the waste products from animals and the bodies of animals and plants specifically digest the proteins. As they break down the protein they excrete **ammonium compounds**. These ammonium compounds are then digested by **nitrifying bacteria** which excrete nitrates, which are returned to the soil to be absorbed by plants again.

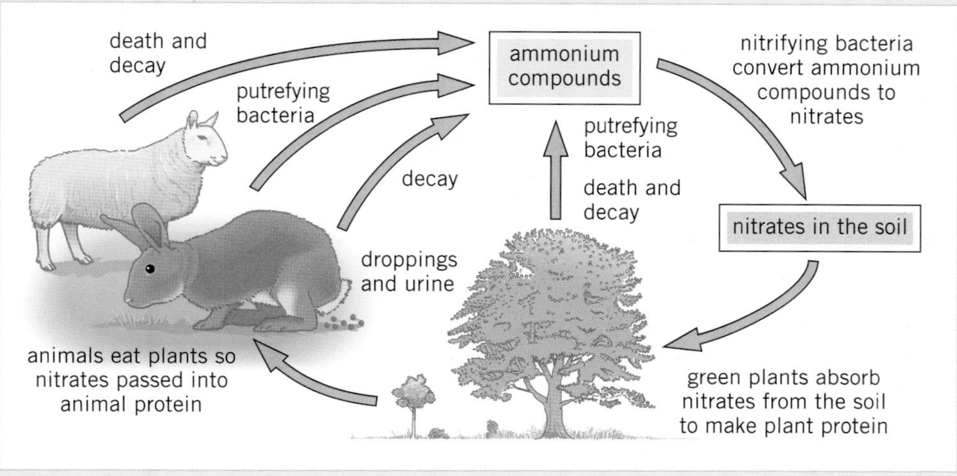

Figure 3: The nitrogen cycle in nature.

By the time the microbes and other animals that feed on decaying organic material (detritus feeders) have broken down the waste products and the dead bodies of organisms in ecosystems, all the energy originally captured by the green plants in photosynthesis has been transferred to other organisms or back into the environment itself as heat or mineral compounds.

? Questions

1 Why are the natural recycling processes like the carbon cycle so important for the continuation of life on Earth?

2 It can be said that no part of our bodies is truly our own – we have borrowed the materials and at a later date they will be used again elsewhere. How would you explain this statement?

H 3 Nitrates are vital for the fertility of the soil.

a Explain why.

b Explain the role of bacteria in maintaining this fertility.

Key Ideas

- In a stable community, the processes which remove materials from the environment are balanced by processes which return materials to it.
- The carbon cycle and the nitrogen cycle are both examples of the cycling of resources in nature.

1 A food web, like this one from a British woodland, links together a number of food chains.

   a What is a food chain?   (1 mark)

   b Give **three** food chains from this food web.   (3 marks)

   c Why is a food web a more accurate way of representing the feeding relationships in a woodland than food chains?   (2 marks)
                                                (Total 6 marks)

2 **a** Explain the following terms used in describing feeding relationships:
     i producer
     ii primary consumer
     iii secondary consumer.   (3 marks)

   b With reference to the food web in question 1, identify
     i two producers   (1 mark)
     ii two primary consumers   (1 mark)
     iii two secondary consumers.   (1 mark)
                                                   (Total 6 marks)

3 Sometimes problems arise because one animal within a food chain or web becomes too dominant. Read the passage.

Glutton up a gum tree

Along the banks of the Cygnet River on Kangaroo Island, the branches of the dying gum trees stretch out like accusing fingers. They have no leaves. Birds search in vain for nectar-bearing flowers.

The scene, repeated mile upon mile, is an ecological nightmare. But, for once, the culprit is not human. Instead, it is one of the most appealing mammals on the planet – the koala. If the trees are to survive and provide a food source for the wildlife such as koalas that depend on them, more than 2000 koalas that must die. If they are not removed the island's entire koala population will vanish.

Illegal killing has already started. Worried about soil erosion on the island, some farmers have gone for their guns. Why not catch 2000 koalas and take them to the mainland? "Almost impossible," says farmer Andrew Kelly. "Four rangers tried to catch some and in two days they got just six, and these fought, bit and scratched like fury."

Use the information from the passage and your own knowledge and understanding to give the arguments for and against killing koalas to reduce the koala population on Kangaroo Island.

(Total 4 marks)
AQA specimen question

4 a What is the role of the **decomposers** in an ecosystem? (2 marks)

b The graph shows the effect of temperature on the rate of decay in a compost heap.

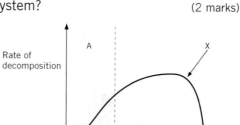

i What happens in part **A** of the graph? Explain your observation. (3 marks)
ii What happens after point **X** on the graph? Explain your observation. (3 marks)
(Total 8 marks)

5 The diagram shows some of the stages by which materials are cycled in living organisms.

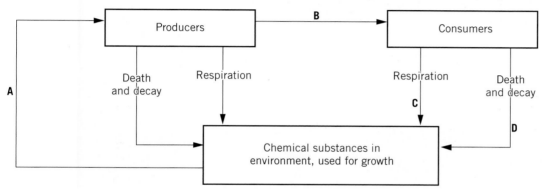

a In which of the stages, **A**, **B**, **C** or **D**
i are substances broken down by microbes
ii is carbon dioxide made into sugar
iii are plants eaten by animals? (3 marks)

b In an experiment, samples of soil were put into four beakers. A dead leaf was put onto the soil in each beaker. The soil was kept in the conditions shown.

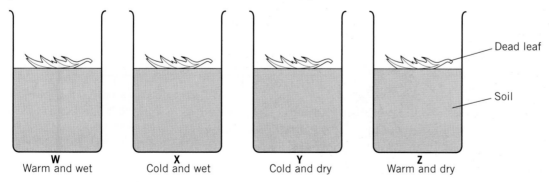

In which beaker, **W**, **X**, **Y** or **Z**, would the leaf decay quickest? (1 mark)
(Total 4 marks)
AQA specimen question

H 6 a Why are nitrates important to plants? (1 mark)
b How do plants obtain nitrates? (1 mark)
c Describe, with the help of a diagram if needed, how nitrogen is cycled in nature between the soil and the bodies of animals and plants. (6 marks)
(Total 8 marks)

10.1 People, people everywhere

People have only been around on the surface of the Earth for a relatively small part of its history, yet their activity has changed the ecology of the planet enormously. Some of the changes we have caused have wiped out other species. The damage we are doing now may even threaten our own survival. How has such a relatively new species had such a major impact on life on Earth?

→ **Figure 1:** The Earth as seen from space – the only planet where we know that carbon-based life forms exist. The question is – for how much longer?

A people explosion

For many thousands of years people lived on the Earth in relatively small numbers – only a few hundred millions. They were scattered all over the world, and the effects of their activities were usually small and local. Any changes could easily be absorbed within the natural cycling of minerals and the processes of decay and regeneration. But in the last 200 years or so, the human population began to grow very quickly. At the end of the 20th century there was an estimated population of over 6 billion people in the world (Figure 2).

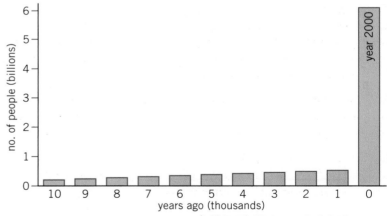

↑ **Figure 2:** The record of the human population shows the massive increase during the last few hundred years.

If the population of any other species of animal or plant had suddenly increased in this way, natural predators, lack of food, build up of waste products or diseases would have reduced it again. But the human population grew partly because we discovered how to grow more food than ever before and how to cure or prevent many killer diseases.

You never had it so good....

Not only has the human population grown hugely, but in large parts of the world the standard of living has also improved enormously. In the UK we use vast amounts of electricity and fuel to heat and light our homes and places of work. We move about in cars, planes, trains and boats at high speed. We have more than enough to eat and if we are ill we can often be made better.

Land grabbing

However, all of this has an effect on the environment. All these humans need more land to live on. More and more land is disappearing in the building of houses, shops, industrial sites and roads (Figure 3). Some of these destroy the habitats of rare species of other living organisms.

← **Figure 3:** In the UK alone it is planned that hundreds of thousands of new homes will be built in the early years of the 21st century. But every time a fresh area of land is cleared for building, the home of uncounted animals and plants is destroyed.

The increased numbers of people means vastly increased amounts of waste. This is both human bodily waste and the rubbish from packaging, uneaten food and disposable goods. The dumping of the waste produced by the ever-expanding human population makes large areas unavailable for any other life except scavengers.

Billions of acres of land around the world are also used for farming, to grow food and other crops for human use. Wherever people farm, the natural animal and plant population is destroyed. Quarrying – digging up great areas of land for the resources it holds such as gravel, metal ores and diamonds – also reduces the land available for other organisms.

Draining resources

The huge human population is also an enormous drain on the resources of the Earth. Raw materials, including non-renewable energy resources and metals, are rapidly being used up by an ever-more demanding world population. Finally, the enormous increase in manufacturing and industry to service the needs of the ever-growing population has led to increased pollution.

The way of life of different people across the world varies immensely. Many people in the developing world live in a similar way to their ancestors many centuries ago.

On the other hand, people in the developed world are surrounded by technology, almost all of which uses a great deal of energy and demands up to 20 times more resources than life only a couple of centuries ago (Figure 4).

↑ **Figure 4:** A world of contrast – in some parts of the world an open fire is all that is available for cooking; in others there is a choice of cooker, microwave, grill, rotisserie, toaster, hob – all of which use energy.

? Questions

1 The usual picture of a population is that it grows and then falls again, then grows and falls again. Why are we not seeing that pattern in the human population?

2 List the main ways in which humans reduce the amount of land available for other animals and plants.

3 a How does the rise in human standards of living affect the environment?

 b Would an increase in the population of America have the same effect on the environment as an increase in the population of Africa? Explain your answer.

⚷ Key Ideas

⊙ Humans have a major impact on the environment of the Earth.

⊙ The rapid growth of the human population in recent centuries has meant that resources are rapidly being used up and lots of extra waste is being produced.

⊙ People reduce the amount of land available for other living organisms in a number of ways.

Human activities can have far-reaching effects on the environment and all the other species of plants and animals which share the Earth. One of the biggest problems is the way people cause pollution (Figure 1).

Air pollution

Everybody needs air – we all breathe it in throughout our lives – and so when the air we breathe is polluted, no-one escapes the effects. This is just one reason why the idea of air pollution is so worrying.

One of the major sources of air pollution is the burning of fossil fuels like oil, coal and natural gas, and all the fuels made from them such as petrol, diesel, and aviation fuel for planes. Fossil fuel is a finite resource – there is a limited amount of it in the crust of the Earth and no more is being formed, so eventually it will all be used up.

When any of the fossil fuels is burned, carbon dioxide is released as a waste product. However, carbon dioxide is not the only waste gas produced when these fuels are burned. Fossil fuels often contain impurities and during burning these react with oxygen to form sulphur dioxide and nitrogen oxides.

These gases dissolve in the rain to form dilute sulphuric acid and nitric acid. As a result the rain which then falls to Earth is acidic – it is known as **acid rain**. Not surprisingly, this acid rain has a damaging effect on the environment. If it falls onto trees, the acid rain can cause direct damage and may kill the leaves and, as it soaks into the soil, even the roots of the tree may be destroyed. In some parts of Europe and America, huge areas of woodland are dying as a result of acid rain (Figure 2).

↑ **Figure 1:** Not all of the pollution we release into the environment is as obvious as this – but it doesn't need to be visible to be deadly!

← **Figure 2:** The fir trees standing dead and bare have been killed by the action of acid rain.

Acid rain has an indirect effect on the environment as well as its very direct effect on plants such as trees. As acid rain falls into lakes, rivers and streams the water in them becomes acidic. If the concentration of acid gets too high, plants and animals can no longer survive and the lake or stream becomes barren, no longer able to support life.

Acid rain is a very difficult form of air pollution to pin down and control. It is formed by pollution from factories but also by cars and other vehicles, unless they have catalytic converters which remove the gases before they are released into the air. So the source of the gases is pretty widespread.

The worst effects of acid rain are often not felt by the country which produced the pollution in the first place. The sulphur and nitrogen oxides are carried high in the air by the prevailing winds, so often it is relatively 'clean' countries, which have stopped their own factories from producing these acidic gases, which get the pollution and the acid rain from their dirtier neighbours. Their own clean air goes on to benefit someone else!

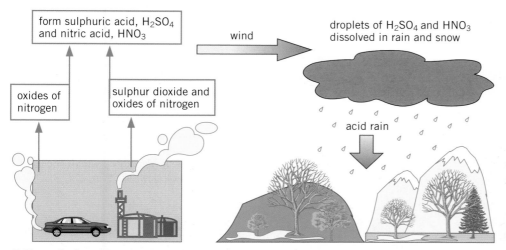

↗ **Figure 3:** Sometimes the level of air pollution is so high that it can be seen, like this brown nitrogen oxide haze in the American city of Los Angeles. More often, however, it is simply the effects that are seen, like the fall of acid rain on trees and lakes elsewhere.

? Questions

1 a How do fossil fuels cause air pollution?

   b Crude oil is also used to make many other things such as plastics and artificial fabrics. Can you think of a way in which oil can be responsible for other types of pollution?

2 Explain how pollution from cars and factories burning fossil fuels can pollute

   a the air

   b the water

   c the land.

3 To get rid of acid rain it is important that all the countries in an area control the production of sulphur and nitrogen oxides. If only one or two clean up their factories and cars it will not be effective. Explain why this is.

⊶ Key Ideas

- ⊙ Human activities may pollute the water, the air and the land.

- ⊙ When fossil fuels are burned carbon dioxide is released into the atmosphere.

- ⊙ Sulphur dioxide and nitrogen oxides may also be released into the air and may lead to the formation of acid rain.

What is the greenhouse effect?

The theory of the 'greenhouse effect' suggests that rising levels of carbon dioxide and methane in the atmosphere are acting like a greenhouse around the Earth, letting the heat from the sun in but stopping some of it from escaping. The levels of carbon dioxide and methane in the atmosphere are certainly rising (Figure 1).

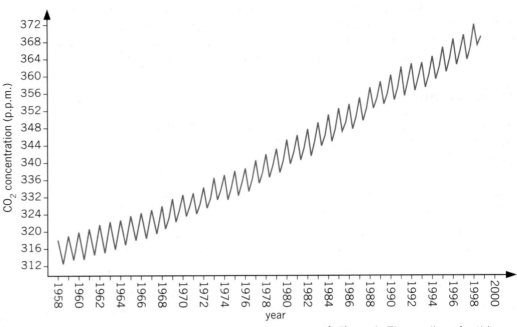

↑ **Figure 1:** The readings for this graph are taken every year on a mountain top in Hawaii. There is a clear upward trend which shows no sign of slowing down.

H An energy trapping system

Carbon dioxide and methane accumulate in the upper atmosphere. The Earth radiates back much of the heat energy it absorbs from the sun. The greenhouse gases absorb much of this energy as it is radiated away and re-radiate it back to the surface of the Earth. The result is that the Earth and its surrounding atmosphere are warmer than they would otherwise be.

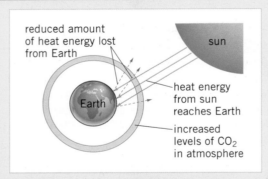

↑ **Figure 2:** Many scientists believe that this simple warming effect could, if it is not controlled, change life on this Earth as we know it.

Why is carbon dioxide rising?

Carbon dioxide is a by-product of the burning of fossil fuels. One of the most common ways in which fossil fuels are burnt world-wide is in the engines of vehicles such as cars. The number of cars around the world is steadily increasing, and although in the developed world new cars now have catalytic converters which greatly reduce the carbon dioxide produced, in much of the world engines are still as dirty as ever.

Cows, rice and methane

The other major greenhouse gas is methane, and levels of that are rising too. Methane has two major sources. One is rice growing – as rice grows in the swampy conditions known as paddy fields methane is released. As the population of the world has grown so has the farming of rice, the staple diet of many countries.

The other source of methane is cattle. Methane is produced during the digestive processes of cows and is released from both ends of the cow at regular intervals. As the demand for food like beefburgers has rocketed, so the numbers of cattle raised for meat have grown, and so the levels of atmospheric methane are rising. What makes this worse is that many of these cattle are raised on farms produced by deforestation, another factor adding to the problems of global warming.

Deforestation

Around the world large-scale deforestation is taking place, with vast areas of land being cleared of trees. These may be used for timber, or they may simply be cleared so that the land can be used for a few years for agriculture. In this case, the trees are felled and burnt in what is known as 'slash-and-burn' farming (Figure 3). The land is only fertile for a short time, after which more forest is destroyed. Once lost, the forest has gone forever.

Deforestation causes problems in two ways. Firstly, burning the trees and the action of the decomposing microorganisms which attack the dead vegetation lead to an increase in carbon dioxide levels.

Secondly, and most importantly, when trees and other plants are destroyed we lose one of the main ways in which carbon dioxide is removed from the atmosphere, because plants use carbon dioxide in photosynthesis. They take it from the air and it is locked up in plant material like wood for years. They and other plants are a carbon dioxide 'sink', that is, they take it out of the air. The oceans are also a carbon dioxide sink because it dissolves in the water.

For most of the Earth's history the carbon dioxide released by living things into the atmosphere has probably been counterbalanced by the oceans and plants taking it out, so that the level in the air stays about the same from year to year. But now the amount of carbon dioxide produced is increasing steadily as the result of human activities. This rate of increase means that the natural sinks cannot cope, and so the levels of carbon dioxide are building up.

↑ **Figure 3:** Tropical rain forests are being destroyed at an alarming rate to supply the developed world with goods like mahogany toilet seats and cheap burgers.

Key Ideas

⊙ Levels of the greenhouse gases carbon dioxide and methane in the atmosphere are steadily rising.

⊙ The burning of fossil fuels, particularly in car engines, causes an increase in atmospheric carbon dioxide.

⊙ Increases in the numbers of cattle and rice fields have increased the amount of methane released into the atmosphere.

⊙ Large-scale deforestation has increased the release of carbon dioxide into the atmosphere and reduced the rate at which it is removed by photosynthesis.

? Questions

1 Why are the numbers of **i** rice fields and **ii** cattle in the world increasing?

2 Give three reasons why deforestation increases the amount of greenhouse gases in the atmosphere.

3 In Figure 1 we can clearly see annual fluctuations in the levels of carbon dioxide recorded each year. These fluctuations are thought to be due to seasonal changes in the way plants are growing and photosynthesising through the year.

  a Explain how changes in plant growth and rate of photosynthesis might affect carbon dioxide levels throughout the year.

  b Explain how this might be used as evidence for the importance of preventing the loss of plant life by deforestation.

4 **a** Use the data in Figure 1 to produce a bar chart to show the maximum recorded level of carbon dioxide in the atmosphere every tenth year from 1970 to the year 2000.

  b Explain the trend which you can see on this graph.

Headlines like that in Figure 1 have become increasingly common over the last few years. But how true is it that a greenhouse effect exists and is causing all this?

Flooding due to global warming

The effect of greenhouse gases in the Earth's atmosphere is to raise the temperature of the Earth's surface by a few degrees. At the moment the lower atmosphere of the Earth is warming at a rate of 0. 06 °C per decade. There is increasing evidence to show that over the last 5 centuries the average temperature of the Earth has risen about by 1 degree Celsius. This might seem trivial, but in fact it is sufficient to cause quite large changes in the climate of the Earth (Figure 2).

Many scientists think that an increase in severe and unpredictable weather will be one of the changes we see due to global warming. Weather is very complex, but the increased energy in the warmer air causes increased convection currents on a massive scale, as well as changing the direction of air currents circulating over vast areas of the globe. The movements of great currents of warm and cold water in the oceans will also be affected by global warming, and these too have a major impact on world climate systems. Some people have suggested that the very high winds and extensive flooding seen in the UK and other countries around the world at the beginning of the 21st century were early examples of the effects of global warming.

Also, as the Earth warms up the ice caps at the North and South poles will melt. There is evidence that this is already happening. As a result, sea levels around the world will rise. This means that the low-lying shores of all countries all over the world will be more prone to flooding and parts of countries, even whole countries – will disappear beneath the seas (Figure 3).

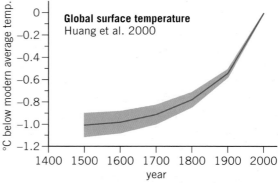

↑ **Figure 2:** Data such as this points clearly to an increase in world temperature over the years, with the major increase over the last century.

Are we sure?

The build up of greenhouse gases cannot be denied, because there is hard evidence for it. However, there is still debate among scientists about whether these really cause the problems which are blamed on the 'greenhouse effect'.

Although some extreme weather patterns have been recorded in recent years, it is possible to go back before fossil fuels were used so heavily and find other equally violent periods of weather in recorded history.

The temperature of the Earth has also fluctuated greatly over millions of years, with both ice ages and times when almost the entire Earth was covered in tropical vegetation before humans ever evolved. So some scientists argue that what we are seeing is the result of natural changes rather than a direct result of human activities.

↑ **Figure 3:** Major floods like these in America are becoming increasingly common.

What can be done?

The majority of scientists now believe that global warming is at least partly linked to human activities such as fossil fuel burning and deforestation. If they are right, what can be done to stop it getting worse?

There are a number of possibilities which would at the very least prevent the problem from getting worse, but it is not always easy to put good ideas into practice. For example:

Cutting carbon dioxide emissions

There are now efforts being made to do this. The problem is that the whole world has to agree because the Earth only has one atmosphere and this is affected by things which happen everywhere in the world. There are enormous problems with this.

The wealthy developed nations who are responsible for most carbon dioxide emissions would have to persuade their citizens to cut back a lot on using their cars and electricity and fear that it would affect their jobs and industry. The developing nations point out that expanding their industries is their chance of becoming less poor and improving the life and health of their people. Why should they have to sacrifice this to ease a problem caused by richer nations?

Preventing deforestation and refusing to buy products produced from the destruction of rain forests by slash and burn

This is very difficult for a number of reasons. Firstly, people always want to buy things as cheaply as possible, so if goods and food which come from areas of destroyed rain forest are cheap, they will find a market. Secondly, the people who do it are often desperately trying to earn a living to support their families and improve their countries. Banning the use of their rain forest resources condemns them to an existence without proper schools, hospitals and infrastructure. There are a number of efforts to monitor and support a more responsible use of the forests but they are difficult to enforce, and there are always people ready to make money fast and illegally.

↑ **Figure 4:** For people who are desperate to provide food, schooling and healthcare for their children, the wider issues of global warming must seem of very little importance.

? Questions

1 a What is the evidence which supports the idea that the greenhouse effect causes global warming?

  b What are the arguments against it?

2 a Use Figure 2 to produce a bar chart to show the increase in global temperature every century from 1500. Take the temperature in 1500 to be 14 °C.

  b Calculate what percentage of the total measured increase took place in each 100-year period.

3 a Why does deforestation take place?

  b How might it be prevented?

  c What are the ethical issues on both sides when we consider preventing deforestation?

4 Why is it so difficult to get everyone to agree on cutting carbon emissions across the world?

5 Plan a presentation to persuade parents, staff and other pupils to change some of their lifestyles to help slow down global warming. You need to convince them that it's worth doing!

⊙—ᴥ Key Ideas

⊙ Greenhouse gases can cause the temperature of the Earth to rise, and this in turn can cause a change in the climate and a rise in sea levels.

Farmers in the developed world produce enormous quantities of food and have increased the yields of their land to keep up with the increasing demands to feed most of the population. They have used and managed the land for centuries, making possible the growth of crops and the raising of animals (Figure 1).

However, in producing lots of cheap, affordable food for everyone, farming has also damaged the environment. This is especially true in the last 50 or 60 years, as farming has become much more technological.

← **Figure 1:** The method of harvesting may have changed over the years, but farmers are still responsible for growing the grain which provides us with our daily bread.

The use of pesticides and herbicides

One of the biggest problems for all farmers is the weeds which compete with crop plants for light, water and mineral resources. On top of that, animal and fungal pests may attack the crop and feed on it. Farmers have increasingly used chemical weapons to help them prevent this destruction of their crops. Weedkillers (or herbicides) kill weeds but leave the crop plant unharmed. Pesticides are designed to kill the insects which might attack and destroy the crop.

The only problem with both of these types of chemicals is that they are poisons, and when they are sprayed onto crops they also get into the soil. From there they are washed out into rivers and streams, where the chemicals can affect other animals and plants which are perfectly harmless to the farmer.

Another problem is that some of the chemicals which are used as herbicides or pesticides become part of food chains. This can lead to dangerous levels of poisons building up in the top predators (Figure 2).

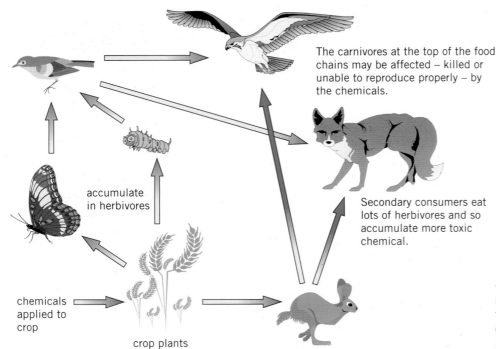

The carnivores at the top of the food chains may be affected – killed or unable to reproduce properly – by the chemicals.

accumulate in herbivores

Secondary consumers eat lots of herbivores and so accumulate more toxic chemical.

chemicals applied to crop

crop plants

← **Figure 2:** The feeding relationships between the different organisms in a food web like this one can lead to dangerous levels of toxins building up in the top predators.

Fertiliser problems

Growing crop plants year after year on the same soil means that the mineral nutrients are used up. To make sure the soil remains fertile, farmers add fertiliser. For many years this was manure – the urine and droppings of farm animals mixed with the straw they stood on.

However, as farming became more intensive many farmers moved to new, cheap chemical fertilisers. But the minerals in these were easily washed from the soil into local waterways, where they caused problems which could eventually lead to the death of all animal life in the water (Figure 3).

← **Figure 3:** A pond like this may look green and healthy, but in fact all the animal life it once supported is dead as a result of all the excess fertiliser which has been washed into the water.

H Eutrophication

When farmers add fertilisers to the soil to replace the nutrients removed by the crops, the excess may be washed into rivers and lakes. The nitrates and minerals lead to the rapid growth of water plants. Some of these die naturally, some die due to the intense competition for light with all the other plants. In turn there is a big increase in the numbers of decomposing microorganisms feeding on these dead plants.

The process of decomposition uses up a lot of oxygen, so the increase in microorganisms results in the levels of oxygen in the water going down. This means that there isn't enough oxygen in the water to support some of the fish and other animals living in it. They die and are decomposed by yet more microbes, using up more of the oxygen for their respiration. The end result is that the oxygen levels in the water become so low that all the fish and other aquatic animals die of suffocation due to lack of oxygen, and the stream becomes effectively dead as far as animals are concerned.

This is known as **eutrophication**. The same process also happens if untreated sewage is released into waterways. Not only do microorganisms feed on the sewage, using up the oxygen in the water, but the sewage also provides nitrates for the water plants, causing a surge in their growth followed by death. So eutrophication results from anything which greatly increases the use of oxygen in the water by microorganisms.

? Questions

1 Farming can be responsible for the pollution of both the land and the water. Explain how this pollution comes about.

2 Produce two separate posters, one showing the positive benefits of farming; one showing farming as damaging the environment, and explain how neither is a full representation of the facts.

H 3 a Produce a flow diagram to show the process of eutrophication.

b Suggest ways in which eutrophication might be prevented.

Key Ideas

- ⊙ Pesticides and herbicides can pollute the land and the waterways and cause problems as they are passed along food chains.

- ⊙ Fertilisers can be washed from the land into waterways and cause the death of animal life in the water.

H ⊙ Chemical waste in waterways can lead to eutrophication.

As our world gets more and more crowded, we are becoming increasingly aware of the need for **sustainable development** which combines human progress and environmental stability.

Sustainable agriculture

Sustainable agriculture means looking after the land. Instead of simply removing crops and applying artificial fertilisers, farmers in the developed world are increasingly ploughing the remains of the crop plants into the soil, and are using animal waste as well as or instead of chemical fertilisers. They are taking measures to prevent soil being lost by erosion, like replanting the hedgerows they grubbed out a few years ago and avoiding deforestation. This type of farming restores the fertility of the soil and means that growing crops will be possible for years to come.

Restoring the land

In the past, when land was taken for industrial use such as quarrying, it was lost as a habitat for animals and plants. Increasingly, companies are using the land to provide a resource which is needed, such as gravel, but once the quarry is worked out they often restore it as a habitat. These reclaimed sites are often very beautiful and when they are relatively secluded can become havens for rare birds, mammals, insects and plants (Figure 1).

Figure 1: A working gravel quarry like this provides us with a resource which we need. But once the active life of the quarry is over, it can be reclaimed as a valuable habitat for all kinds of living organisms.

Sustainable building

There is now a move in the UK towards building houses and businesses on land which has already been spoiled by development rather than using land which is still fairly wild. This called 'brown field' rather than 'green field' development. It has a great deal of potential in urban areas. Similarly, in many industrial areas, old worked out quarries are often filled in and housing built on top.

Keeping the trees

Another important form of sustainable development is in the farming of trees. As a society we use an enormous amount of tree products, both in the form of wood and paper. Centuries ago much of Britain was covered in woodland, but now we have fewer trees than almost all of our European neighbours. However, over the last 80 years or so the Forestry Commission has developed commercial woodlands which are planted and harvested in carefully controlled cycles. Felling can only take place as long as replanting replaces the felled trees. Originally much of the planting was of conifers, which grow fast and straight, but produce dark forests where there is relatively little variety of life. In recent years the planting has included many more broad-leaved trees and open glades, so that farmed woodlands not only provide a sustainable resource but also a rich environment for a wide variety of species (Figure 2).

↑ **Figure 2:** Sustainable woodland development not only provides a constant supply of timber and a rich habitat, it also gives people a place to enjoy at their leisure.

Managing the oceans

People have fished for food throughout human history. However, in the last 50 years or so commercial fishing fleets have grown up capable of taking huge quantities of fish on a regular basis. The result of this type of uncontrolled over-fishing is that the stocks of edible fish in some areas – like the North sea – are on the point of collapse. People have been warning about the problems of taking more fish than can be replaced for many years, but it is only now that the fish could actually disappear altogether that serious restrictions on fishing are to be put in place. Ways of protecting the fish populations include controlling the size of the holes in the nets, so only the biggest fish are caught, banning fishing altogether during the breeding season of the fish and imposing very strict quotas on fishermen – in other words, putting a strictly enforced limit on the amount of fish they are allowed to catch. Only with protection like this in place will fish like cod survive in many areas of the world.

? Questions

1 a List the main ways in which humans reduce the amount of land available for other animals and plants.

   b Explain why each of these land uses is necessary.

   c Suggest ways in which two of these different types of land use might be reduced.

2 Some farmers farm their land intensively, which means growing their crops or raising their animals using as little space as possible. This usually involves using lots of artificial fertiliser and feedstuffs. Others farm extensively, taking up much more land but using fewer chemicals. Discuss the advantages and disadvantages of each from the point of view of the farmer and of the environment.

3 a Explain how the fishing industry has reached a point of crisis.

   b How might fish stocks be protected?

   c Why do you think such measures were not enforced a long time ago?

🔑 Key Ideas

⊙ Sustainable development means working out ways of harvesting resources whilst maintaining the conditions needed for future crops as well.

1 The table shows the world population from the year 1 AD to the year 2000.

Date (AD)	World population (billions)
1	0.25
1750	0.5
1927	2.0
1974	4.0
1987	5.0
2000	6.0

  a Plot a graph to show the increase in the human population from the beginning of the 20th century. (4 marks)

  b Give **two** factors which have contributed to the enormous growth of the human population in the last century compared with the growth since 1 AD. (2 marks)

(Total 6 marks)

2 Lichens are simple plants. The table shows how many different types of lichen were recorded at set distances from a city centre.

Distance from city centre (km)	Number of types of lichen found in a given area
0	4
2	7
3	10
5	20
6	25
7	40

  a Draw a graph of these results. (3 marks)

  b Use your graph to estimate the number of types of lichen at a distance of 4 km from the city centre. (1 mark)

  c Use information from your graph to describe how the number of types of lichen is linked to the distance from the city centre. (1 mark)

  d Lichens are killed by air pollution. Name **two** gases that pollute the atmosphere of a city. (2 marks)

(Total 7 marks)

3 The graph shows the levels of carbon dioxide in the atmosphere over the last 30–40 years.

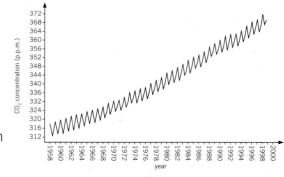

  a What do these readings, taken on the top of a mountain in Hawaii, tell us about the level of carbon dioxide in the atmosphere? (1 mark)

  b Why do you think the readings are taken from a mountain top in Hawaii rather than from a tall building in London? (2 marks)

  c Give **two** reasons why the carbon dioxide levels are changing in this way. (2 marks)

  d Methane levels in the atmosphere are known to be rising – why is this? (2 marks)

  e What is the effect on the Earth of these changes in carbon dioxide and methane levels? (1 mark)

(Total 8 marks)

H **4** Around the world, large-scale deforestation is taking place, and this is thought to be having a major effect on the balance of carbon dioxide in the atmosphere.

  a What is **deforestation**? (1 mark)

  b Explain how deforestation affects the balance of carbon dioxide in the atmosphere. (2 marks)

c The graph in question 3 shows a yearly fluctuation in carbon dioxide levels. The lowest levels are during summer months, the highest levels in the winter. How could you use this evidence to help explain the importance of plants in controlling the levels of atmospheric carbon dioxide? *(3 marks)*

d Explain, using clear English, how increased levels of carbon dioxide and methane in the atmosphere might bring about what is known as the 'greenhouse effect'. *(3 marks)*

(Total 9 marks)

5 The graph shows the increase in car ownership in a number of different countries.

a What has been the increase in car ownership per 1000 people in the following countries since 1955?
 i UK
 ii Germany
 iii USA. *(3 marks)*

b What is the overall trend for all countries? *(1 mark)*

c How does this effect the problem of global warming due to a build up of greenhouse gases? *(2 marks)*

d Give **two** possible results of global warming. *(2 marks)*

e Suggest **two** ways in which levels of greenhouse gases might be reduced. *(2 marks)*

(Total 10 marks)

6 a Farmers in the developed world use many chemicals on their crops to help them produce as much food as possible. These include fertilisers, pesticides and herbicides. What is
 i a fertiliser
 ii a pesticide
 iii a herbicide? *(3 marks)*

b Peregrine falcons like the one shown here used to be a relatively common sight in Britain. They feed on pigeons and other smaller birds as well as rabbits, mice and other small mammals which often feed on farm crops. But in the 1950s and '60s their numbers fell dramatically as the use of pesticides by farmers increased.

 i Draw a food web with a peregrine falcon as the top predator. *(4 marks)*
 ii Use the web you have drawn to explain how an increase in the use of pesticides by farmers led to the death of so many peregrine falcons. *(3 marks)*

(Total 10 marks)
AQA specimen question

7 a Around the world there is an increasing awareness of the need for sustainable development. What is meant by the term '**sustainable development**'? *(2 marks)*

b In the UK fishing is an industry in crisis. The stocks of fish are running so low that drastic measures have been introduced to help conserve the fish stocks and make sure that there is a sustainable population of fish for the future. Give three of the ways in which fish stocks are being protected. *(3 marks)*

c Give another example of sustainable development in the UK. *(1 mark)*

(Total 6 marks)

Skeletons are very important to animals for support and movement. In soft-bodied animals like worms the skeleton usually depends on fluid trapped within the body of the animal (a **hydrostatic skeleton**) (Figure 1). This is sometimes combined with a protective shell. Arthropods (which include insects and crustaceans) have developed a rigid external skeleton. In vertebrates the skeleton is also a strong, rigid structure but it is found inside the body.

The vertebrate skeleton

The vertebrate skeleton is an internal structure made of bone and cartilage which provides a framework in the body for support. Without a rigid internal skeleton there would be a limit on the size of land animals. Whilst there are reports of invertebrates like the giant squid reaching 10 metres long and more, that is only possible because they live in water, which supports them. Invertebrates which live on land are much more limited in size, even when they develop a rigid external skeleton like the arthropods have done. The vast majority of land invertebrates are very small indeed, and those which do reach large sizes are unable to lift their bodies far from the ground (Figure 2).

The support provided by a bony skeleton makes a great variety of sizes and shapes possible for animals, and enables them to exploit a wide range of ecological niches on the land. Without it we would all resemble slugs!

↑ **Figure 1:** The fluid-based skeleton of an animal like an octopus allows it to move about and to use its tentacles both for delicate tasks and when it needs great strength.

← **Figure 2:** Even the biggest land invertebrates, like this giant Brazilian millipede, cannot match the size and mobility of many land vertebrates, because their fluid-based skeleton simply does not offer enough support.

Because it is strong and rigid the skeleton also protects delicate internal organs from damage. The bones of the skull protect the brain; the vertebrae (backbones) protect the spinal cord; the ribs protect the heart and lungs; and the pelvis protects some of the digestive organs, and the reproductive organs in the female.

The bony internal skeleton is very important in movement too. The bones act as levers and move both with gravity and against gravity. The skeleton is not a solid framework – it is made up of lots of bones which are attached at the **joints**, and these allow movement to take place. These joints are of vital importance in a skeleton. If the bony structure was all in one piece our bodies would be supported and internal organs would be protected, but movement would be completely impossible, and so would life as we know it. Fortunately the body contains a large number of joints of different types and so we (and all other vertebrates) can move freely.

Living bone

When we look at skeletons we always see a dead, white structure. However, living bone is very different. It has a rich blood supply and is constantly being broken down and built up where it is needed. Your skeleton is a surprisingly fluid structure, constantly changing even as you sit reading this book! Yet bones are very strong and rigid, which allows them to carry out their function of supporting the weight of your body. The bones also provide a rigid framework for muscle attachment, which makes it possible to move different parts of the skeleton independently.

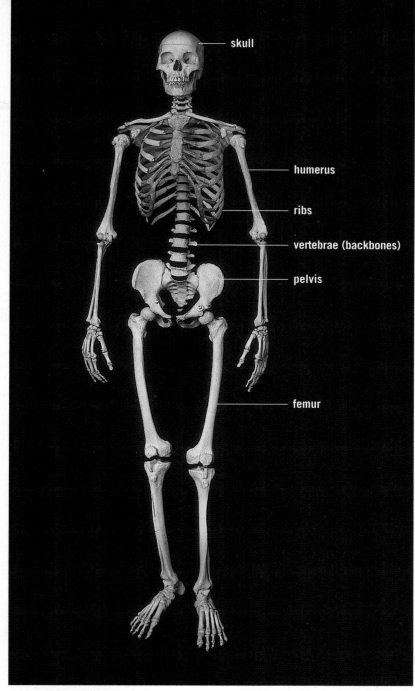

↑ **Figure 3:** The human skeleton.

Labels: skull, humerus, ribs, vertebrae (backbones), pelvis, femur

? Questions

1 List as many advantages as you can of having a bony, internal vertebrate skeleton.

2 Look at Figure 3. Make a table to show which bones are involved in movement and the type of movement it is (e.g. the ribs – breathing movements), which bones have a protective function and which bones are important in support. Some bones may appear in more than one column of your table.

3 Why are joints such an important part of the skeleton?

⊙╍ Key Ideas

- ⊙ Vertebrates have an internal skeleton which provides the framework for support and movement.

- ⊙ Bones are rigid to provide support for the body and for muscle attachment.

- ⊙ The skeleton provides protection for internal organs.

- ⊙ Movement of the skeleton takes place at the joints.

All about joints

The structure of a joint

At a joint, two bones meet and in most cases they move against each other. There are a number of very different types of joints. In some, like those in our skull and pelvis, the bones are fused together and allow little or no movement. Some, like the joints in our fingers, knees and elbows, are known as hinge joints because they work like a hinge – they allow an opening and closing movement. Yet other joints, like our shoulders and hips, allow very free movement. There is a 'ball' of bone on the end of one bone in the joint, and a smooth socket on the other bone in the joint into which it fits. This gives lots of free rotational movement and these joints are known as ball and socket joints (Figure 2).

To keep the bones in position as the joints move they are held together by strong fibres called **ligaments**. This makes sure that the bones move against each other smoothly in the right alignment and do not slip apart, even when we are doing vigorous exercise.

When materials rub against each other they tend to wear each other away. If the bones in a joint rubbed against each other the bone would quickly be worn away. However, this doesn't happen, because the ends of the bones in a joint are covered with a layer of a tissue called **cartilage**. Cartilage is smooth and rubbery. It cushions the joint and makes sure that the bone ends do not come into contact. The cartilage is continually replaced by new growth as it wears down.

Very active joints, like the hip, knee, shoulder and elbow, are used almost constantly, and the movements made by the joint are very big. Cartilage cover alone is not sufficient to keep these joints moving smoothly. However, a special membrane in these joints secretes an oily fluid called **synovial fluid**. This bathes the joint, making the surface of the cartilage slippery and making sure that the joint moves easily (Figure 3). Synovial fluid is a lubricant, and it works in a similar way to the oil which bathes the moving parts of a car, preventing friction and sticking, and keeping the whole system working smoothly. Unlike a car, we don't need regular oil changes because used synovial fluid is removed by the body and new fluid is always being made.

↑ **Figure 1:** When we see a top gymnast performing like this it brings home to us exactly how much movement our bodies are capable of, and how flexible our joints can be.

↙ **Figure 2:** The different types of joints in the skeleton allow for very different degrees of movement.

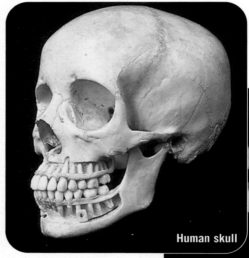

Human skull

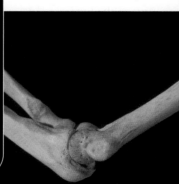

Elbow joint

Ball and socket joint of pelvic girdle

Locomotion

When things go wrong

Most of the time we never give our joints a second thought, because when they are working properly they are pain-free and allow us to move exactly as we want to. However, if things go wrong with our joints it is a very different story. In young people, the most common problems with the joints come about as a result of exercising too hard in the wrong way, or as the result of an accident on the sports field or on the road. Particular care needs to be taken during exercise to avoid two of the most common joint injuries – **sprains** and **dislocations**. If a joint is wrenched suddenly in a direction it would not usually move in, it may be sprained. The ligaments which hold the bones together and the other tissues in the joint are torn by the sudden wrench. They swell up and the whole joint becomes extremely painful. There is little that can be done to help except take painkillers, so it doesn't hurt so much, and anti-inflammatory drugs to reduce the swelling. Depending on how severe the strain is, the joint may need resting. This may be simply a case of strapping it up for a few days so the wrench cannot be repeated while the joint is weak, or in severe cases when the ligaments are actually torn it may involve encasing the joint in plaster to hold the bones still until the ligaments heal.

Dislocations occur when the bone is actually forced out of its position in a joint. Some of the most common dislocations are fingers, shoulders and knees (Figure 4). A dislocated joint is excruciatingly painful – but the pain does ease dramatically as soon as the bone is returned to it's proper place. Sometimes this can be done immediately, but at times it can only be done under a general anaesthetic. Depending on the severity of the dislocation and its position, you may be able to use the joint as normal almost immediately or it may need a prolonged period of rest.

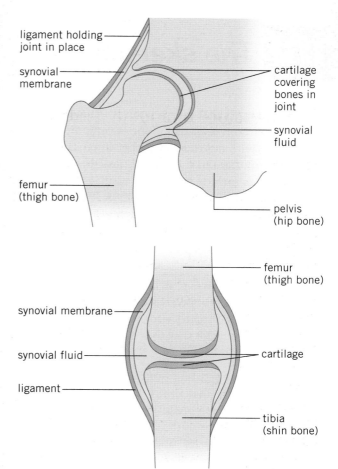

↑ **Figure 3:** A synovial joint – perfectly adapted to allow smooth, free movement where we really need it.

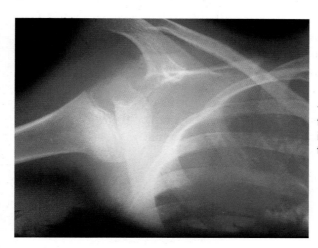

← **Figure 4:** A dislocated shoulder like the one in this X-ray is a very painful injury and the joint can take a long time to regain its strength and flexibility.

Questions

1 Make a table to summarise the main types of joints, examples of where they are found and the type of movement which takes place.

2 Arthritis is a disease which affects the joints. Often associated with old age, it can also affect even very young children. It is associated with very painful joints which may be swollen, and with a reduction in the mobility of the joint. In osteoarthritis the cartilage in the joints is worn away, while in rheumatoid arthritis bony growths develop within the joint capsule between the two surfaces of the bones. Explain why these two conditions cause problems in relation to the normal way in which the joint works.

Everyone knows that the skeleton is made up of bone, but there is much more to it than that. Bone is certainly an important part of the skeletal system, but there are other important tissues associated with it that are important to the smooth functioning of the system as a whole. These tissues include ligaments, cartilage and tendons. All of the skeletal tissues have distinctive physical properties which adapt them for their functions within the body.

The bone itself

Living bone is an active, dynamic tissue. It is a composite material, made up of living bone cells embedded in a matrix or mesh of special protein fibres (collagen) which are hardened by calcium phosphate deposited within the structure. These hard calcium salts make up 70% of the bone (Figure 1).

Bone is extremely strong – it resists compression (squashing), bending and stretching, so that almost regardless of what we do our skeleton remains intact. This strength is the result of the cells and proteins within the structure of the bone. The combination of the calcium salts which make bone hard, and the proteins and living cells which prevent it from being brittle and breaking easily, mean that bone tissue is perfectly adapted to the jobs it has to carry out. Bone needs to be hard and strong to support the weight of our body as we move around, but it also needs to be as light as possible. If bones were solid structures they would be so heavy that they would be impossible to move around. However, our bones are not solid – they are hollow tubes which are themselves made up of two different types of bone. Compact bone is heavy, dense and very strong. It is found in areas like the shafts of the long bones (for example in the arms and legs). Much of the rest of the skeleton contains large amounts of spongy bone which has a much lighter, open structure.

Inside the bones is bone marrow. The white bone marrow in the long bones is the site of white blood cell production, whereas the red bone marrow in short bones like the ribs is where red blood cells are produced (Figure 2).

Cartilage

Cartilage is another very strong tissue but it is flexible rather than rigid. Its structure is rather like bone without the calcium salts, with cartilage cells embedded in a collagen matrix (Figure 3). Much of the skeleton is first formed as cartilage, which is then hardened when

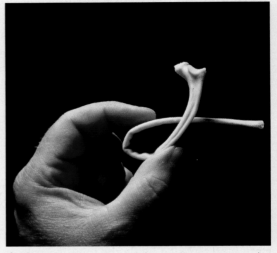

↑ **Figure 1:** When the calcium salts are removed from bone it becomes a relatively soft, floppy tissue – no good for supporting the weight of a human body!

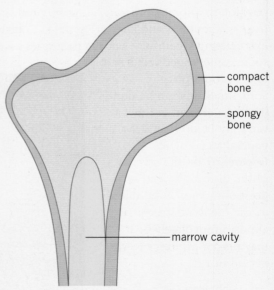

— compact bone

— spongy bone

— marrow cavity

↑ **Figure 2:** The arrangement of the different types of bony tissue within a bone like the femur is adapted to give an ideal combination of lightness and strength.

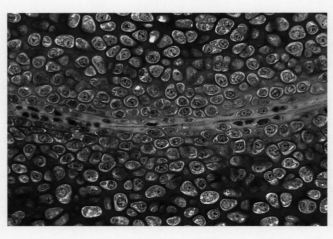

← **Figure 3:** Cartilage is important as a shock absorber and as the forerunner to many of our bones.

calcium salts are deposited in it. Because cartilage is not rigid it can be slightly compressed, and this makes it very important to the body as a shock absorber. Cartilage is found covering the bones in most joints, and pads of cartilage which act as shock absorbers are found between the vertebrae.

Ligaments and tendons

Ligaments attach bones to other bones in joints – they form the capsule of the joint which holds the whole arrangement of bones in place. Ligaments have a great deal of tensile strength – that means they can withstand a lot of stretching or pulling – and they have a certain amount of elasticity, so that as the bones move within a joint the ligament capsule stretches to allow that to happen without damage.

Tendons, on the other hand, attach muscles to bones. Like ligaments they have a great deal of tensile strength – they can withstand large pulling forces – but they have very little elasticity (they don't stretch). This is very important, because if tendons stretched, when muscles contracted they wouldn't move the bones, they would simply stretch the tendons.

Ideas and Evidence

Skeletal tissues are very strong, but if the forces applied to them are strong enough, e.g. when we jump, or fall, or are in an accident, they will tear or break. For centuries, broken bones could only be diagnosed by the appearance of the limb, or the sight of the broken ends of bones sticking out through the surface of the skin in very severe breaks. Then, in 1895, while he was investigating something else entirely, Wilhelm Roentgen discovered X-rays. This invisible radiation could pass through paper and the soft tissues of the body but was absorbed by dense materials such as bone. Within a very short time doctors realised the enormous potential of X-rays for diagnosing problems of the skeleton which had previously been hidden – and the diagnostic use of X-rays continues today (Figure 4).

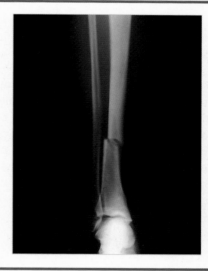

← **Figure 4:** It is easy to spot the fracture in this leg bone using X-rays, although from the outside the leg would have looked relatively normal.

Questions

1 Make a table to compare and contrast the properties and the functions of the four main skeletal tissues – bone, cartilage, ligaments and tendons.

2 Bone is particularly good at withstanding compression forces. Why is this so important to its role in the body?

3 The long bones of the body like the femur in the leg are very strong.

   a Describe how the bones are made both as strong and as light as possible.

   b In children and young people there is an area of cartilage at the top and bottom of the long bones. By adulthood those areas of cartilage have gone. What might be the function of these cartilage areas in the bone?

Key Ideas

⊙ Skeletal tissues have properties which mean they are well adapted to perform their functions.

⊙ Bone is hardened by calcium salts and resists compression, bending and stretching.

⊙ Cartilage is strong but not rigid, so it can be compressed and absorb shock.

⊙ Ligaments have tensile strength and some elasticity, so joints can bend without the bones dislocating.

⊙ Tendons have tensile strength but little elasticity.

Muscle tissue is closely associated with the skeleton and is vital for its roles of movement and support. Muscles are joined to bones by tendons, and they move the bones at a joint when they contract.

The structure of muscle

Muscle tissue is made up of protein fibres which are able to contract when supplied with energy from respiration (Figure 1). They contract in response to messages from the nervous system – they are **effector organs** which enable us to respond to the world around us. Muscle fibres usually occur in big blocks or groups known as muscles.

The contraction of muscles holds us upright against the pull of gravity and allows us to make the millions of tiny adjustments to our posture which keep us upright throughout the day. The contraction of muscle fibres is also responsible for the much larger movements our bodies make as we move around carrying out all the normal functions of life.

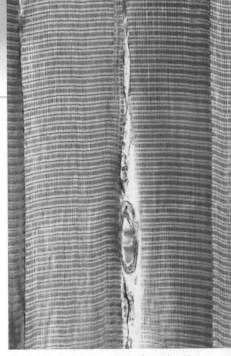

↑ **Figure 1:** All the work done by the muscles is based on these very special protein fibres.

How do muscles work?

Muscles are attached to bones in pairs. Muscle fibres are always either contracted or relaxed. When a muscle contracts, it shortens and pulls on the bones to which it is attached, moving one of them. When it relaxes, it is capable of being stretched out to its original length, but it cannot push the bone back into place. This can only be done by another muscle, contracting and pulling in the opposite direction to the first one. This is why muscles always come in pairs, known as **antagonistic pairs** because they work in the opposite direction to each other (Figure 2).

Muscles and exercise

Even when we are resting, our muscles use up a certain amount of oxygen and glucose because some of our muscle fibres are constantly contracting to keep us in position and to carry out processes associated with breathing and circulation, etc. However, when we begin to exercise, the increased muscle activity means that glucose and oxygen need to be supplied at a much faster rate to fulfil the needs of the contracting muscle fibres. As they contract and use up energy, the muscle fibres also produce increased amounts of carbon dioxide and heat, and these need to be removed so the muscles can continue to work effectively. This means that when muscular activity increases, both the breathing rate and the heart rate also need to increase (Figure 3). The increase in breathing means that more oxygen is brought into the body to be carried in the blood to the exercising muscles, and also more carbon dioxide can be removed from the blood in the lungs

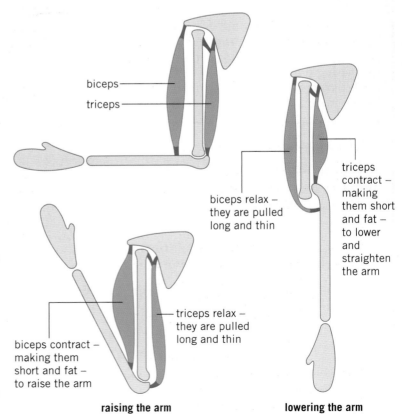

biceps
triceps

triceps contract – making them short and fat – to lower and straighten the arm

biceps relax – they are pulled long and thin

triceps relax – they are pulled long and thin

biceps contract – making them short and fat – to raise the arm

raising the arm

lowering the arm

↑ **Figure 2:** The biceps and the triceps form the antagonistic pair of muscles which we use to raise and lower our arms.

and exhaled. Similarly, the increased beating of the heart ensures that plenty of blood arrives in the exercising muscles, carrying oxygen and glucose and removing carbon dioxide and heat. The heat is used to warm the whole body and excess heat is lost by sweating.

The benefits of exercise

Regular exercise has been shown to have a number of benefits for health and fitness. It keeps the muscles toned, so that the fibres are constantly slightly tensed and ready to contract. This speeds up your reaction time and uses up energy, helping to maintain a healthy body weight. When the muscles are used regularly, the strength of the muscles increases as more muscle fibres develop, and also the muscles are much less likely to feel stiff and sore after exercise. The blood supply to the muscles increases, bringing glucose and oxygen to the tissues more efficiently, removing carbon dioxide and avoiding oxygen debt (see page 31). The joints tend to work more smoothly if regular exercise is taken, because the blood flow is increased so the body maintains and repairs the cartilage in the joints and produces plenty of synovial fluid.

The benefits of regular exercise are not confined to the musculo-skeletal system – the heart and lungs benefit too. Both the heart and the lungs become larger, and they both develop a bigger and very efficient blood supply which allows them to function as effectively as possible at all times, whether exercising or not.

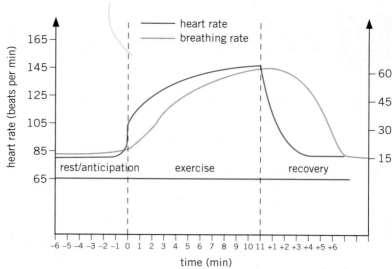

↑ **Figure 3:** During exercise, the heart and breathing rate increase to supply the muscles with what they need and remove the extra waste produced.

? Questions

1 The lower leg is raised and lowered by a pair of muscles attached to the top of the femur and the top of the tibia (Figure 4).

Redraw the diagram to show how these muscles work to

a straighten and

b bend the leg at the knee joint.

2 a Using Figure 3, describe the effect of exercise on the heart rate and the breathing rate and explain why these changes happen.

b The graph uses information from a fit person and the heart and breathing rates begin to increase just before exercise. Why do you think this happens? What advantage does it give?

3 Regular exercise benefits many of the body systems. Draw a table listing four body systems and, for each system, describe and explain the changes produced by regular exercise.

→ **Figure 4:**

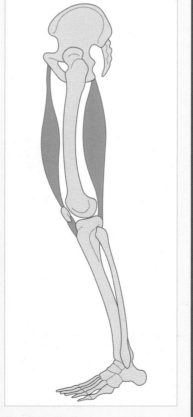

0ᴍ Key Ideas

⊙ Muscles contain fibres which contract to move bones at a joint when supplied with energy from respiration.

⊙ Increased muscle activity requires glucose and oxygen to be supplied at a faster rate, and the rate of removal of carbon dioxide and heat from muscle tissues to be increased.

⊙ Regular exercise benefits the muscles, joints, heart and lungs.

Fish are superbly adapted to life in water, and have evolved a very different way of moving to the way animals move on land (Figure 1).

The world of water

Land animals move through air, which offers very little resistance to their movement but also very little support for their weight. Water, on the other hand, is much denser than air and it is also much more viscous (thicker). As fish live in water they can grow quite large with only relatively small skeletons, because much of the supporting role of the skeleton is taken over by the water. The main function of the skeleton becomes protection of the internal organs and the attachment of the muscles needed for movement. However, compared with air, water offers more resistance to movement, so to move at any speed fish must have a streamlined body shape to help reduce resistance as they move along.

↑ **Figure 1:** Fish move with speed and grace through their environment, whether it is the salt water of the seas and oceans or the fresh water of rivers, lakes and ponds.

Adaptations for moving in water

Fish are adapted for moving in water in a number of ways in addition to the streamlined shape mentioned above. In many fish, movement is brought about by lashing movements of the spine caused by the contraction of the zigzag arrangement of muscles along the vertebrae. This produces wave-like movements of the body. In some fish, like eels, these waves pass visibly along the whole body. In others, the wave is kept mainly to the rear part of the fish, and particularly the tail (Figure 2).

Most fish have a big tail fin (with a large surface area) that pushes backwards against the water as the fish flexes its spine. This moves the fish forward (Figure 3).

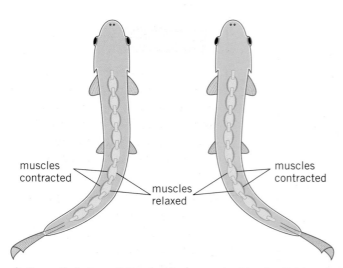

muscles
contracted

muscles
relaxed

muscles
contracted

↑ **Figure 2:** Antagonistic muscles on each side of a fish's spine contract alternately, bending the backbone from side to side.

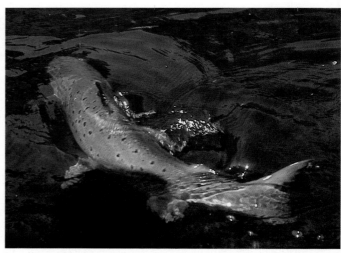

↑ **Figure 3:** Fish tails come in a variety of shapes and sizes but they all have the same function of providing forward thrust through the water.

Manoeuvring in water

If fish only had a tail fin they would struggle to swim in anything like a straight line – or even to stay the right way up! Most fish have a combination of other adaptations which not only help them to keep upright and balanced, they also make them extremely manoeuvrable in the water.

Many fish have a **swim bladder**. This is a gas-filled sac which provides buoyancy. By changing the amount of gas in the swim bladder the fish can keep its relative density the same as the water. This means it does not have to use energy trying to stop itself sinking but instead can use its energy for controlling its lateral position in the water and for moving forwards.

The other major adaptation that fish have to keep them stable in the water and to allow them to manoeuvre is the fins they have positioned strategically around their bodies (Figure 4). For example, the **median fins** found at the top and bottom of the fish increase the vertical surface area. This is important for helping to keep the fish upright – it is much less likely to simply roll over uncontrollably if there is a large surface area pushing against the water. The **paired fins** which stick out at the sides of the fish help to improve stability and also make it possible for controlled movements up, down and backwards to take place. Changing the angle of the fins will make the fish swim upwards or downwards, just as the flaps on the edge of an aeroplane wing change the angle of flight.

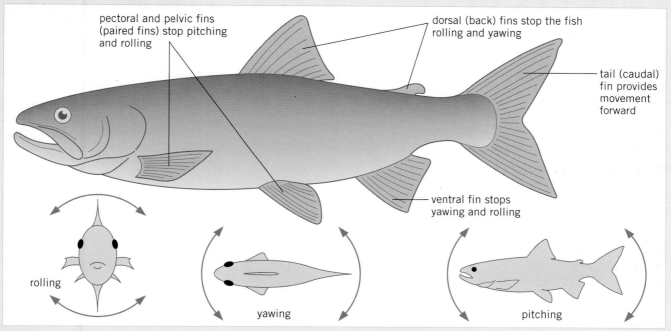

↑ **Figure 4:** Without these fins, fish would find stable movement in the water almost impossible.

? Questions

1. What are the main differences between air and water as a medium for movement?

2. Explain with the aid of diagrams how fish swim through the water.

3. How do the swimming movements of a fish like an eel differ from those of a goldfish?

H 4. Explain why, without special adaptations, fish might tend to

     a sink to the bottom

     b roll around uncontrollably.

5. Explain how the swim bladder and fins contribute to controlled and highly manoeuvrable swimming in fish.

0—m Key Ideas

⊙ Fish are adapted for movement in the water by having a zigzag arrangement of muscles which produce wavelike movements of the body, a tail fin with a large surface area and a streamlined body shape.

H ⊙ Swimming in fish is assisted by a swim bladder to provide buoyancy, and fins which provide stability and allow the fish to change direction.

Air offers virtually no support and no purchase for the limbs, yet birds of many different shapes and sizes manage to move through it with apparent ease. How do they do it?

The wonders of wings

The single biggest adaptation for flight which is seen in all birds is a pair of wings. Wings provide a very large surface area which pushes down on the air to lift the bird upwards. The large surface area of the wings is largely produced by the big flight feathers which stick out well beyond the edge of the limb itself. The structure of the feathers means that they can provide this big surface area while being very strong and, most importantly, very light (Figure 1).

As a bird flaps its wings downwards, the large surface area results in enough uplift for the bird to fly. The only problem is that if it brings the wings straight up again it will be pushed downwards instead of up, and end up going nowhere!

The problem is solved because birds tilt their wings on the upstroke so the wings go up at an angle, reducing the downwards force which is created (Figure 2). Try modelling the down and up strokes holding a flat piece of paper or card.

↑ **Figure 1:** The wing of a bird, with the feathers providing a large surface area, is vital for successful flight. The Andean condor seen here has the largest wingspan (around 3.2 m) of any bird, but smaller wings are just as effective for flying.

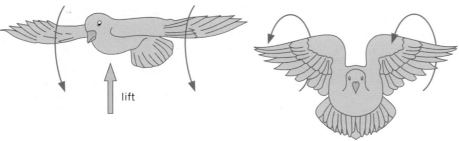

downstroke –
the whole flat surface of the wing pushes down through the air with the front edge leading to give maximum lift

upstroke –
the wing is bent and twisted so that the front edge of the wing moves through the air first, then the rest of the wing at an angle to minimize the downwards effect

← **Figure 2:** By changing the angle of their wings, birds make the most of the uplift they create and minimise the downwards forces.

Other adaptations for flight

A streamlined body shape is very important for a bird in flight because it reduces the air resistance, which in turn reduces the energy needed for flight.

Another very important factor for successful flight is lightness – the heavier a bird is, the less successful it will be at flying. Bird bones have a very open, honeycomb structure which means they retain considerable strength yet have a much reduced mass compared to the bones of land-dwelling mammals of the same size (Figure 3).

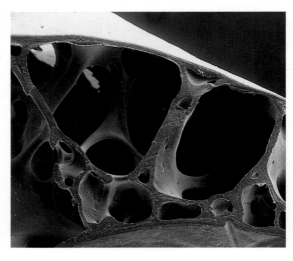

← **Figure 3:** The honeycomb structure of bird bones means that a bird skeleton is very light, making it relatively easy to lift off the ground.

More about flight

The light bones are not the only adaptation of the bird skeleton for flight. The very large breast bone (sternum), and the keel which has developed on it, together give a very large surface area and a rigid framework for the attachment of the great flight muscles across the chest (Figure 4). We can see this very clearly when we carve a chicken to eat. The wing itself is an adaptation of the typical five-fingered (pentadactyl) limb so common among the vertebrates. The structure is comparable to the skeleton of the human arm (see page 153), but with a reduced number of digits and wrist bones. This explains the way the wing can be rotated during flight – it simply involves a movement at the 'shoulder'.

The wings and feathers also display a number of specialised adaptations for flight. The cross-sectional shape of the wing is an **aerofoil**. As air passes over it, it has to travel faster over the longer top surface of the wing than over the shorter bottom surface. This results in a lower pressure above the wing than below it – the air particles are more spaced out – and this generates lift (Figure 5).

The feathers on the surface of the wing are very important in flight. The flight feathers have interlocking barbs in their structure which help to maintain a flat, smooth surface during flight. The main shaft of the feathers is hollow, which makes them as light as possible. This hollow shaft was used in the days

when people wrote using quills. Not all feathers are the same. The big primary flight feathers are easily recognised, but the wings also have smaller, secondary feathers. The arrangement of these primary and secondary feathers is such that they create a big surface area on the downbeat of the wings to provide both lift and forward movement. However, on the upbeat the feathers unlock, allowing air to flow between the feathers and so helping to make sure that the bird is not forced downwards again.

the bones of the front limbs are adapted to form wings

the large keel on the breast bone is for the attachment of the big muscles needed for flight

↑ **Figure 4:** Adaptations like these, along with the honeycomb structure of the bones, make birds' skeletons ideally suited to flight.

← **Figure 5:** A bird needs to create enough lift to stop itself falling out of the sky and the aerofoil shape of the wings is a big help.

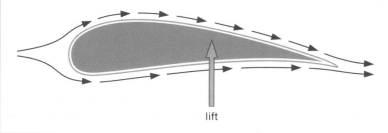

air travels faster over the top, longer surface. This causes reduced pressure above the wing and creates lift, helping to keep the bird up in the air.

lift

? Questions

1 Give three adaptations of birds which are important for successful flight.

2 Ostriches and emus are large, flightless birds. Suggest reasons to explain why they are not able to fly.

H 3 Compare the adaptations of a bird for flight with the adaptations of a fish for swimming in water and a human for movement on land.

O—ᵐ Key Ideas

⊙ Birds are adapted for flight by having wings with a large surface area, light feathers and bones, and a streamlined body shape.

H ⊙ The large sternum and keel and the specially adapted pentadactyl limb are important for bird flight.

⊙ The wing acts as a aerofoil.

⊙ The structure and arrangement of the feathers play a part in successful flight.

1 The drawing shows some of the structures of the human knee joint.

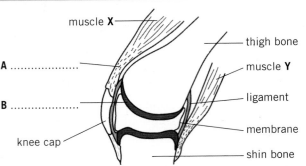

   a Label parts **A** and **B** on the drawing.

(2 marks)

   b Explain how muscles **X** and **Y** straighten the leg at the knee.

(2 marks)
(Total 4 marks)
AQA specimen question

2 Birds and bats have skeletons which are both adapted for flight. The drawings show the body and wing structure of the small brown bat and the frigate bird. The drawings are not to the same scale.

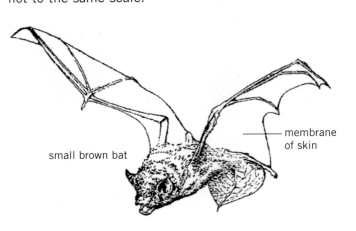

Use the drawings to help you to answer the questions.

   a How are the wings of the frigate bird adapted to give maximum lift? (2 marks)

   b Scientists think that during evolution the wings of birds and bats were adapted from the front legs of animals that did not fly.

     i Look carefully at the drawings. Give **one** piece of evidence that supports the idea that the wings evolved from the legs of animals that did not fly. (1 mark)

     ii There are two suggestions to explain how bats' wings evolved.
Suggestion 1: Bats' wings were adapted from the wings of a bird.
Suggestion 2: Bats' wings were adapted from the front legs of a small mammal.
Using evidence from the drawings, which suggestion do you think is more likely? Give **two** reasons for your answer. (2 marks)
(Total 5 marks)
AQA specimen question

Ⓗ 3 a The diagram shows part of a human backbone. Give the normal function of the discs and describe **two** properties of cartilage which suit it to this function.

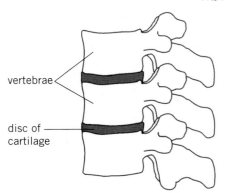

(3 marks)

b The diagram shows the bones and some muscles in the wrist and hand of an adult human.

Use the diagram, together with your own knowledge of muscle action and the properties of muscles and tendons, to explain how the thumb and forefinger can grip and then release an object.

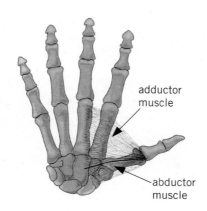

adductor muscle

abductor muscle

(4 marks)
(Total 7 marks)
AQA specimen question

4 The diagram shows a section through a human hip joint.

a Label parts **A**, **B** and **C** on the drawing. (3 marks)

b **i** What would you expect to find in the space marked **X**? (1 mark)
ii What is it's function in the joint? (1 mark)

c Osteoarthritis in the hip affects many people as they get older. How would the structure and function of the hip joint of a person affected by osteoarthritis differ from the normal hip joint shown in this diagram?

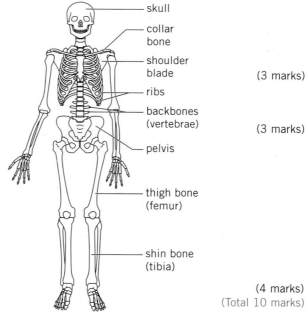

pelvis

B
X

C

A

(2 marks)
(Total 7 marks)

5 The diagram shows a human skeleton.

a The skeleton of a vertebrate like a human being carries out three main functions within the body. What are these three functions? (3 marks)

b For each function, give an example of a part of the skeleton which carries it out. (3 marks)

c The bones of the skeleton are held together in the joints by ligament capsules, whilst muscles are attached to bones by tendons.

Give **two** properties of ligaments and **two** properties of tendons which show they are well adapted for the job that they do.

skull

collar bone

shoulder blade

ribs

backbones (vertebrae)

pelvis

thigh bone (femur)

shin bone (tibia)

(4 marks)
(Total 10 marks)

H **6** **a** Give two ways in which fish are well adapted for moving through water. (2 marks)

b Fish have to be able to swim in a straight line and to stay upright in the water. Explain the roles of the fins labelled
i A, **ii B**, **iii C** in enabling fish to do this.

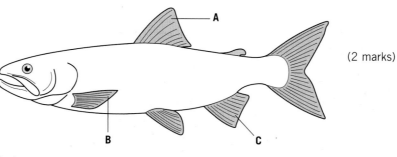

A

B

C

(5 marks)
(Total 7 marks)

Plants can make their own food in the process of photosynthesis. Animals can't – they have to obtain food from a wide variety of sources. In order to feed, animals have evolved an enormous range of adaptations to obtain food and take it into their bodies.

Filter feeders

Many animals which live in water are **filter feeders** – in other words they pass the water they live in through some kind of filter or sieve which lets the water through but traps tiny animals and plants – phytoplankton (plant plankton), zooplankton (animal plankton) and creatures such as krill (Figure 1). The range of animals which use some form of filter feeding is very wide – from the blue whale which, at around 30 m long, filters up to 1.5 tonnes of food from the sea water each day through its baleen plates, through flamingos which have fringed filters in their bills, to invertebrates such as mussels (Figure 2).

Mussels are typical invertebrate filter feeders. They live attached to rocks and stones in shallow coastal waters. They do not move around so their food has to come to them. Mussels have two shells with the muscular body of the animal contained within them. They have a pair of **gills**, one on each side of the body, which are covered in **cilia**. These hair-like cilia beat together, drawing a current of water through the body of the mussel. The water comes in at one end through a tube called a siphon, passes over the gills and then leaves the animal through another siphon. As the water passes over the gills, any food it contains (plankton or other organic particles) is extracted.

← **Figure 1:** At the bottom of most marine food chains are the plankton – microscopic organisms found throughout the oceans. The big problem is how to catch it!

↑ **Figure 2:** Mussels are molluscs which feed on plankton in the water where they live.

The gills act like sieves as the water flows over them, trapping food in the sticky mucus which they secrete. Yet more cilia then beat to move the trapped plankton into the mouth of the mussel, where it enters the digestive system. The water is kept continually moving across the gills, in at one end and out at the other. Gas exchange, with oxygen moving into the mussel and carbon dioxide moving out into the water, takes place at the same time.

When the tide is low, mussels are often left exposed to the air. They shut themselves tightly inside their shells with a little bit of trapped sea water and wait without feeding until the sea returns.

Blood suckers

Insects are another group of invertebrates which have a wide range of feeding methods, one of the most unpleasant of which – at least as far as people are concerned – is feeding on blood. Mosquitoes are one of the best known groups of insects which feed on blood. In fact it is usually the female which takes a blood meal to provide the protein she needs before laying her eggs (Figure 3).

It takes some very special adaptations of the mouthparts to be a successful blood feeder, taking blood from the capillaries of an unwary victim. Mosquito mouthparts include a sharp, needle-like hollow tube known as the **proboscis**. This enables them to pierce the skin without their victim noticing, and the blood can then travel up the hollow tube. The saliva of mosquitoes contains a special substance which prevents the blood from clotting. Saliva is secreted into the capillary as the mosquito bites. This is a very important adaptation, because without it the blood might clot around the mouthparts, trapping the insect so the victim could see it and kill it. Equally important, it stops the blood from clotting in the proboscis, blocking it and making further feeding impossible.

Finally, mosquitoes have special, strong muscles in their throat which help them to draw the blood up from the capillaries into their digestive system. Feeding on blood from another living organism is a risky way to get food, but with the right adaptations it can be a very successful way of feeding (Figure 4).

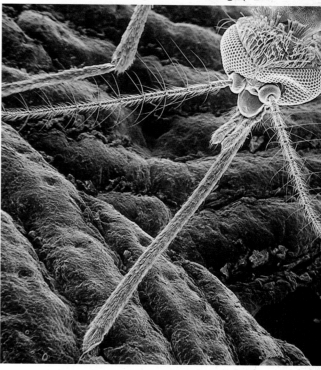

↓ **Figure 3:** The specialised mouthparts of this female mosquito look very impressive when they are magnified in a scanning electron micrograph.

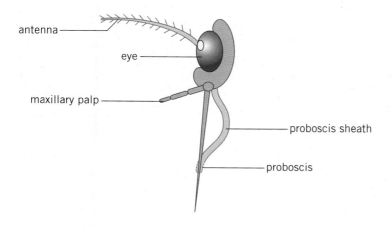

antenna

eye

maxillary palp

proboscis sheath

proboscis

← **Figure 4:** The mouthparts of a blood-sucking insect like the mosquito are very complex, with different parts adapted to different functions.

Key Ideas

- Mussels are filter feeders, feeding on microscopic organisms in the water.

- The feeding method of mussels involves beating, hair-like cilia which draw a current of water through the body, gills which act like sieves to trap plankton, and other cilia which move the plankton to the mouth.

- Mosquitoes feed on blood.

- The feeding method of mosquitoes involves a sharp proboscis to penetrate the skin, saliva which contains a substance that prevents the blood from clotting and muscles in the throat that help to draw up the blood from a capillary.

Questions

1 a How do mussels keep a flow of water moving over their gills, regardless of the state of the tide?

 b How is food material extracted from this water?

2 A constant flow of water over the gills of a marine invertebrate like a mussel is not only important for feeding. Why else is it important?

3 Make a table to show the main adaptations of a mosquito for feeding on blood and the reasons why each adaptation is so important.

4 Eating mussels which have been living in water affected by pollutants or sewage can lead to serious illness. Why are shellfish like this particularly likely to cause problems when we eat them?

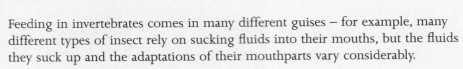
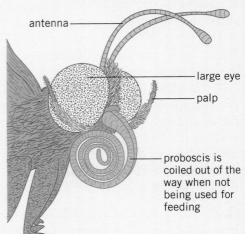

Feeding in invertebrates comes in many different guises – for example, many different types of insect rely on sucking fluids into their mouths, but the fluids they suck up and the adaptations of their mouthparts vary considerably.

Houseflies, aphids and butterflies

Butterflies and moths have mouthparts which are adapted to suck liquid food – usually nectar – from flowers (Figure 1). They have a very long, hollow proboscis (tube) which reaches into the nectar stores in flowers and the sugary liquid is then sucked up. When the insect is not feeding, the delicate proboscis is coiled up out of the way.

Aphids also feed on plants, but they have a very different approach to their diet. They have long, piercing mouthparts which they use to penetrate the plant tissues. Once the mouthparts are in the phloem, food-rich sap is forced up the tube into the body of the insect. There is enough fluid pressure in the phloem to do this – the insect does not even have to suck! (Figure 2)

Houseflies are yet another type of fluid feeder. Their mouthparts are well adapted for their (disgusting to us!) eating habits. The wide **labium** has a large surface area to be in contact with the food, and a number of tubes running down into it. The mouthparts are extended for feeding, when the fly pumps saliva down onto solid food. The enzymes in the saliva partially digest the food and the resulting liquid is then pumped up by muscles in the pharynx through a number of small tubes into the body of the fly (Figure 3).

antenna

large eye

palp

proboscis is coiled out of the way when not being used for feeding

↑ **Figure 1:** Butterflies are some of our most beautiful insects. They feed on nectar which they suck from flowers.

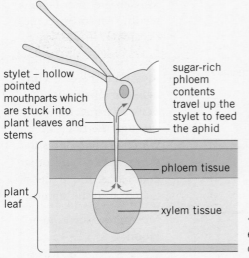

stylet – hollow pointed mouthparts which are stuck into plant leaves and stems

sugar-rich phloem contents travel up the stylet to feed the aphid

phloem tissue

plant leaf

xylem tissue

← **Figure 2:** Aphids are very effective fluid feeders that can cause great damage to plants.

↘ **Figure 3:** Flies emerge from maggots in rotting meat or faeces and may then regurgitate the germ-laden remains of their last meal onto food in our homes. It is not surprising that they can carry many diseases and are often killed by outraged humans!

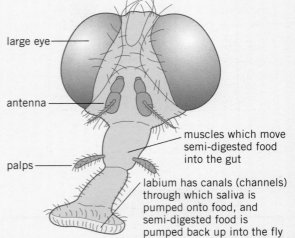

large eye

antenna

palps

muscles which move semi-digested food into the gut

labium has canals (channels) through which saliva is pumped onto food, and semi-digested food is pumped back up into the fly

Mosquitoes and malaria

Flies can cause disease by transferring bacteria from decaying material to our food. In some cases the transfer is even more sinister. A number of organisms can transfer a parasite from one host to another as part of their feeding cycle. A **parasite** is an organism that lives in or on another organism and obtains food from it. A **host** is the organism that the parasite lives off. The worms which live in the guts of many animals (including people) are one example of parasites, while the fleas which may plague your pet dog or cat are another.

One particularly deadly parasite is the organism which causes malaria. This single-celled organism (called *Plasmodium*) feeds and reproduces inside human blood cells. These blood cells rupture periodically, releasing more *Plasmodium*. Each new organism then invades another red blood cell, so each time the cycle is repeated more and more red blood cells are destroyed. Every time the blood cells rupture, the sufferer has a high fever, caused by the response of the body to the parasites released inside it.

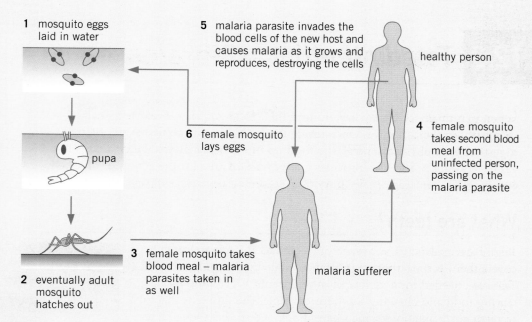

1 mosquito eggs laid in water

2 eventually adult mosquito hatches out

pupa

3 female mosquito takes blood meal – malaria parasites taken in as well

5 malaria parasite invades the blood cells of the new host and causes malaria as it grows and reproduces, destroying the cells

healthy person

6 female mosquito lays eggs

4 female mosquito takes second blood meal from uninfected person, passing on the malaria parasite

malaria sufferer

↑ **Figure 4:** Malaria affects almost 300 million people around the world, mainly in the developing countries, and it causes up to 2 million deaths every year – all this suffering is caused by the feeding habits of the mosquito.

Drugs for treating malaria are available, although it is difficult to attack the parasite hidden in the red blood cells. However, many people in the parts of the world most affected by malaria cannot afford the drugs they need. Without treatment, some affected people will die – malaria kills up to two million people every year.

Malaria is passed on from one person to another by the feeding processes of mosquitoes. Female mosquitoes need at least two blood meals before laying their eggs. If a female bites a malaria sufferer, the parasite is taken in with the blood meal and goes through part of its life cycle inside the mosquito. If she then bites someone unaffected by the disease, some of the malaria parasites will enter their bloodstream when anti-coagulant saliva is pumped into the bite (see page 167). The *Plasmodium* will then infect the red blood cells of their new host, and yet another person will be affected by the terrible symptoms of malaria (Figure 4).

? Questions

1 Compare and contrast the adaptations of butterflies, aphids and houseflies to liquid feeding.

2 Both the butterfly and the housefly keep their proboscis out of the way close to their body when they are not feeding. Why do you think this might be?

3 Use the information about mosquitoes and malaria, including Figure 4, to help you answer these questions:

a Spraying waterways with DDT and other chemicals which kill insect larvae, in areas where malaria is a major problem, can help to control the spread of the disease.

b It is difficult to develop effective drugs against the malarial parasite once it is in the human body. Why do you think this might be?

c Controlling the amount of standing water in Singapore – even making it illegal to leave old bottle tops and tins lying around – has greatly reduced the levels of malaria in the country. Why are measures such as these so effective?

⚷ Key Ideas

⊙ Aphids, butterflies and houseflies feed by sucking fluids into their mouths, but they all have different adaptations to different food sources.

⊙ The saliva of the mosquito may contain parasites which cause diseases such as malaria. The parasites are transmitted from one person to another through the bite made as the insect feeds.

⊙ Parasites are organisms that live in or on another organism and obtain food from it.

12.3 Totally teeth

When mammals feed, they have to find their food and then break off small pieces to get it into their mouths. Once inside the body, one of the first stages of digestion is to physically break the food up into smaller pieces which makes it easier to swallow and also provides a large surface area for the action of digestive enzymes. The teeth are vitally important in these early stages of digestion.

What are teeth?

Teeth have evolved to be very strong – in fact the **enamel** which covers them is the strongest substance made by the human body. Teeth are needed for a variety of different jobs – gripping food, tearing food and chewing food, for example. The different shapes of teeth are adaptations which have developed so that the teeth are ideally suited to their different functions. Because as humans, we have a very varied diet (we are omnivores so we eat animal and plant food) we also have a variety of different types of teeth. The **incisors** and **canines** are used for biting, while the **premolars** and **molars** are used for chewing and crushing food (Figure 1).

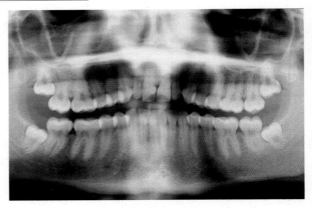

↖ Figure 1: The structure of teeth makes them very well adapted to their various functions.

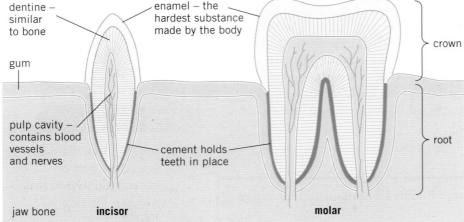

The importance of teeth becomes clear when we look at animals living in the wild. For both carnivores and herbivores, if their teeth become lost or worn out it is usually the end of their lives, as they can no longer feed effectively. Only people have so far overcome this problem, by cooking and softening their food, by developing dental treatment to preserve the teeth and by producing false teeth to wear when the natural ones are lost.

Carnivore adaptations

Carnivores have more problems in obtaining their food than many other groups of animals, because it tends to run away from them. Then, when they have caught and killed their prey they have to tear the meat away from the bones – and it is very firmly attached by tendons and ligaments. The teeth and jaws of a carnivore such as a dog are obviously adapted to overcome all of these problems (Figure 2). The teeth are large and sharp, and the food is hardly chewed at all. This works because meat is protein and is relatively easily digested.

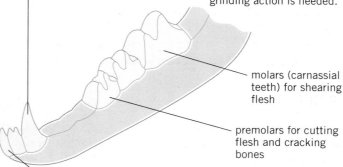

the canines are very sharp, pointed teeth which are extremely long and obvious in some carnivores. They are often used to grip prey, both to bring it down and hold it as it struggles and dies, and also for tearing meat

Carnivore jaws move only up and down to give a firm scissor action for gripping prey and using the slicing teeth. There is no sideways movement because no grinding action is needed.

molars (carnassial teeth) for shearing flesh

premolars for cutting flesh and cracking bones

the incisors are relatively small. They are used to pull meat apart. They are biting teeth

↗ Figure 2: The mouth of a carnivore, like this dog, is well adapted to catching prey and tearing meat from the bones.

Herbivore adaptations

Herbivores have rather different problems to those of carnivores – their food does not escape, but the cellulose walls make it difficult to digest so the cells need to be broken open as much as possible. So for herbivores the premolars and molars are the most important teeth. They have large, flat, ridged surfaces and the jaws move from side to side as well as up and down, so that the plant material is thoroughly crushed as it is repeatedly ground up by the teeth. The teeth at the front of the mouth are usually peg-like for gripping, pulling and tearing plant material (Figure 3).

In some herbivores there are no front teeth in the upper jaw, just a hard pad. Grass is gripped between the teeth of the lower jaw and the pad so the teeth can cut or tear it.

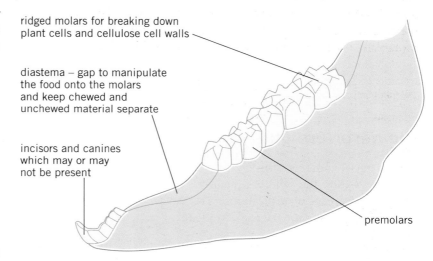

ridged molars for breaking down plant cells and cellulose cell walls

diastema – gap to manipulate the food onto the molars and keep chewed and unchewed material separate

incisors and canines which may or may not be present

premolars

↑ Figure 3: Herbivores, like horses, sheep and cows, have teeth which are very well adapted to their plant-based diet.

The human gut gives us a good picture of the main adaptations needed to eat food which is a mixture of plant and animal material (see page 18). But just as the teeth of a carnivore are very different from the teeth of a herbivore or of an omnivore like ourselves, so the digestive systems of mammals are adapted to cope with the diet they eat.

The carnivore gut

The diet of carnivores is very largely made up of protein from the muscles of the animals they eat. Protein is relatively easy to digest, with much of the process being carried out in the stomach and then continued in the small intestine. As a result, carnivores have relatively short guts and they produce a relatively small amount of waste faecal material (Figure 1).

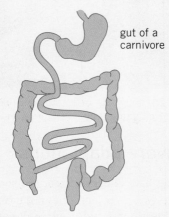

gut of a carnivore

↖ **Figure 1:** The digestive processes in a carnivore are relatively straightforward, so they have short, simple guts – much shorter even than the human version.

The herbivore gut

Plant material contains many useful chemicals, but the cell contents are all contained within the cellulose plant cell walls. Mammals do not produce an enzyme that breaks down cellulose, and yet a great many mammals, including all of the largest land animals, feed on plants.

Herbivorous mammals often rely on cellulose-digesting bacteria in their digestive system to make use of the food they eat (Figure 2). These bacteria make the enzyme **cellulase** which breaks down cellulose into sugars. Both organisms benefit from this type of arrangement – the bacteria get a regular supply of cellulose and other nutrients when the herbivore feeds, whilst the herbivores get the sugar from the cellulose and also gain access to the rest of the cytoplasm when the cell wall is broken down. An arrangement like this, where two organisms live together with both of them benefiting, is a form of **symbiosis** (living together) known as **mutualism**, because the advantages are mutual.

↓ **Figure 2:** Many plant-eating animals rely on cellulose-digesting bacteria to enable them to break down their food. Wood-eating termites have guts full of these flagellates which produce cellulase and break down the wood for them.

Ruminants like sheep and cows have a special extra area in their gut between the oesophagus and the stomach which is known as the **rumen**. This contains the cellulose-digesting bacteria. The grass or other plant material is bitten off, chewed and passed into the rumen where cellulose digestion takes place. The partly digested food is then passed back into the mouth where it is re-chewed to complete the breaking open of any cellulose cell walls which are still intact. This enhances digestion when the food is passed on into the real stomach for further digestion to take place (Figure 3).

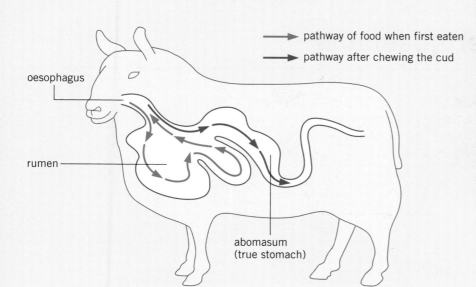

pathway of food when first eaten

pathway after chewing the cud

oesophagus

rumen

abomasum
(true stomach)

↖ **Figure 3:** Chewing food twice – once when it is first eaten and then when 'chewing the cud' – helps make the digestive system of ruminants very successful.

Other herbivores deal with the whole problem rather differently. Rabbits, for example, have cellulose-digesting bacteria in a large appendix/caecum which opens into the junction between the small and the large intestine. Food is eaten and has been partially broken down once before it reaches these cellulose digesters. The faeces which the rabbit produces at this stage are still very moist and bulky, so the rabbit eats them to take advantage of the newly digested cellulose. The faeces produced after a second passage through the gut have relatively little goodness left in them and form the familiar dry pellets of rabbit droppings (Figure 4).

Because of the problems of digesting plant material, even with the help of cellulose-digesting bacteria, most herbivores have very long guts to give themselves the maximum opportunity to extract the nutrients from their food. In spite of this, most herbivores also fail to digest a large amount of what they take in and so produce large quantities of very bulky, cellulose-rich faeces (see Figure 2 on page 130). Compared with carnivores, herbivores have to spend a large percentage of their time eating, in order to get the nutrients they need.

↑ **Figure 4:** Children and many adults find rabbits cute and adorable – if everyone knew about their habit of eating their own partially digested droppings they might not seem quite so appealing!

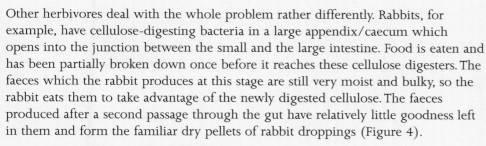

? Questions

1 Summarise the main problems facing the digestive systems of a carnivore and a herbivore, and the way the guts of these two different types of animal are adapted to cope with these difficulties.

2 Sheep, which are ruminants, deal with the cellulose in plant material very differently to other herbivores like rabbits.

   a Explain how each type of animal deals with the digestion of cellulose in plant food.

   b What are the advantages and disadvantages of each way?

3 A human gut is longer than a carnivore gut but much shorter than a herbivore gut, and the amount of faeces produced by a human on a healthy diet is similarly more than a carnivore but less than a herbivore.

   a Why is the human gut like this?

   b How might the human gut be modified to make it better adapted to the diet we eat?

O━ Key Ideas

⊙ The digestive systems of mammals are adapted to the diet they consume.

⊙ Carnivores have short guts, adapted for digesting mainly protein.

⊙ Herbivores have long guts which often contain cellulose-digesting bacteria in different areas.

⊙ Cellulose-digesting bacteria break down cellulose into sugars which are then available for use by the mammal.

1 The drawings show the arrangement of the teeth in the lower and upper jaws of an adult human.

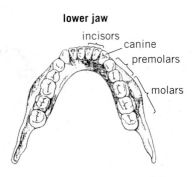

lower jaw
incisors
canine
premolars
molars

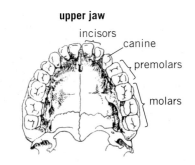

upper jaw
incisors
canine
premolars
molars

a How many teeth in total does this adult have? (1 mark)

b Choose words from the box as you copy and complete the sentences. You may use each word once or not at all.

bite	chew	front
pointed	ridged	side

The incisor teeth are placed at the .... of the mouth and their function is to .... off pieces from the food. Human canine teeth are smaller in proportion and less .... than those of a carnivore. Their molar teeth are less .... than those of a herbivore.

(4 marks)
(Total 5 marks)
AQA specimen question

2 a The mosquito feeds by sucking human blood. Describe one way in which the mouthparts of the mosquito are adapted for sucking blood. (1 mark)

b Herbivores are animals which feed almost entirely on plants. They have teeth, jaws and digestive systems which are specially adapted to processing their food.

Photograph **A** shows the skull of a llama, which is a herbivore.

i What is the importance of the hard pad on the upper jaw in obtaining small pieces of vegetation?

ii State **two** similarities, related to feeding, between the skull of a sheep and that of a llama. The features must be visible in the photograph.

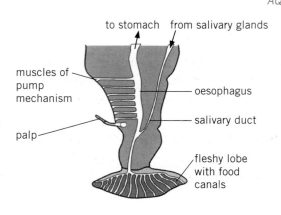

hard pad

(2 marks)

(2 marks)
(Total 5 marks)
AQA specimen question

3 The housefly feeds on organic material such as dead animals, dung and human food. It secretes saliva onto the food and then sucks the digested food through its proboscis into its stomach. The diagram shows a section through the proboscis of a housefly.

to stomach   from salivary glands

muscles of pump mechanism

oesophagus

salivary duct

palp

fleshy lobe with food canals

a Suggest **two** ways in which the proboscis of the housefly is adapted to the way in which it feeds. (2 marks)

b Suggest how houseflies can transmit diseases to humans through their feeding habits. (2 marks)

(Total 4 marks)

AQA specimen question

4 The diagram shows a mussel. Use it to help you answer the following questions.

mussel with one shell removed

gill

threads attaching mussel to rock

a Mussels are filter feeders. How does a filter feeder get its food? (2 marks)

b Give **one** other example of a filter feeder. (1 mark)

c Mussels live in the tidal zone, so for part of the day when the tide is out they may be left exposed to the air. How do they cope with this? (2 marks)

(Total 5 marks)

5 Female mosquitoes need a blood meal to provide them with protein before they lay their eggs.

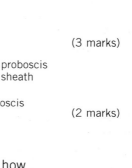

antenna

eye

maxillary palp

proboscis sheath

proboscis

a Give three important ways in which mosquitoes are adapted for feeding on blood. (3 marks)

b Mosquitoes spread malaria, a disease which affects millions of people world-wide. How do mosquitoes spread the disease? (2 marks)

c Aphids (greenflies) have similar sharp pointed mouthparts to mosquitoes, but they feed on plants rather than animals. Suggest how you would expect the mouthparts of a greenfly to differ from the mouthparts of a mosquito. (2 marks)

(Total 7 marks)

6

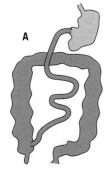

A

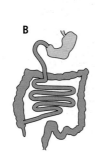

B

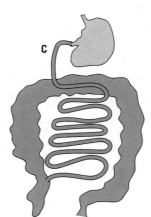

C

The diagrams show the guts of three very different types of animals. Use the diagrams and your knowledge of different digestive systems to help you answer this question.

One of the guts shown is from an omnivore, one is from a carnivore and one is from a herbivore.

a Explain what is meant by the terms carnivore, herbivore and omnivore. (3 marks)

b State the type of diet eaten by the animals to which the three different guts **A**, **B** and **C** belong. In each case explain your choice. (6 marks)

(Total 9 marks)

13.1 The germ theory of disease

Changing ideas

Although people have suffered and died from infectious diseases for thousands of years, it was only in the 19th century that we really began to understand what actually causes them. Simply observing what happened when illness struck was not enough to help people grasp what was causing the problem, and so most European explanations of diseases in earlier centuries relied heavily on the idea of illness as a punishment or trial from God.

One man who began to develop an understanding of infectious diseases was the Hungarian doctor Ignaz Semmelweiss (see page 54). He realised that the infections suffered by women after childbirth were the result of some infectious agent carried on the hands of the doctors who attended to them (Figure 1).

John Snow continued with the development of the germ theory of disease. In the 19th century, cholera was a new disease in Britain. People who are affected produce large quantities of watery diarrhoea and may vomit as well, and it is often fatal. John Snow saw its effects among miners in Newcastle in 1831 and then again in London. He took careful details of all the cholera cases he came across and developed a hypothesis that the disease was spread from one person to another by something in the vomit and diarrhoea of cholera victims. For many years he was ignored, but then in 1854 another terrible cholera epidemic broke out in London – in one small area where Snow was working, 500 men, women and children died in the space of 10 days. Snow kept precise records of all the deaths and where they occurred and realised that all the affected people got their drinking water from the same place – the Broad Street pump (Figure 2). He thought the infective agent must be in the water. Once the handle of the pump was removed, people could no longer drink the infected water and the disease was controlled – and Snow's ideas became accepted.

Louis Pasteur

The work of people like Semmelweiss and Snow gradually led doctors and scientists to recognise that infectious diseases were brought about by an infectious agent or 'germ' (the germ theory of disease), but progress was very slow. Much of the credit for the development of a widely accepted germ theory of disease must go to Louis Pasteur, the great 19th century French scientist, helped on his way by the development of microscope techniques by people like Robert Koch, which made microbes visible and identifiable for the first time.

↑ **Figure 1:** Ignaz Semmelweiss realised that the lives of thousands of women could be saved by simple hand-washing, and had a breakdown when he could not convince others of his findings.

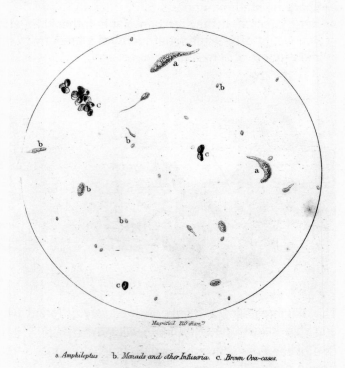

FROM WATER FROM PUMP IN BROAD ST GOLDEN SQUARE. Pl.9.

Magnified 220 diam.

a. *Amphileptus*   b. *Monads and other Infusoria.*   c. *Brown Ova-cases.*

↑ **Figure 2:** The water from the Broad Street pump, contaminated by sewage from cholera victims, caused the deaths of over 500 people before it was put out of action by John Snow. This drawing of the water and the organisms it contained, magnified 220 times using a microscope, was made in 1854.

- Pasteur showed that fermentation is the result of the action of microorganisms on sugar.

- Many people believed that living things could arise from non-living things by the action of God – a theory known as spontaneous generation. Pasteur was convinced that any growths that appeared – for example mould on food as it decayed – were from microscopic organisms already present in the air. First he showed that the experiments of his main opponent were dubious. Then he showed that if he boiled broth and sealed the container it would stay clear until he introduced material exposed to the air, when microorganisms grew and the broth turned cloudy. Finally he designed a very elegant series of experiments which again showed clearly that any microbes which appear in boiled broth are present in the air (Figure 3).

- A mystery disease almost wiped out silkworms throughout the world. Pasteur showed that the disease was caused by a microbe found only in the tissues of diseased silkworms, moths and eggs, which could be seen using a microscope. He devised a way of avoiding the disease by identifying eggs which were free from infection, saving the silk industry. This was the first clear conclusive evidence of microbes or germs causing disease.

- After the death of three of his daughters from infectious diseases, Louis Pasteur focused his work on them, at first in animals and later in humans. He was enormously successful at developing vaccines, which further confirmed his germ theory of disease, and his work influenced Lister in the development of antiseptic surgery.

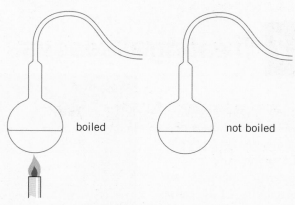

1 Pasteur prepared a series of flasks and drew the necks out into narrow curved extensions. Without sealing he boiled the broth in some of them for several minutes and left others unboiled.

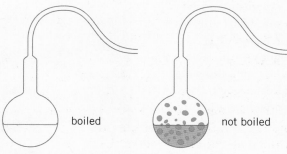

2 All the flasks were left in calm air and within 36 hours the unboiled flasks were full of microbes and moulds, while the boiled flasks remain unchanged.

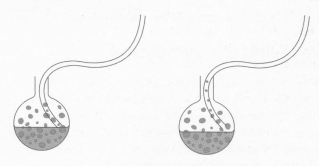

3 If the curved necks were snapped off and dipped into the broth of the boiled flasks, microbes immediately began to grow.

↑ **Figure 3:** From these experiments, Louis Pasteur concluded that the 'swan necks' trapped germs from the air, preventing them reaching the broth and growing.

? Questions

1 How did John Snow's observations on cholera help to confirm the germ theory of disease?

2 What are the similarities and differences between the work of John Snow on cholera and the work of Ignaz Semmelweiss on childbed fever?

3 By the time Louis Pasteur was doing his great work on germ theory, microscopes were greatly improved and staining techniques to make different microorganisms visible were becoming available. How would this have made it easier for Pasteur's ideas to become accepted?

4 Give five examples which demonstrate how our modern acceptance of the germ theory of disease influences our everyday behaviour, e.g. wiping down work surfaces in a kitchen.

Long before anyone understood the causes of infectious diseases, people tried to relieve the symptoms of illness. As our understanding of the causes of different infections grew, so gradually did our ability not only to make ourselves feel better but also to actually cure the diseases which affected us. The microorganisms which cause infectious diseases – often referred to as **pathogens** – can cause a variety of symptoms that may affect specific areas or the whole body (Figure 1).

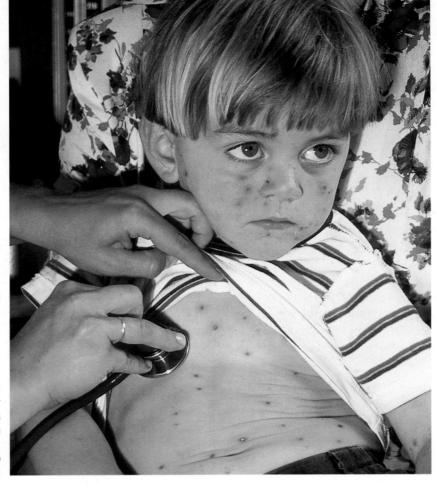

→ **Figure 1:** When pathogens invade our bodies they can make us feel very uncomfortable and ill. Not surprisingly, we want something to make us feel better!

Relieving the symptoms

When we have an infectious disease, whether it is something common and relatively minor like a cold, or something more serious like tuberculosis, we will often be treated with medicines which contain useful drugs. Frequently, particularly for mild illnesses, the medicine has no effect on the pathogen at all – it simply relieves the symptoms. So, for example, drugs like aspirin and paracetamol are very useful as painkillers. When we have a cold, they will help to relieve the headache and sore throat, but they will have no effect on the virus which has invaded our tissues and caused the symptoms. Particularly in small children, paracetamol is also useful in reducing fevers. Many of the medicines we buy at a chemists are like this – they are symptom relievers rather than pathogen killers and do not speed up our recovery. We have to wait for the immune system of our body to overcome the invading microorganisms.

Making us better

While drugs which relieve our symptoms are useful, the drugs which have really revolutionised the treatment of infectious diseases are **antibiotics**. Antiseptic and disinfectant chemicals kill bacteria outside of the body, but they are far too poisonous to be used inside the body – they would kill the patient and the pathogens at the same time!

Penicillin, the first antibiotic, was discovered in 1928 by Alexander Fleming, and then ignored by him and everyone else for a further 10 years before Ernst Chain and Howard Florey saw its potential and set about developing its human use. The effect of penicillin was almost miraculous. Factory production was soon taking place to satisfy the demands during the Second World War, and has continued ever since. Penicillin destroys bacteria by weakening their cell walls so they burst open and die. As human cells do not have walls they are not affected, so the drug affects only the pathogen and not the host. Over the years, other antibiotics have been developed which also allow us to cure bacterial diseases by killing the infective bacteria inside the body.

Unfortunately, antibiotics have not been a complete answer to the problem of infectious diseases, which still kill millions of people world-wide every year. One of the problems is that antibiotics have no effect on diseases caused by viruses. What is more, developing drugs which do have an effect on viral diseases is proving very difficult indeed, and there has so far been only limited success. The problem with viral pathogens is that they live and reproduce inside the cells of the body. This means it is extremely difficult to develop drugs which kill the viruses without damaging the cells and tissues of the body at the same time.

Antibiotic-resistant bacteria

Many strains of bacteria have developed resistance to antibiotics as a result of natural selection (see page 99). Because of this it is very important to have a range of different antibiotics and to select the one which is most effective at killing the bacteria which cause a particular infection. For example, penicillin is often prescribed for tonsillitis, while trimethoprim, a different antibiotic, is prescribed for infections of the bladder. Most frightening of all, some bacteria have become resistant to all known types of antibiotics and at the moment we do not have any new antibiotics to use against these 'superbugs'. To prevent the development of further antibiotic-resistant strains of bacteria, it is important both that people finish the course of any antibiotic they are given (see page 58), and that antibiotics are not overused. For many years, doctors gave patients antibiotics for bacterial infections which their own bodies would have been able to deal with relatively easily, creating more opportunities for the development of resistant strains. Increasingly, doctors are saving antibiotics for more serious infections in an attempt to prevent further resistance arising.

↑ **Figure 2:** In the 1930s Gerhard Domagk made an anti-bacterial drug from a red dye. His first human trial was on his own young daughter, dying of an infection she picked up in his laboratory. She lived! Later her father was awarded the Nobel prize for developing the first sulphonamide drug, giving people an effective weapon against some infectious diseases.

Questions

1 What is the difference between drugs like paracetamol and drugs such as penicillin?

2 Use material from 7.3 Evolution today, and these pages to explain how bacteria develop resistance to antibiotics.

3 How can completing a course of antibiotics and avoiding the overuse of antibiotics help prevent the development of further resistant strains of bacteria?

4 Explain why it is so much more difficult to develop an effective anti-viral drug than it has been to develop anti-bacterial drugs.

Key Ideas

- Microorganisms that cause disease are called pathogens.

- Diseases may be treated using medicines which contain drugs which relieve symptoms, like painkillers, or drugs which destroy pathogens, like antibiotics.

- Many strains of bacteria have developed resistance to antibiotics.

- It is difficult to develop drugs to destroy viral pathogens.

Drugs can be used to relieve the symptoms of a disease or destroy the pathogen which is making us ill – but it is better still to avoid catching the disease in the first place. One of the most effective ways of doing this is by vaccination.

Q Ideas and Evidence

The defeat of smallpox

Smallpox was a terrible disease which killed millions of people, and disfigured and disabled millions more all over the world. When Lady Mary Wortley Montagu was travelling in Turkey in 1718 she found that the Turks tried to give people mild, controlled doses of smallpox, which then made them immune to serious illness later on, by giving them a small dose of pus from smallpox blisters. Lady Mary was so impressed that she brought the technique back to England where it was known as variolation. Prisoners who had been condemned to death were offered their freedom if they took part in a trial of the method – and they all survived and were set free (Figure 1).

Some years later, as Dr Edward Jenner worked among farmers in Gloucestershire, he noted that girls who milked the cows often caught cowpox, which gave them spots on their hands. However, they rarely caught smallpox. Jenner began to wonder if deliberately infecting people with cowpox would protect them against smallpox. Finally, in 1794, when one in five of all deaths was the result of smallpox, Jenner decided to try out his idea. He took pus from the cowpox spots of a milkmaid and scratched it into the skin of a healthy young boy called James Phipps, who then developed cowpox. Two months later Jenner scratched pus from a smallpox victim into the boy's arm. As a result of Lady Mary Montagu's ideas, this had become a fairly common procedure as a way of preventing a serious infection. Fortunately James did not develop smallpox at all, and the idea of inoculating someone against a fatal illness by exposing them to a similar but mild illness began to be accepted. From that time onwards a programme of **vaccination** (from the Latin word for a cow because of the link to cowpox) began to take place. By 1842, as the use of the safer cowpox vaccination spread, the technique of inoculating people with smallpox was banned in England (Figure 2).

↑ **Figure 1:** Lady Mary Montagu had her own children protected against smallpox in Turkey before bringing the technique back to England.

Even in the 1960s, up to 2 million people died of smallpox each year, and millions more were infected. Then, between 1967 and 1977 a world-wide vaccination programme was put in place and in 1980 the World Health Organisation declared that smallpox had officially been eliminated from the world. The virus is now kept in a small number of laboratories and children are no longer vaccinated against a disease which does not exist!

← **Figure 2:** Not everyone approved of vaccination. This nightmare scenario of the results of cowpox vaccination imagined by the cartoonist Gillray put many people off the new treatment!

How does immunisation work?

Each organism has special protein markers known as **antigens** on the outside of its cells. When our bodies are invaded by a pathogen, our immune system responds to these foreign proteins and we produce antibodies which in turn destroy the pathogen carrying the foreign antigens. While our body is working out the correct antibodies we suffer the symptoms of the disease. However, once we have been exposed to a particular pathogen and made the right antibodies we become immune to it — we can always call up the right antibodies to get rid of the pathogen before we fully develop the disease (Figure 3). Unfortunately some pathogens cause such serious symptoms that we are at risk of dying before our body can make antibodies, and so we are often vaccinated to immunise us against these diseases (see Chapter 4).

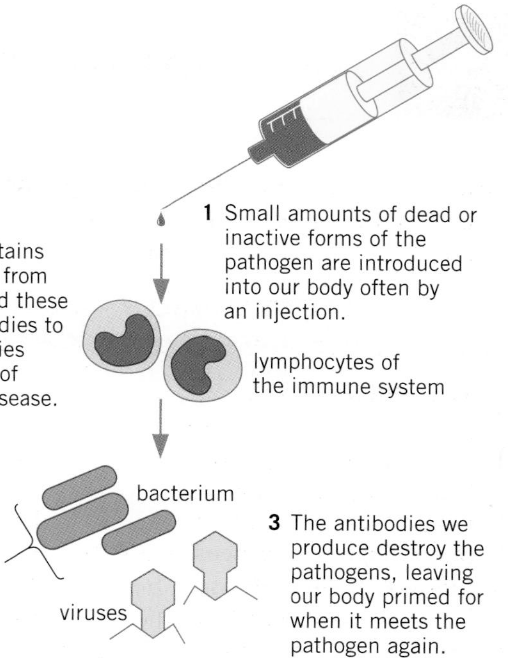

After vaccination against a particular disease (see Figure 3) we are able to deal immediately with any live pathogens of that type we might meet in the future, because our bodies respond by making the correct antibody just as if we had once had the disease. This **active immunity** makes us immune to any future infection, protecting us against harmful diseases such as polio, tetanus and diphtheria. The MMR is another commonly used vaccine, which protects children against measles, mumps and rubella (German measles). Each vaccine takes a major investment of time and money to develop.

Unlike antibiotics, vaccination is equally effective against bacterial diseases (e.g. tetanus, diphtheria and tuberculosis) and viral diseases (e.g. polio, measles, mumps and rubella). However, there are times when a person has already been exposed to a dangerous pathogen and it is too late for a normal vaccine. In this case they can be given an injection of ready-made antibodies to provide them with protection. This is called **passive immunity** because the antibodies have not been made by the person concerned. Examples of when this might be used include the injection of rabies antibodies when a person has been bitten by a dog which might be rabid, and the injection of tetanus antibodies if a person has cut themselves and may have been exposed to tetanus pathogens.

1 Small amounts of dead or inactive forms of the pathogen are introduced into our body often by an injection.

lymphocytes of the immune system

2 The vaccine contains protein antigens from the pathogen and these stimulate our bodies to produce antibodies without any risk of us getting the disease.

disease-causing antigens which may enter through the eyes, nose, mouth, skin or any other opening to the body

bacterium

viruses

3 The antibodies we produce destroy the pathogens, leaving our body primed for when it meets the pathogen again.

↑ **Figure 3:** The development of active immunity.

? Questions

1 a How did the method of immunising against smallpox introduced by Lady Mary Montagu differ from Jenner's ideas?

   b Why do you think Jenner's method was so much more successful?

2 There are aspects of the way both Lady Mary and Jenner tested their ideas which would be quite unacceptable today. Explain this statement.

3 Produce a flow chart to explain the process of developing active immunity following

   a natural infection

   b vaccination.

4 There are vaccines for diseases such as diphtheria, polio, tetanus and meningitis but not for the common cold or tonsillitis. Suggest reasons why this is so.

O—ⁿ Key Ideas

⊙ People can be immunised against disease by introducing small quantities of dead or inactive pathogen into the body, which responds by making antibodies. This is active immunity.

⊙ People who have been exposed to a dangerous pathogen can be injected with ready-made antibodies — this is passive immunity.

Ideas and Evidence

As we can see in Figure 2 on page 180, there were many people who had reservations about vaccinations when the idea was first developed. In the 21st century, the debate still continues. Looking at the whole population in the UK and world-wide there is no doubt that vaccination programmes are very successful and save many lives. Smallpox has been eradicated. In the UK, swimming pools are no longer closed regularly because of outbreaks of polio and people crippled or paralysed by the disease are rare indeed (Figure 1).

World-wide too, an intensive polio vaccination programme has made sure that the disease is becoming increasingly rare and there are hopes that polio will go the same way as smallpox and eventually be eliminated completely.

Meningitis is a disease which involves the infection of the membranes which surround the brain. It takes hold rapidly and often kills within a day or two of the symptoms first appearing. Babies, infant school children, teenagers and university students are particularly high risk groups. A vaccination against meningitis C was developed and brought into general use at the beginning of the 21st century. The uptake was very high, with almost all school children being vaccinated – and the rate of meningitis C infections fell by 98%. This represented many young lives saved, and more saved from brain damage, deafness or other problems (Figure 2).

However, any medical procedure carries some risk, and every so often research is done which suggests there may be a risk to children in taking a particular vaccine. When a disease is no longer visible in the population it can be easy to forget the risks associated with the disease and focus on the risks which might be linked to the vaccine. For example, in the 1970s some research was done which suggested that a very tiny number of children might have been brain damaged by the whooping cough vaccination. Many parents then – understandably – refused to have their children vaccinated against whooping cough and the incidence of the disease increased considerably (see page 59) until the vaccination levels went up again.

Measles, mumps and rubella are three childhood diseases which used to be very common but have become a relatively rare occurrence thanks to the MMR vaccination programmes. Measles makes children feel very unwell. More importantly, it can cause fits, brain damage, blindness and death. Similarly, mumps can result in meningitis and sterility in men. Rubella is rather different. It is not a serious disease in itself, but if a pregnant woman gets rubella then her developing baby can be born seriously damaged. So, when children are vaccinated against the disease, it gives young girls the

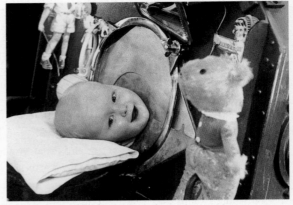

↑ **Figure 1:** When polio was common, children and adults alike would find themselves dependent on an 'iron lung' – a machine which 'breathed' for you when polio paralysed all the muscles in your chest.

Meningitis C Reduce the risk
Your guide to the new meningitis C vaccine

NHS

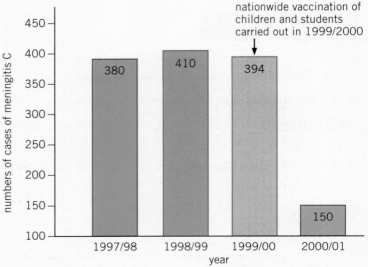

↑ **Figure 2:** Meningitis is a swift and deadly killer, but a nationwide vaccination programme in the UK massively reduced the impact of one form of the disease in just 12 months.

immunity they will need when they are adults. When young boys receive this vaccination, it is for the good of society – it means they will not carry or contract the disease and pass it to any unvaccinated pregnant women.

In 1988, 86 000 people caught measles, most of them children. Sixteen of them died. After a big vaccination campaign, again involving lots of children in schools, the number of people getting measles had dropped to 2500. However, towards the end of the 20th century some research was published which suggested that the MMR vaccine might be linked in some children to the development of bowel problems and autism. (Autistic children tend to be very withdrawn from people and cannot cope easily with normal life.) This got a lot of media coverage, and by the start of 2001 uptake of the vaccine had dropped from 92% of the population to only 75%. In 2000, Ireland had an alarming increase in the number of measles cases, and for the first time in years two babies died of the disease. There are fears that the same thing will happen in England.

Making decisions about immunisations is always difficult. For the sake of society as a whole it is important that as many people as possible are immunised against as many diseases as possible to reduce the pool of infection in the population. For the sake of each individual, no parent wants their child exposed to potentially life-threatening diseases. Yet, on the other hand, there is only a chance that your child will get one of these diseases, and then another remote chance that they will be permanently damaged or killed by it. By taking a healthy child along for a vaccination, you are deliberately exposing them to the remote chance that something will go wrong.

It can be difficult to decide what is unbiased information to help make a decision. The media emphasise scare stories which make good headlines. The pharmaceutical companies want more rather than less vaccination to go on so they can sell more of their product. Doctors and health visitors can weigh up all the information, but they have vaccination targets set by the government. The consensus is that vaccination is almost always a good thing for both individuals and society. The great majority of parents still choose to protect their children – but it is not always an easy choice.

↓ **Figure 3:** This graph shows clearly the effect of measles vaccinations on the number of children under 15 years who have died of measles in England and Wales (1980–2000).

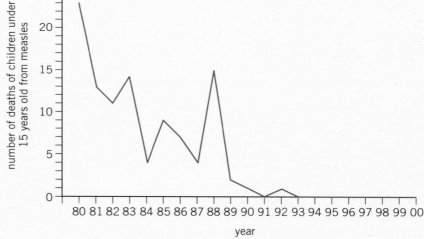

? **Questions**

1 When people stopped having their children vaccinated against whooping cough in the 1970s because of fears of the risk of brain damage, there were three epidemics of the disease, with more than 300 000 notified cases and at least 70 deaths. No link was ever proven between the vaccine and brain damage.

Use this evidence along with the information on these pages to plan a speech in a debate. Choose whether you wish to speak for or against the motion: 'It is in the best interests of both individuals and society for all children to be vaccinated against common and serious infectious diseases'.

Key Ideas

⊙ There are many advantages to vaccination but there are some disadvantages. Both need to be considered when taking the decision to vaccinate a child.

Two types of white blood cells (lymphocytes) are involved in the immune response of the body. These are the **T-cells** and the **B-cells**. As we have already seen, every organism carries a unique set of protein markers called antigens on the surface of its cells. The body makes a huge range of different white blood cells, each with receptors on their surface which recognise and attach to different antigens.

The working of the immune system

T-cells and B-cells both have surface receptors, but they react to antigens in very different ways (Figure 1).

When T-cells recognise and attach to a cell carrying a foreign antigen they destroy the cell. The T-cell then divides rapidly to produce many more T-cells with the right surface receptors to bind to the antigen and destroy it. T-cells also stimulate B-cells to multiply.

B-cells, unlike T-cells, do not destroy the foreign cell directly. When their surface receptors recognise and attach to an antigen, the B-cell immediately reproduces and multiplies itself to form many identical cells (or clones) which secrete antibodies. Antibodies are specific to a particular antigen. They travel around the body, binding with any cells carrying the specific antigen and deactivating them. These antigen–antibody complexes are then removed by yet another type of white blood cell which engulfs and digests them (Figure 2).

It can take some time for the immune system of the body to produce enough T- and B-cells with the right receptors to overcome a particular pathogen. It is while the immune system is producing these defences that the pathogen can reproduce rapidly and cause the symptoms of disease.

The dividing of the B-cells also results in **memory** cells. These remain in the body, and mean that if an antigen enters the body for a second time antibody production takes place very rapidly. This time the pathogen is disabled before it has time to make us feel ill – we have developed immunity to the disease.

It is this immunological memory which gives us immunity to diseases both following a natural infection, when we have actually been ill, and following vaccination (Figure 3).

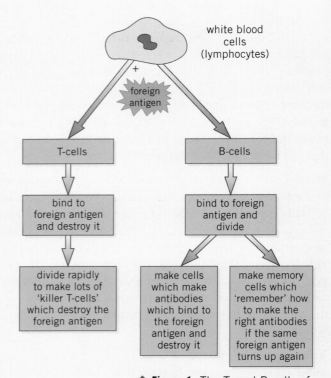

↑ **Figure 1:** The T- and B-cells of the immune system form a very effective defence against foreign antigens which get into the body.

↑ **Figure 2:** Once a pathogen has been destroyed by antibodies, it is removed by white blood cells which 'eat' the remains.

← **Figure 3:** The Heaf test is given before the BCG vaccination against tuberculosis, because some people will have built up their own natural immunity to TB. A small dose of inactivated bacteria is injected – just enough to produce an immune reaction in people already exposed to the disease as the memory cells make sure that antibodies are produced very rapidly to a pathogen which has been met before (the person on the left has natural immunity to TB). Only the people who do not react to the Heaf test (the great majority!) are then given the full vaccination.

Human blood groups

A number of different antigens are found specifically on the surface of the red blood cells. These give us the different human blood groups. There are several different blood grouping systems but the best known is the ABO system. In this system there are two possible antigens on the red blood cells – **A** and **B**. There are also two possible antibodies in the plasma – known as **a** and **b** – and unlike other antibodies these are there all the time, not made in response to a particular antigen. Table 1 shows the four combinations of antibodies and antigens which give the four ABO blood groups.

Blood group	Antigen on red blood cells	Antibody in plasma
A	A	b
B	B	a
AB	A and B	none
O	none	a and b

↑ **Table 1:** The ABO blood grouping system

If blood from different groups is mixed, there may be a reaction between the antigen and the complimentary antibody which causes the blood cells to **agglutinate** (stick together). This means they cannot work properly and clog up capillaries and even larger vessels. Most of the time this is not important, because everyone keeps their own blood in their own circulatory system. But if someone loses a lot of blood in an accident or during an operation, then blood may need to be given from one person to another in a **blood transfusion**. Before a transfusion it is vital that the blood groups of both the donor and the recipient are known, so that the right blood can be given to prevent agglutination. It is not usually the case that only one type of blood can be given – simply that blood containing a particular antigen must not be mixed with blood containing the matching antibody (Figure 4 and Table 2).

↑ **Figure 4:** There are 2.5 million blood donors in the UK. 10 000 donations of 470 cm³ of blood – that's 4700 litres in total – are given each day. Each bag of blood must be clearly labelled so it can be given to someone with a compatible blood group.

Donor	Recipient O	A	B	AB
O	✓	✓	✓	✓
A	✗	✓	✗	✓
B	✗	✗	✓	✓
AB	✗	✗	✗	✓

↑ **Table 2:** Compatibility in the ABO blood groups. If a recipient is given blood from a donor with the wrong blood group the blood will clot which may be fatal

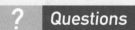

Questions

1 Make a table to compare and contrast the T-cells and the B-cells of the immune system.

2 Use your knowledge of the immune system to explain

  a why we suffer the symptoms of a disease the first time we meet a pathogen

  b why we do not suffer the symptoms of disease the second time we meet a pathogen

  c how vaccinations protect us from suffering from a particular disease.

3 Produce a leaflet or poster to be used by doctors to help patients in their surgeries understand why they need vaccinations, e.g. for yellow fever before they travel to certain holiday destinations.

4 **a** Explain why someone with blood group O is particularly welcome as a blood donor.

  b Explain why there can be problems when a person of blood group O needs a blood transfusion. How are these problems resolved?

Key Ideas

- Two types of white blood cells are involved in the immune response – T-cells and B-cells.

- In the ABO blood grouping system there are antigens on the red blood cell surface and antibodies in the plasma.

Controlling disease   185

Infectious diseases can cause serious problems while people are actually suffering from them, but they can also cause serious long-term damage to organ systems in the body. Some of the organs most commonly affected by serious infection are the heart, the lungs, the liver and the kidneys.

Kidney failure

The kidneys can be damaged and destroyed by kidney infections, but they can also suffer damage from severe infections which affect the whole body. Not all kidney failure is due to infectious diseases. Sometimes there is a genetic problem which means the kidneys fail, and sometimes the kidneys are damaged during an accident. Whatever the cause, untreated failure of both kidneys leads to death, as toxins such as urea build up in the body and the salt and water balance of the body is upset (see page 48 on the structure and function of the kidney).

Dialysis – an artificial kidney

For centuries kidney failure meant certain death, but now there is an effective method of treating kidney failure by carrying out the function of the kidney artificially. The first 'artificial kidney' was developed in 1943 by the Dutch doctor Wilhelm Kolff, and the technology of these amazing machines was welcomed and rapidly developed (Figure 1).

The machine which carries out the functions of the kidney is known as a dialysis machine, because it relies on the process of dialysis to clean the blood. In this machine a person's blood leaves the body and flows between partially permeable membranes. The concentration of the solutes on one side of the membrane makes sure that waste urea passes out of the blood by diffusion into the dialysis fluid. Similarly, excess salt is also removed from the blood (Figure 2).

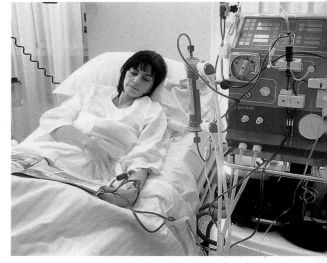

↑ **Figure 1:** These 'artificial kidney machines' have not only saved countless lives, but allow sufferers from kidney failure to lead full, active lives.

Without normally functioning kidneys the concentration of dissolved substances such as urea and salt build up in the blood. Treatment by dialysis restores the concentrations of these dissolved substances to normal levels. Then, as the patient carries on with normal life, urea and other substances build up again, so the dialysis has to be repeated at regular intervals. It takes around 8 hours for dialysis to be complete, so people with kidney failure have to remain attached to a dialysis machine for many hours, several times a week. They also have to manage their diet carefully, particularly restricting their intake of protein and salt, so that their blood chemistry stays as stable as possible. The only time they can eat exactly what they want is during the first few hours of dialysis!

→ **Figure 2:** A dialysis machine relies on simple diffusion to clean the blood, removing the waste products which would damage the body as they built up.

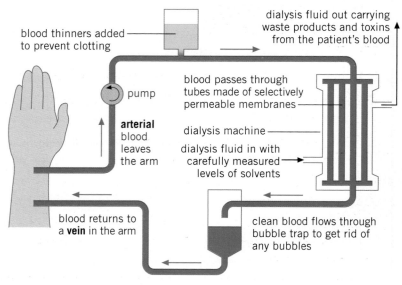

blood thinners added to prevent clotting

pump

arterial blood leaves the arm

blood returns to a **vein** in the arm

dialysis fluid out carrying waste products and toxins from the patient's blood

blood passes through tubes made of selectively permeable membranes

dialysis machine

dialysis fluid in with carefully measured levels of solvents

clean blood flows through bubble trap to get rid of any bubbles

Many people go to hospital to receive dialysis, but in 1964 home dialysis machines were made available for the first time. This meant that at least some people with kidney failure could set up their dialysis in their own home, removing the need for regular hospital visits. Even more recently, methods of carrying out dialysis *within* the body have been devised so that people can carry out dialysis without a cumbersome machine.

Dialysis certainly has some disadvantages – the need for a carefully controlled diet, the need for regular sessions connected to a dialysis machine and the fact that, over many years, the balance of substances in the blood can become more difficult to control however careful the dialysis. But for people with kidney failure, dialysis means life rather than death, because we have learned to copy successfully the action of the living organ in the body.

(H) More about dialysis

During dialysis, whilst it is vital that patients lose the excess urea and salt which has built up in their systems, it is equally important that they do not lose useful substances such as glucose and mineral ions from their blood. The loss of these substances is prevented by the careful control of the dialysis fluid. It contains no urea, so there is a strong concentration gradient from the blood to the fluid for this substance. It contains normal plasma levels of salt so excess salt is lost but no more. However, the dialysis fluid contains the same concentrations of glucose and mineral ions as the blood plasma, so there is no net movement of these substances out of the blood (Figure 3).

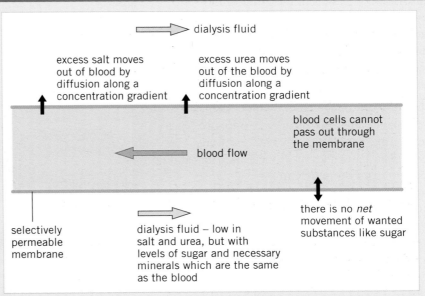

↑ **Figure 3:** Changing the concentration of substances in the dialysis fluid allows unwanted substances to be removed from the blood whilst the concentration of useful substances remains unchanged.

(?) Questions

1 Why is kidney failure potentially life threatening?

2 Produce a flow chart to explain how a dialysis machine works.

3 a Why do people with kidney failure have to control their intake of protein and salt?

   b Why can patients with kidney failure eat and drink what they like during the first few hours of dialysis?

(H) 4 a Explain the importance of dialysis fluid containing no urea and normal plasma levels of salt, glucose and minerals.

   b Both blood and dialysis fluid are constantly circulated through the dialysis machine. Explain why the constant circulation of dialysis fluid is so important.

(0→) Key Ideas

⊙ People suffering from kidney failure may be treated by dialysis.

⊙ In a dialysis machine the concentration of dissolved substances in the blood is restored to normal levels.

(H) ⊙ The levels of useful substances in the blood are maintained while urea and excess salt are lost.

13.7 Kidney transplants

When the kidneys fail, survival is made possible by using a dialysis machine. However, once the body has been returned to health and the blood is kept balanced by regular dialysis, another treatment becomes possible – a kidney transplant.

What is a transplant?

In a kidney transplant the diseased kidneys are replaced by a single healthy kidney from a donor. The donor kidney is attached to the normal blood vessels in the groin of the recipient and, if all goes well, it will function normally to cleanse and balance the blood (Figure 1). One kidney is quite capable of keeping the blood chemistry in balance and removing waste urea for a person for a lifetime.

The great advantage of receiving a kidney transplant is that the recipient no longer has to behave like someone with kidney failure. Transplant patients can eat what they like and are free from the restrictions which are inevitable with regular dialysis sessions. An almost completely normal life is the dream of everyone waiting for a kidney transplant.

However, there are some problems. The main physical problem is that the kidney comes from a donor so it will have slightly different antigens from the recipient on the cell surfaces. Everything is done to make sure that the match between the donor and the recipient is as close as possible, but there is still the risk that the donor kidney will be rejected by the immune system unless precautions are taken. When this happens the immune system destroys the new organ.

There are a number of ways in which the risk of rejection can be kept as low as possible. Only donor kidneys with a 'tissue-type' similar to the recipient are used – in other words the antigens of donor and recipient are as similar as possible. Before the transplant takes place, the bone marrow of the recipient is irradiated to stop the production of white blood cells in the early days of the transplant, to give it time to become established. The recipient is kept in sterile conditions for some time after the transplant surgery. This is to reduce the risk that they will get an infection while their immune system is not functioning properly, and also to reduce the chance that their immune system will be stimulated to fight the infection and will then attack and reject the donor kidney. Finally, anyone who has a transplant of any kind will be given immunosuppressant drugs – drugs that suppress the immune response and stop it working – for the rest of their lives (Figure 2).

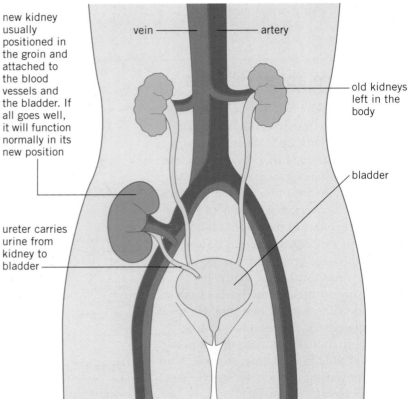

↓ **Figure 1:** A donor kidney is placed in the body and takes over the functions of the organs which have failed.

new kidney usually positioned in the groin and attached to the blood vessels and the bladder. If all goes well, it will function normally in its new position

vein —— artery

old kidneys left in the body

bladder

ureter carries urine from kidney to bladder

↑ **Figure 2:** This infant has had a transplant operation and is being given Cyclosporin-A, an immunosuppressant drug. Immunosuppressants can have unpleasant, long-term side effects, although most people feel that is a relatively small price to pay for the hope of a normal life.

The disappointment of rejection after a transplant operation must be enormous, so patients willingly take the drugs which reduce the effectiveness of their immune systems. The down-side of this is that they are less able to fight off infectious diseases, and have to take great care if they become ill in any way.

Finding the donors

The main source of kidneys for transplant operations is from people who die suddenly and unexpectedly either from road accidents or from strokes and heart attacks. In the UK, organs can only be taken from people if they carry an organ donor card giving permission for the organs to be used in this way, or if they have registered on-line as a donor, or if the bereaved relatives give consent. Because many people do not carry donor cards, and many doctors feel unable to ask grieving relatives for the use of organs, there are never enough donor kidneys to go around – at any time there are thousands of people having kidney dialysis who would love to have a kidney transplant but who never get the opportunity (Figure 3).

↑ **Figure 3:** This 9 year old boy has been given a new lease on life by a kidney transplant. Not everyone who suffers from kidney failure is so lucky, due to a lack of donors.

Blood transfusions

One of the important tissue matches which must be made when deciding if a kidney is suitable for a particular patient is the blood-group matching. Not only is this important for the organ itself – if the blood groups are incompatible blood will go sticky and block the kidney capillaries as soon as the organ is in place – but also for any blood transfusions which might be necessary during transplant surgery. The blood group of the donor organ or the donor blood must match that of the recipient to avoid the dreadful consequences of agglutination (see page 185).

? Questions

1 How does a kidney transplant overcome the problems of kidney failure?

2 Sometimes – in very rare cases – a healthy kidney is taken from a live donor to be given to someone with kidney failure. Usually the live donor is a close family member – the parent, brother or sister. Live donor kidney transplants have a higher rate of success than normal transplants from dead, unrelated donors.

   a Suggest two reasons why live transplants have a higher success rate than normal transplants.

   b Why do you think that live donor transplants are relatively rare?

3 Compare the advantages and disadvantages of treating kidney failure with dialysis or with a kidney transplant. Which treatment do you think is preferable and why?

Key Ideas

⊙ In a kidney transplant a diseased kidney is replaced by a healthy one from a donor.

⊙ The donor kidney may be rejected by the recipient's immune system, so precautions are taken to prevent this, including a careful matching of the blood groups.

1 Colds and influenza ('flu') are infectious diseases caused by viruses. The drawing shows the percentage of people who were affected by colds and flu in different parts of the UK in November 1997.

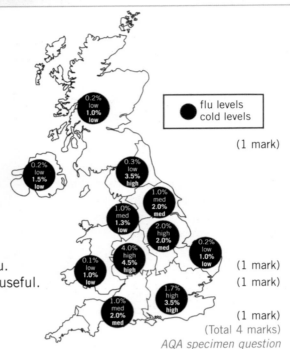

● flu levels
cold levels

a What was the highest percentage of people suffering from colds?

(1 mark)

b The symptoms of flu include headache, aching muscles and fever. The treatment is to keep warm and to drink plenty of liquid. Antibiotics are of no use in treating flu.

   i Suggest **one** medicine that would be useful in treating the symptoms of flu.
   ii Explain how this medicine would be useful.
   iii Explain why antibiotics are of no use in treating flu.

(1 mark)

(1 mark)

(1 mark)
(Total 4 marks)
AQA specimen question

2 Read the following passage and then answer the questions.

Helicobacter – the secret enemy

For many years doctors believed that ulcers in the stomach and the duodenum were caused by stress, which in turn caused extra acid to be secreted by the stomach which damaged the gut wall. The biggest selling drugs in the world were drugs which relieved the symptoms of gut ulcers. Both doctors and scientists also believed that bacteria could not live in the stomach because they are killed off by the acid produced there.

In the 1980s an Australian doctor, Dr Barry Marshall, noticed that there seemed to be a type of bacterium actually living in the stomachs of all his ulcer patients. He began to suspect that the bacteria were causing the ulcers and set up a series of tests to try and prove his theory. Eventually he started treating his ulcer patients with antibiotics which he had discovered would kill the new bacterium known as *Helicobacter pylori*. His patients recovered rapidly and their ulcer symptoms did not return. It took many years before other doctors would accept Dr Marshall's findings, but now this long-hidden bacterium is known to cause not only the great majority of stomach ulcers but also certain types of stomach cancer as well.

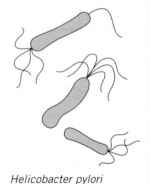

Helicobacter pylori

a Why did doctors find it hard to believe that stomach ulcers are caused by bacteria?

(1 mark)

b Suggest one test by which Dr Marshall might have proved his idea about the cause of stomach ulcers.

(1 mark)

c How might a doctor or scientist investigate which antibiotic could be used to successfully treat the diseases caused by *Helicobacter pylori*?

(3 marks)
(Total 5 marks)

3 a Sometimes kidneys fail. Two ways of treating kidney failure are the use of a dialysis machine and kidney transplants.

   Describe what happens to the composition of a patient's blood as it passes through a dialysis machine.

(2 marks)

b In the treatment of kidney failure:
   i Give **two** possible advantages of using a kidney transplant rather than a dialysis machine.

(2 marks)

   ii Give **two** possible disadvantages of using a kidney transplant rather than a dialysis machine.

(2 marks)
(Total 6 marks)

H **4** **a** In the UK, immunisation of children against polio was started in 1956. Children are given the vaccine, often on a sugar lump, by mouth. The vaccine contains a non-virulent form of the polio virus.

Explain as fully as you can how this vaccine prevents a child from getting polio. (6 marks)

b In some countries polio is still common. Give **two** advantages of continuing with a polio immunisation programme in the UK. (2 marks)

(Total 8 marks)

5

Year	1965	1970	1975	1980	1985	1990	1995	2000
% uptake of vaccination	78	78	39	53	73	90	95	95

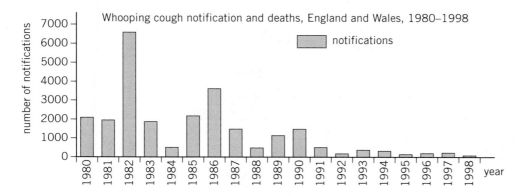

Whooping cough notification and deaths, England and Wales, 1980–1998

Whooping cough is a very unpleasant disease which can cause death and more frequently brain damage. Children have been vaccinated against it for many years but during the 1970s there was a health scare which suggested some children might have been brain damaged as a result of receiving the whooping cough vaccination. Use the data given above to answer the following questions:

a Draw a graph using the data in the table and use it to explain the effect of the health scare on the uptake of whooping cough vaccination. (4 marks)

b What was the effect of the scare on the numbers of cases of whooping cough that were reported in the 1980s? Why do you think this happened? (2 marks)

c When did the uptake of whooping cough vaccination reach over 90%? (1 mark)

d What effect did the increased uptake of vaccine have on the number of cases of whooping cough reported and why? (2 marks)

e No link was ever proved between the whooping cough vaccine and brain damage in children. Why do you think so many parents stopped vaccinating their children against this disease during the 1970s? (2 marks)

(Total 11 marks)

H **6** The human immune system enables the cells of the body to recognise its own cells and foreign cells which may get into the body. The immune system recognises cells by the antigens on the surface membranes. The T-cells and the B-cells are both very important in the immune system.

a Explain the role of the T-cells in the immune response. (2 marks)

b Explain the role of the B-cells in the immune response, including the part played by the memory cells. (4 marks)

c The diagram shows a phagocyte in action. What is the importance of the phagocytes in the immune response? (1 mark)

(Total 7 marks)

14.1 What is microbiology?

Microbiology is the study of microorganisms – tiny living organisms which are usually too small to be seen with the naked eye. To see and understand them properly we need to use a microscope (Figure 1).

There are many different reasons for studying microorganisms. One of these is their role in decay and the recycling of nutrients in the environment (see page 134). Another is their role in causing disease – for example the bacteria and viruses which we have looked at earlier in this book (see page 52). Yet another very good reason for studying microorganisms is that they are enormously useful to people, and with the advent of new technologies like genetic engineering they are becoming more useful all the time.

↑ **Figure 1:** The beauty and detail of the world of microorganisms is only made available by the use of microscopes – this bread mould is magnified 300 times!

Bacteria and viruses

Bacteria and viruses are microorganisms which are widely used in a number of different ways. Their basic structure, discussed earlier in Chapter 4, is summarised in Figure 2.

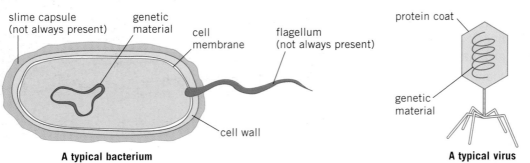

← **Figure 2:** The structure of bacteria and viruses is different from that of the fungi shown in Figure 3.

slime capsule (not always present)
genetic material
cell membrane
flagellum (not always present)
cell wall

A typical bacterium

protein coat
genetic material

A typical virus

Moulds and yeasts

Some of the microorganisms which are most useful to people are moulds and yeasts. These are both fungi – living organisms which obtain their food from other dead or living organisms. Both moulds and yeasts are extremely important as decomposers, breaking down animal and plant material and returning nutrients to the environment.

The yeasts are single-celled organisms. Each yeast cell has a nucleus, cytoplasm and a membrane surrounded by a cell wall. The main way in which yeasts reproduce is by asexual **budding** – splitting in two to form new yeast cells (Figure 3).

Moulds are rather different. They are made up of minute, thread-like structures called hyphae. The hyphae are not made up of individual cells – they are tubes consisting of a cell wall containing cytoplasm and lots of nuclei. Moulds, like yeasts, generally reproduce asexually but they do it by producing fruiting bodies containing spores (Figure 4).

↓ **Figure 3:** Yeast cells – these microscopic organisms have been useful to us for centuries.

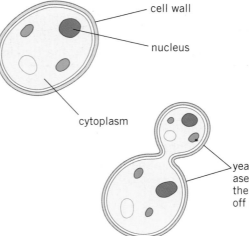

cell wall
nucleus
cytoplasm
yeast cells reproduce asexually by budding – the new yeast cell breaks off to grow and bud itself

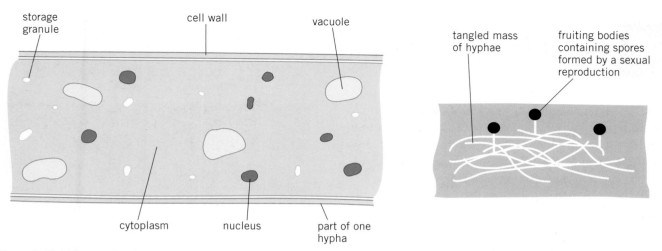

storage granule   cell wall   vacuole

tangled mass of hyphae   fruiting bodies containing spores formed by a sexual reproduction

cytoplasm   nucleus   part of one hypha

↑ **Figure 4:** Moulds are closely related to yeasts, but they are very different in structure.

Using microorganisms

One of the fastest-growing areas of industry is **biotechnology** – the use of microorganisms to make things that people want. However, although some biotechnology is very new, much of it has been in use for thousands of years. People have used microorganisms to make food and drink almost as far back as our records go. Bacteria are used in the manufacture of yoghurt and cheese, and moulds too are often involved in cheese production to give them their distinctive colour and flavour, whilst yeasts are used in the making of alcoholic drinks and bread (Figure 5).

↑ **Figure 5:** This cheese is produced using bacteria and moulds to give it its characteristic texture and taste, whilst the bread and the wine are made using yeast – a microorganism-based feast!

? Questions

1 List five things made using microorganisms.

2 Compare the structure of a yeast with that of a mould. Why do you think they are both classified as fungi?

3 Use the diagrams on page 192 to compare the structure of moulds and yeasts with those of bacteria and viruses. In what ways are they similar and how do they differ?

⊙━ Key Ideas

- ⊙ Microorganisms are used to make food and drink such as cheese, yoghurt, beer, wine and bread.

- ⊙ Moulds and yeasts are fungi.

- ⊙ Yeasts are single-celled organisms; moulds are made of thread-like structures called hyphae.

Yeasts and fermentation

Yeasts can respire aerobically, breaking down sugar to provide energy for the cells and producing water and carbon dioxide as waste products. But the reason yeasts are so very useful to human beings is because they can also respire anaerobically, and when yeast cells break down sugar in the absence of oxygen they produce ethanol (commonly referred to as alcohol) and carbon dioxide. Aerobic respiration is necessary because it provides more energy than anaerobic, so it is needed for the yeast cells to grow and reproduce. However, once the yeast cells are present in sufficient numbers, they can survive for a considerable amount of time in low oxygen conditions and will break down the available sugar to produce ethanol. The anaerobic respiration of yeast is sometimes referred to as **fermentation**.

↑ **Figure 1:** The fermentation reaction of yeast was being used centuries ago in ancient Egypt to make bread.

Baking bread

Bread is basically flour and water mixed together and cooked. Bread made like this is thin, flat and fairly dense in texture. When yeast is used in bread-making it provides a way of raising the dough, giving it a lighter, softer texture.

The yeast is mixed with sugar to provide it with a substrate (food!) for respiration. The yeast and sugar are then mixed with flour, water and/or milk and sometimes extras such as salt or butter to give extra flavour. The mixture is kneaded to make sure the yeast is evenly spread throughout the dough and to improve the texture. The mixture is then left at a warm temperature and as the yeast grows and respires it produces carbon dioxide which makes the dough rise. The dough is then kneaded again and formed into loaves or rolls before it is left to rise a second time in the warm. Then, when the bread is baked the bubbles of gas expand in the high temperature, giving the cooked bread a light texture. The yeast cells are killed during the cooking process (Figure 2).

← **Figure 2:** Dough is usually left to rise at least twice, to give the yeast a chance to make as much carbon dioxide as possible.

Making alcoholic drinks

When ripe fruits fall to the ground and begin to decay, wild yeasts present on the skin break down the fruit sugar and form ethanol and carbon dioxide. These fermented fruits can cause animals to become intoxicated when they eat them – our ancestors probably discovered alcohol in this way. This same reaction is harnessed and used in a controlled way in the making of beers and wines. In both cases the yeast has to be supplied with carbohydrates to act as an energy source for respiration. Beer-making depends on a process called **malting**. Barley grains are soaked and kept warm until they begin to germinate. The starch in barley grains is broken down into a sugary solution by enzymes in the germinating grains and this sugary solution is extracted from the barley and used as an energy source for the yeast. The yeast and sugar solution mixture is fermented to produce alcohol, and hops may be added to give flavour. Finally, the beer is allowed to clear and develop flavour before being put in barrels, bottles or cans, and sold (Figure 3).

← **Figure 3:** Thousands of litres of beer are brewed in the UK alone every year!

Wine making, in contrast, uses the natural sugar found in fruit such as grapes as the energy source for the yeast. The grapes are pressed, and the juice is mixed with yeast and water and then allowed to respire anaerobically until most of the sugar has been used up. The wine is then filtered, to remove the yeast, and put in bottles where it will remain for some time to mature before it is sold. Most commercially sold wine is made from grapes, but wine can actually be made from almost any fruit or vegetable as the yeast isn't at all fussy about where the sugar it uses comes from!

? Questions

1 Produce word equations to show the difference between aerobic and anaerobic respiration in yeast.

2 **a** In bread-making, why is the yeast mixed with sugar before it is added to the flour and water?

  b Why is the bread dough kept warm while it is rising (proving)?

  c Why are the cooked rolls or loaves bigger than the risen dough which is placed in the oven?

3 Make a flow chart to explain the process of making beer.

4 **a** Correct temperature is vital for successful beer and wine making. Why is it so important?

  b To make sparkling wine or champagne, a small amount of yeast is left in the bottle. What effect does this have and what is the gas which makes the bubbles in the drink?

Key Ideas

⊙ Yeast can respire anaerobically, producing ethanol and carbon dioxide in a process known as fermentation.

⊙ The fermentation reaction of yeast is used to raise the dough in the baking of bread and to produce ethanol in the production of beer and wine.

People began to domesticate animals quite early in their history, and whether the animals were cows, sheep, horses or camels, the milk produced by the female animals as food for their calves was quickly recognised as a useful potential food for people too (Figure 1). Unfortunately there is a great drawback in using milk as part of the diet – it very rapidly goes off and becomes completely unpalatable. However, it didn't take people long to discover ways of changing the milk and turning it into milk-based foods which had a much longer life than the original milk itself. These changes depended on the action of microorganisms. Yoghurt has long been a staple part of the diet in the Middle East, but has only relatively recently become popular in the UK. Cheese, on the other hand, has been around for a very long time almost all over the world.

→ **Figure 1:** We get almost all of our milk from the domestic cow, but around the world a number of different animals are used for milking.

Making yoghurt

Traditionally, yoghurt is fermented whole milk, but now it can be made from semi-skimmed milk, skimmed milk and even soya milk. It is formed by the action of bacteria on the lactose (milk sugar) in the milk. A starter culture of the right kind of bacteria is added to warm milk and the mixture is then kept warm so the bacteria begin to grow, reproduce and ferment. This is known as **lactic fermentation** because as the bacteria break down lactose they produce lactic acid which gives the yoghurt its sharp, tangy taste. The lactic acid causes the milk to clot and solidify into yoghurt, while the action of the bacteria gives the yoghurt a smooth, thick texture. Once the yoghurt-forming bacteria have worked on the milk, they also help prevent the growth of the bacteria which normally send the milk bad. Yoghurt, if it is kept cool, will last almost three weeks before it goes bad, whereas milk manages only a few days – and then only if it's kept really cold.

Making cheese

Like yoghurt-making, cheese-making depends on the reactions of bacteria with milk changing the texture and taste and also preserving the milk. Cheese-making is very successful at this, and some cheeses can survive for years without decay. Around 900 different types of cheeses are made around the world, but the basis of the production method is the same for them all.

Again, just as in yoghurt making, a starter culture of bacteria is added to warm milk. The difference is in the type of bacteria added. The bacteria in cheese-making also make lactic acid, but in greater quantities, so that the milk is more acidified and the curds which are produced are much more solid than the yoghurt ones. Enzymes are also added to increase the separation of the milk. When it has completely curdled, the solid parts (curds) are cooked with the liquid whey, after which the curds are separated and used for cheese-making while the whey is often used as animal feed.

The curds are cut and mixed with salt along with other bacteria or moulds before they are packed and pressed and left to dry out. The bacteria and moulds which are added at this stage of the process are very important in the development of the final flavour and texture of the cheese as it ripens – a process which may take months or years depending on the cheese being made (Figure 2).

↑ **Figure 2:** The curds on which a cheese-maker depends are formed by the action of one set of bacteria on the milk, and the final flavour and texture of the cheese may well depend on other bacteria added at this stage of the process.

Questions

1 Produce a flow chart to summarise the production of

   a yoghurt and

   b cheese from milk.

2 Compare the processes of yoghurt- and cheese-making and summarise the differences between them.

3 In cheese-making, the milk is usually kept at around 18 °C for about 24 hours after the bacterial starter culture has been added. Why do you think these conditions are chosen?

Many microorganisms can be grown in the laboratory, which allows us to learn a lot about them – from the nutrients they need to survive to the chemicals which will kill them, from the microbes which we can put to work for our benefit to the pathogens which cause deadly disease.

Laboratory culture of microorganisms

To find out more about microorganisms we need to culture them – in other words grow very large numbers of them so that we can see the colony as whole (Figure 1).

To culture microorganisms we must provide them with all they need. This usually involves providing a culture medium containing carbohydrate to act as an energy source, along with various mineral ions and in some cases extra, supplementary proteins and vitamins. Usually warmth and oxygen also need to be provided (Figure 2).

The nutrients are often contained in an agar medium. **Agar** is a substance which dissolves in hot water and sets to form a jelly. Hot agar containing all the necessary nutrients is poured into a Petri dish and left to cool and set before any microorganisms are introduced. The other way in which nutrients may be provided for growing microorganisms is as a **broth** in a culture flask.

Great care has to be taken when we culture microorganisms, because even when the microbes we want to grow are completely harmless, there is always the risk that a mutation may take place, resulting in a new and dangerous pathogen. Also, the culture may be contaminated by disease-causing pathogens which are present in the air, soil or water around us.

Not only do we want to avoid contamination by any dangerous microorganisms, we also want to keep any pure strains of bacteria that we are growing free from other microorganisms – harmful or otherwise – from the air or our own skin. So whenever we are culturing microorganisms, strict health and safety procedures are always carried out (Figure 3).

↓ Figure 1: Bacteria can grow and divide very rapidly if they are given the right conditions, which is why it is relatively easy to culture them in the laboratory.

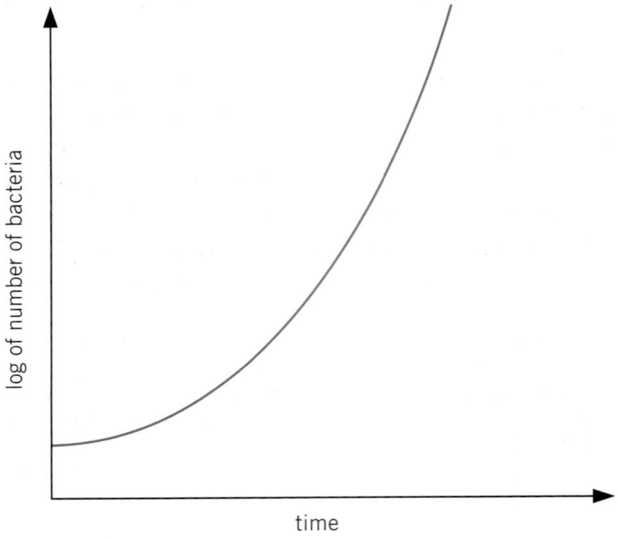

(graph: y-axis labelled "log of number of bacteria", x-axis labelled "time", showing an exponential rising curve)

↑ Figure 2: Culturing microorganisms like bacteria makes it possible for us to see what they are like and find out what they need to grow.

← Figure 3: When people culture the most dangerous pathogens, extreme safety measures have to be taken. The situation in the school laboratory is not quite as risky as this, but sensible safety precautions have to be taken when dealing with any microorganisms.

Growing useful microorganisms

When we want to prepare useful products, whether in industry or in the laboratory, we need uncontaminated cultures of microorganisms. In the laboratory we achieve this by observing a number of steps.

Both the Petri dishes on which the microbes are to be grown and the nutrient agar which will provide their food must be sterilised before they are used to kill unwanted microorganisms. This sterilisation is done by heat, often in a special oven known as an autoclave which uses steam at high pressure. The sterile nutrient agar is then inoculated with the microorganism we want to grow as shown in Figure 4.

Once these steps have been taken, the sealed Petri dishes should be incubated to allow the microorganisms to grow. In school and college laboratories, the maximum temperature at which cultures should be incubated is 25°C, because this greatly reduces the likelihood of pathogens growing which might be harmful to people. In industrial conditions, bacterial cultures are often grown at higher temperatures to promote rapid growth of the microbes. Once the microbes have been used and observed, the Petri dishes, complete with their cultures, should be re-sterilised by heating to 100°C, and then thrown away.

↓ **Figure 4:** Culturing microorganisms in the laboratory.

1 The inoculating loop which is used to transfer microorganisms to the media is sterilised by heating it to red hot in the flame of a Bunsen and then leaving to cool.

2 The sterilised loop is dipped in a suspension of the bacteria we want to grow and then used to make zig-zag streaks across the surface of the agar. The lid is then replaced on the dish as quickly as possible.

3 The lid of the Petri dish is sealed with adhesive tape to prevent microorganisms from the air contaminating the culture, or microbes from the culture escaping.

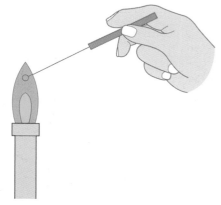

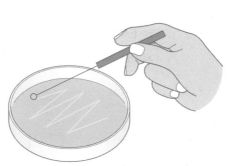

? Questions

1 Why do we culture microorganisms in the laboratory?

2 Why do you think that all bacteria need a carbohydrate energy source as part of their nutrient medium?

3 Explain why cultures are not incubated at 37°C in a school laboratory.

4 Make a poster or a safety leaflet which could be given to pupils working in the laboratory with microorganisms for the first time, to make sure they realise the need for care and good hygiene.

5 Look at the graph in Figure 1.

  a What does this tell you about the growth of bacteria in ideal conditions?

  b A Petri dish provides ideal conditions for bacteria as they start to grow, but the ideal conditions do not last forever. What might limit the growth of the bacteria in a culture on a Petri dish?

0━ Key Ideas

⊙ Microorganisms can be grown in an agar culture medium with a carbohydrate energy source and various minerals, vitamins and proteins.

⊙ To obtain uncontaminated cultures of microorganisms and to avoid the growth of harmful pathogens, careful safety measures must be taken and all the equipment sterilised.

It is one thing growing microorganisms in the laboratory on a small scale in a Petri dish. In those conditions it is relatively easy to provide everything the microorganisms will need to grow – food, oxygen and warmth – and cultures are not usually kept for long enough for the build up of waste products to be a problem. But it becomes a very different story when we want to grow microorganisms on an industrial scale. Often, we want to make use of materials made by the microbes, either as drugs or as food. This means we need to keep a very large fermentation going for a long time so we can harvest the products (Figure 1).

↑ **Figure 1:** Scaling up brings problems of its own – when we move a culture of microorganisms from an agar plate to vessels which might hold $1\,000\,000\,dm^3$ of medium it is a very big step to manage successfully.

Getting bigger

Figure 1 on page 198 shows how bacteria grow in ideal conditions. However, ideal conditions are rare and what usually happens in a bacterial culture is shown in Figure 2.

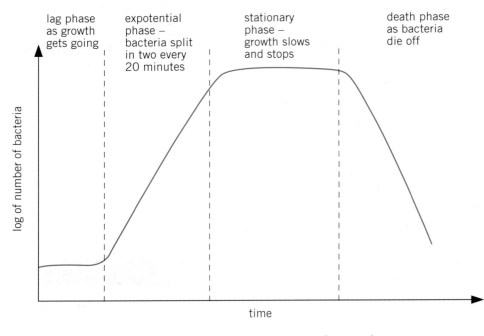

← **Figure 2:** In real life rather than ideal conditions, all sorts of factors make bacterial growth slow down.

As the numbers of microorganisms begin to rise, conditions change:

⊙ The food begins to be used up.

⊙ The metabolism of all the millions of microorganisms causes the temperature to rise.

⊙ Oxygen levels fall as the oxygen is used up in respiration, and the carbon dioxide produced as a waste product can alter the pH of the culture and stop it growing.

⊙ Other waste products begin to build up and poison the culture.

In industrial fermentations, such as those producing antibiotics or the meat substitute ™Quorn, very large cultures are involved and these types of problems develop very rapidly.

In industrial processes, microorganisms are grown in large vessels known as **fermenters**. Industrial fermenters usually have a range of features which overcome the problems which can stop a culture from growing satisfactorily. These include:

⊙ an oxygen supply to provide oxygen for the respiration of the microorganisms

⊙ a stirrer to keep the microorganisms in suspension, to maintain an even temperature, and to make sure that oxygen and food are evenly distributed through the culture

⊙ a water-cooled jacket which removes excess heat produced by the respiring microorganisms – any rise in temperature heats the water which is constantly removed and replaced with more cold water

⊙ measuring instruments which constantly monitor factors such as the pH and temperature so that adjustments can be made if they start to become a problem (Figure 3).

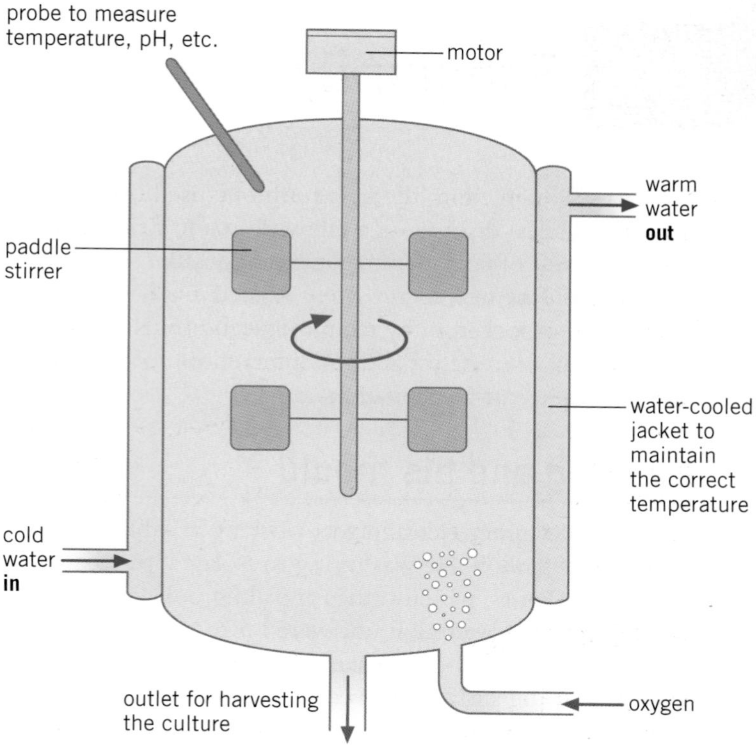

↑ **Figure 3:** The design of fermenters is improving all the time as new ways are developed of keeping conditions inside the fermenter as stable as possible all of the time.

What can we make?

The industrial use of microorganisms includes all the technology we have met in previous sections for making cheese, yoghurt, wine and beer, but it goes well beyond that now. Moulds produce antibiotics, and these drugs, which are still in most cases extremely effective against bacterial diseases, are in demand all over the world. Thousands of tonnes are produced by microbes every year.

Specially selected microbes also produce the basis of ™Quorn, a high protein, low fat meat substitute which was developed some years ago and which is now a major competitor in the food market. The microorganisms grow and reproduce rapidly in large, specialised fermenters, using a relatively cheap sugar syrup as their basic food.

Another increasingly important use of microorganisms industrially is in the production of specific drugs or human proteins which are needed by people with very specific diseases. For example, genetic engineering has made it possible for bacteria to produce human insulin. These engineered microbes are cultured in big fermenters and the insulin they produce is used to treat the great majority of people who suffer from diabetes – a lack of insulin. So the production of microorganisms on a large scale is not only here to stay, but is a technology which is growing and developing all the time.

? Questions

1 a Describe how Figure 1 on page 198 differs from Figure 2 on page 200.

 b What causes the difference between the growth pattern in ideal conditions and that in real conditions?

2 Why are microorganisms so useful in industrial processes?

3 How might an industrial fermenter be adapted to ensure the best possible conditions for the growth of a particular microorganism?

4 Why do the following factors tend to change during a fermentation process?

 a temperature   b oxygen levels   c pH levels.

0⃞ Key Ideas

⊙ Microorganisms can be grown in large vessels known as fermenters to make useful products such as antibiotics.

⊙ Industrial fermenters usually have a range of features to make sure the fermentation takes place in the best possible conditions for a maximum yield of the product.

The story of penicillin, the first antibiotic used on a large scale in the battle against bacterial diseases, is a tale with many strands to it. The initial discovery was the result of lax laboratory procedures, the sort that would cause serious trouble with the health and safety executive today. The potential of the discovery was seen, but locked in by technological difficulties which were only solved with a World War as a catalyst and the intervention of American companies with money and experience in fermentation.

↓ **Figure 1:** The keen eyes of Alexander Fleming noticed the clear areas on his plates. He realised he had made a discovery of enormous potential.

Fleming and his mould

In 1928, Alexander Fleming was working as a bacteriologist at St Mary's hospital in London. He was trying to isolate a particular bacterium, *Staphylococcus aureus*, which causes appalling boils and skin infections. His inoculated plates were left uncovered near an open window, and when he remembered to look at them he found that, while the bacteria were growing on the surface of his dish as he expected, there were areas of clear medium where the bacteria were either not growing or had died. Something had blown in through the window and was growing on the plates and producing a chemical which killed the bacteria (Figure 1).

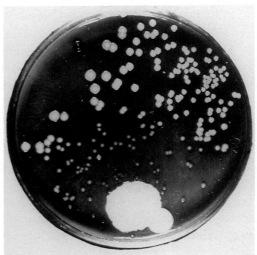

Fleming removed and cultured the microorganism which had invaded his Petri dishes. He found that it was a common mould called *Penicillium notatum* and set about trying to extract the substance which killed bacteria. It was almost impossible with the technology available, but he managed to extract a tiny amount and used it to treat an infected wound. However, unable to extract a useful amount of the miracle substance he had christened penicillin, Fleming saved his mould cultures and returned to other areas of research.

Passing the baton

As the Second World War began to rage, the need for a drug to kill bacterial infections became ever more urgent. Howard Florey and Ernst Chain were working at Oxford University in a desperate search to find an antibacterial drug (Figure 2). They turned to the mould which Fleming had so carefully conserved for 11 years, and after months of work they extracted enough penicillin to prove that this was the substance they needed.

After successful animal trials, they tried to save the life of a London policeman dying of a blood infection. The dying man made an amazing recovery, but the supply of penicillin ran out, the infection regained its hold and he died. More months of work produced enough penicillin to save the life of a boy dying of a bacterial infection, but what was needed was huge amounts of the drug – not tiny quantities to treat one lucky patient but enough to treat thousands of wounded and sick soldiers.

In Britain, most factories were dedicated to the war effort, so Chain and Florey turned to the American pharmaceutical industries for help. Three companies, Pfizer, Merck and Squibb, gave them both expert scientists and the facilities they needed to make progress.

↑ **Figure 2:** Alexander Fleming, Howard Florey and Ernst Chain each received a well-deserved Nobel Prize for their work on the miracle drug penicillin.

The right mould

Whatever they did with Fleming's original mould they were going to struggle – it was incredibly difficult to grow in large cultures and it yielded only I part penicillin for every million parts of fermentation broth. Then another amazing stroke of luck saw one of the researchers discover a mouldy melon in a market, and the mould from that melon yielded 200 times more penicillin than the original. What was more, *Penicillium chrysogenum* also grew relatively easily in deep tanks, making large-scale production possible. Tonnes of antibiotic were made, saving the lives of thousands of Allied soldiers throughout the rest of the war. By the end of the war, 7000 billion units of penicillin were being produced each year – enough to treat 7 million people.

Modern penicillin production

The production of penicillin certainly did not stop with the end of the war. The antibiotic is still made by growing *Penicillium* mould – modern forms with even higher yields – on a medium containing sugar and other nutrients which is made from steeping corn in water. The fermenters have strong paddles to keep stirring the broth because the penicillin mould needs lots of oxygen to thrive. During the first part of the process (the first 40 hours of the fermentation) the mould grows extensively, using up much of the nutrients in the broth. Only after most of the nutrients have gone does the mould begin to make penicillin, and then over a period of about 140 hours broth is removed and small amounts of nutrients are added to get the maximum yield of the drug, which is then extracted from the broth (Figure 3).

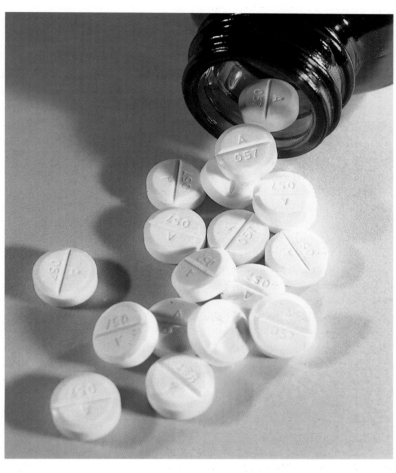

→ **Figure 3:** Penicillin tablets – the drug can be produced in many different shapes and forms, but it all has the same fatal effect on bacteria. For most of us at some stage in our lives, antibiotics are lifesavers.

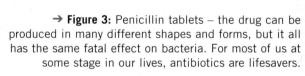

? Questions

1 Produce a timeline to show the stages in the discovery and development of penicillin.

2 Why has the development of penicillin had such an impact on the quality of human life?

3 Produce a flow chart for the production of penicillin in a commercial fermentation process.

O—ᴛᴛ Key Ideas

⊙ The antibiotic penicillin is made by growing the mould *Penicillium* in a fermenter.

⊙ The medium contains sugars and other nutrients.

⊙ The mould only starts making penicillin after most of the nutrients are used up.

14.7 Biogas – a fuel of the future?

Everywhere in the world fuel is important. We use it for heating, cooking, lighting, refrigeration and electricity generation. In many developing countries, wood and peat fires are used for cooking. There is only a finite amount of fossil fuels like coal, oil and gas, and even wood and peat are getting scarcer, so there is a quest for other, renewable forms of fuel. One which is becoming increasingly important in the developing world and which is beginning to arouse interest in the developed world is the generation of **biogas** from human and animal waste (Figure 1).

What is biogas?

Biogas is the flammable mixture of gases formed when bacteria break down plant material or the waste products of animals – or humans – in anaerobic conditions. It is mainly made up of methane but the composition of the mixture varies depending on what is put into the generator and which bacteria are present (Table 1).

How is it made?

Biogas is made by the fermentation of dung or any other material which contains a high level of carbohydrates. Around the world, millions of tonnes of faeces and urine are made by animals like cows, pigs, sheep and chickens. Humans, too, produce their fair share of waste materials. Also, in many parts of the world, particularly in the tropics, plant material grows freely and rapidly. Both the plant material and the animal waste make up a potentially enormous energy resource – but how can it be exploited?

To produce biogas, dung or plant material is collected and put into a biogas generator or digester. A mixed population of many different types of bacteria are needed to digest the carbohydrate, closely resembling the mixture of bacteria in the stomach of a ruminant like a cow or sheep. Some break down the cellulose in plant cell walls whilst others break down the sugars formed to produce methane and other gases. The biogas which is produced is passed along a pipe into the home where it is burned to produce a source of heat, light or refrigeration.

The bacteria involved in biogas production work best at a temperature of around 30°C, so the generators work best in hot countries. However, the process is exothermic – it generates heat – so, as long as energy is put in to start things off and there is good insulation to prevent heat loss, the generators will work anywhere (Figure 2).

Under ideal conditions, 10 kg of dry dung can produce 3 m³ of biogas, and that is enough to provide 3 hours of cooking, 3 hours of lighting or 24 hours of running a refrigerator. Not only that, but the waste from the generator makes a useful fertiliser.

What is the potential?

So far, most biogas generators around the world operate on a relatively small scale. Often they supply one family, a farm or at most a whole village. What is.

↑ **Figure 1:** Biogas generators are providing cheap and readily available fuel to many families in the developing world – and they may have a role internationally in reducing our dependence on fossil fuels.

Type of gas	% in the mixture by volume
Methane	50–80
Carbon dioxide	15–45
Water	5
Other gases including hydrogen	0–1
Hydrogen sulphide	0–3

↑ **Table 1:** How the composition of biogas varies

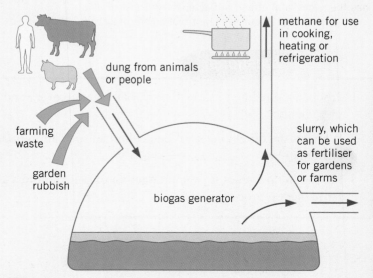

↑ **Figure 2:** Biogas generators take in waste material or plants, and biogas and useful fertilisers come out at the other end.

Applied microbiology

put in to these small generators has a big effect on what comes out. In China – where there are well over 7 million biogas units producing fuel energy equivalent to 22 million tonnes of coal – waste vegetables, animal dung and human waste are used. The digesters produce excellent fertiliser but relatively low-quality biogas. In contrast, in India, where there are religious and social taboos against using human waste in biodigesters, only cattle and buffalo dung is put into the biogas generators. This produces very high-quality gas, but much less fertiliser (Figure 3).

However, many countries are now experimenting with using biogas generators on a larger scale. The waste material from sugar factories, sewage farms and rubbish tips all has the potential to act as a starting point for the production of biogas. There are problems to be overcome with scaling the process up, but the early progress looks promising. Biogas could well be an important fuel for the future for us all, helping us to get rid of much of the waste we produce as well as providing a clean and renewable energy supply.

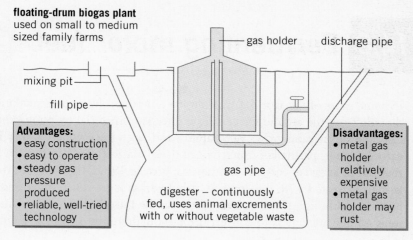

floating-drum biogas plant
used on small to medium sized family farms

gas holder   discharge pipe

mixing pit

fill pipe

Advantages:
• easy construction
• easy to operate
• steady gas pressure produced
• reliable, well-tried technology

gas pipe

digester – continuously fed, uses animal excrements with or without vegetable waste

Disadvantages:
• metal gas holder relatively expensive
• metal gas holder may rust

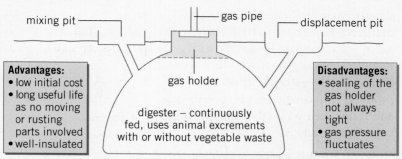

fixed-dome biogas plant

mixing pit   gas pipe   displacement pit

Advantages:
• low initial cost
• long useful life as no moving or rusting parts involved
• well-insulated

gas holder

digester – continuously fed, uses animal excrements with or without vegetable waste

Disadvantages:
• sealing of the gas holder not always tight
• gas pressure fluctuates

↑ **Figure 3:** Different types of biogas generators have different advantages and disadvantages – it is a case of choosing the right design for the conditions available.

? Questions

1 **a** Using Table 1, produce bar charts to compare high-quality biogas (high methane, low carbon dioxide) with poor-quality biogas (low methane, high carbon dioxide).

   b What effect do you think differences in composition like this will have on the use of the gas as a fuel?

2 Why is it important that there are many different bacteria present in a biogas generator rather than a culture containing just one or two microbes?

3 Some types of biogas generator are designed for batch feeding. In other words they are set up with a large amount of biological material and a starter mixture of bacteria, and left to produce gas. They are very effective with fibrous plant material as a raw material. Once gas generation begins to drop, the biogas generator is emptied and cleaned out and the process starts again.

   a Using a generator like this, what would be necessary to ensure a continuous supply of gas for cooking, etc?

   b What are the advantages of a batch-type digester over the types shown in Figure 3?

   c What are the advantages over a batch-type digester of

      i a floating drum and

      ii a fixed dome biogas plant?

4 Write a letter to your local authority explaining why you think they should look into the idea of installing a biogas generator at your school, including where the fuel supply for the generator might come from and how the biogas produced might be used.

O─ⅲ Key Ideas

⊙ Biogas – mainly methane – can be produced by anaerobic fermentation of a wide range of plant products and waste materials that contain carbohydrates.

⊙ Many different organisms are involved in the breakdown of material in biogas production.

14.8 Fermenting motor fuel H

↑ **Figure 1:** In areas where there is plenty of sun and rain, plants like this maize grow very rapidly. All we need is a way of turning them into usable fuel.

In some parts of the world, plants produce biomass very quickly, taking up carbon dioxide from the air and converting it into plant material by photosynthesis. For example, sugar cane grows very rapidly, and has a juice which is very high in carbohydrates, particularly sucrose. Similarly, maize (which in the UK is usually referred to as sweet corn) is another fast grower. When the starch in the maize kernels is treated with the enzyme carbohydrase it is broken down into glucose. However, although these carbohydrates can be burned, they do not make very good fuels – the challenge is to convert the carbohydrates into clean and efficient fuels.

Alcohol-based fuels

If sugar-rich products from cane and maize are fermented anaerobically with yeast, the sugars are broken down incompletely to give ethanol and water. The ethanol is extracted from the products of fermentation by distillation, and it can then be used in motor vehicles as a fuel.

Car engines need special modification to be able to use pure ethanol as a fuel, but it is not a major job, and many cars can run on a mixture of petrol and ethanol without problems (Figure 2).

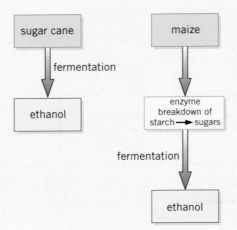

← **Figure 2:** Making ethanol from maize takes one extra step compared to making it from sugar cane because the starch needs to be broken down by enzymes before the yeast can use it.

Ideas and Evidence

The advantages and disadvantages of ethanol as a fuel

Ethanol is in many ways an ideal fuel. It is efficient and it does not produce toxic gases when it burns, so it is much less polluting than conventional fuels which produce carbon monoxide, sulphur dioxide and nitrogen oxides. In addition, ethanol reduces pollution even when it is simply mixed with conventional petrol to make a fuel such as **gasohol**, increasingly being used in the USA. There is no overall increase in carbon dioxide in the atmosphere when it burns – the CO_2 removed by the source plants in photosynthesis is simply returned to the air.

The biggest difficulty with the use of plant-based fuels for cars is that it takes a lot of plant material to produce the ethanol. Ethanol as a fuel has therefore been limited to those countries with enough space and a suitable climate to grow lots of the right sort of plant material as fast as possible. Brazil was the trail-blazer for ethanol as a fuel when oil prices shot up in the 1970s. By growing its own 'green petrol', Brazil was able to reduce the amount of oil imports which were costing the country so much money. The Brazilians were very successful, and in the 1980s 90% of the cars produced in Brazil had ethanol-powered engines (Figure 3).

However, when oil prices dropped again it became uneconomic for the Brazilian government to support and subsidise ethanol as a fuel, and as a result they began to move back to petrol-driven cars.

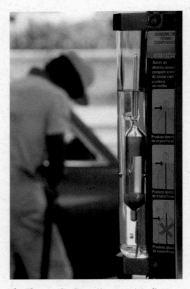

↑ **Figure 3:** Brazil was the first country to develop ethanol-powered cars – but now they use many petrol cars again.

Now, in the 21st century, people all over the world are recognising the damage which the burning of fossil fuels is doing to the environment, and interest is soaring in clean alternatives such as ethanol. Brazil is again taking a lead, supporting countries such as India with advice on technology for producing ethanol from plants.

In America, the use of gasohol – a mixture of 90% petrol and 10% ethanol – is becoming an increasingly important factor in their drive to reduce air pollution. The ethanol is fermented and distilled from maize grown within the USA itself (Figure 4).

The problem with using gasohol as a petrol substitute will continue to be the provision of an adequate supply of ethanol. If Europeans added 5% ethanol to their fuel to help reduce carbon dioxide emissions, this would result in an additional demand for 7.5 billion litres of ethanol a year – more than half of the total production level in Brazil!

Attempts to produce economically viable quantities of ethanol from plants which grow in Europe, such as pine trees and beet, have not yet been very successful.

→ **Figure 4:** The production of ethanol for fuel in the USA has increased almost 10-fold in the last 20 years – and it continues to climb.

In addition, current methods of ethanol production leave large quantities of unused cellulose. To make ethanol production financially viable in the long term, this cellulose must be used in some way. Biogas generators might be able to break down the excess cellulose into methane, another fuel. Genetically engineered bacteria may even be able to break down the cellulose and make it available to the yeast for anaerobic fermentation to make more ethanol. At the moment, no-one is quite sure what the future will hold, but it seems likely that ethanol-based fuel mixes will be part of it.

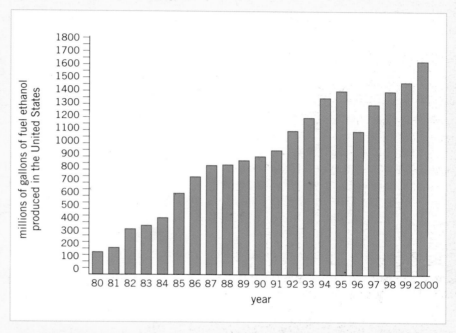

Questions

1 Produce a flow chart to summarise the making of ethanol fuel from sugar cane.

2 Make a table to summarise the advantages and disadvantages of ethanol as a fuel for cars.

3 Use the data in Figure 4 to help you answer the following questions:

a What was the percentage increase in ethanol production in the US between

   i 1980 and 1985   ii 1985 and 1990   iii 1990 and 1995?

b Much of the ethanol made is mixed with normal petrol to make a more ecologically sound motor fuel. If each gallon of gasohol sold contains 10% ethanol, how many million gallons of gasohol could have been produced in 1990?

c Describe what happened to ethanol production between 1995 and 2000. Suggest reasons which might explain the trends you see.

4 Produce a presentation to explain to your peers the potential value of ethanol in helping to prevent the greenhouse effect and global warming.

Key Ideas

⊙ Ethanol-based fuels can be produced by the anaerobic fermentation of sugarcane juices and from glucose derived from maize starch by the action of the enzyme carbohydrase.

⊙ The ethanol is distilled from the fermentation products and can be used in motor vehicles.

1 a The drawings show some products in a shop. List the products that are made by using microbes. (2 marks)

bread   wine   sugar   yoghurt   cigarettes   antibiotics

b A new disease was found to be caused by a type of bacterium. An investigation was carried out to find out which antibiotics were effective against this type of bacterium. Each of four paper discs **A** to **D** was soaked in a different antibiotic. A fifth disc, **E**, was a control.

A culture containing the bacteria was used to inoculate the surface of the growth medium in a Petri dish. The five paper discs were put on the surface, and the dish was incubated for 24 hours. The drawing shows the results of this investigation.

i The growth medium was heated to a high temperature before pouring it into the Petri dish. Why was this necessary? (1 mark)

ii After inoculating the dish with the culture, the lid was sealed with tape. Why was this necessary? (1 mark)

c Explain why there were clear areas around some discs after 24 hours. (2 marks)

d From the results shown in the diagram, what is the order of effectiveness of antibiotics **A** to **D** against this type of bacterium? (2 marks)

(Total 8 marks)

AQA specimen question

2 The drawing shows a section through a fermenter used to produce the antibiotic penicillin. The fermenter contains the mould *Penicillium*.

a Name **two** nutrients which moulds such as *Penicillium* need for growth.

b Explain why air must be bubbled through the fermenter.

c Explain why the water-cooled jacket is necessary.

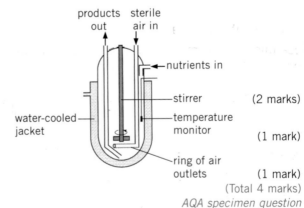

products out   sterile air in

nutrients in

stirrer   (2 marks)

water-cooled jacket

temperature monitor   (1 mark)

ring of air outlets   (1 mark)

(Total 4 marks)

AQA specimen question

3 The drawing shows a commercial yoghurt-manufacturing process.

a i Suggest how the fresh milk is sterilised.

ii Suggest why it is necessary to sterilise the fresh milk.

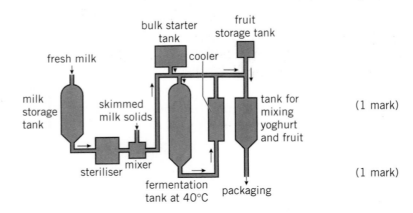

bulk starter tank   fruit storage tank

fresh milk   cooler

milk storage tank   skimmed milk solids   tank for mixing yoghurt and fruit   (1 mark)

steriliser   mixer

fermentation tank at 40°C   packaging   (1 mark)

b *To gain full marks in this question you should write your ideas in good English. Put them into a sensible order and use the correct scientific words.*

The bulk starter tank contains a culture of bacteria. Describe the effect of these bacteria on the milk.

(3 marks)

(Total 5 marks)

AQA specimen question

H 4 The antibiotic streptomycin, is produced by a mould which is grown in a fermenter. The graph shows the concentrations of mould, glucose and streptomycin in a fermenter over a period of ten days.

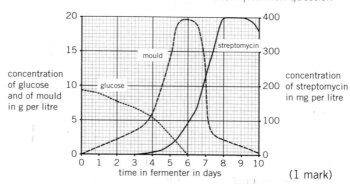

a Describe the relationship between glucose concentration and streptomycin production.

(1 mark)

b Explain

  i the change in glucose concentration (2 marks)

  ii the decrease in concentration of the mould. (2 marks)

(Total 5 marks)

AQA specimen question

5 The diagram shows several different types of microorganism.

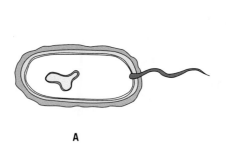
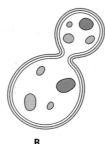
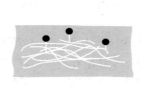
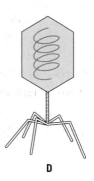

A   B   C   D

a Identify the four different types – **a**, **b**, **c** and **d**. (4 marks)

b For each of these microorganisms, give **one** example of a way they might be put to use by people.

(4 marks)

(Total 8 marks)

H 6 The diagram shows a generalised biogas generator.

a What is biogas? (2 marks)

b Label parts **A**, **B** and **C** on the diagram. (3 marks)

c Biogas generators are already quite widely used in the developing world. Give **three** reasons why generators like this are so useful.

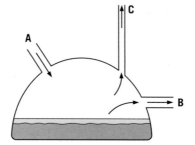

(3 marks)

d Interest in biogas generation has been increasing in the developed world. Suggest **two** ways in which this type of fuel production might be advantageous and **one** difficulty which might arise.

(3 marks)

(Total 11 marks)

Index